Pascal Precisely for Engineers and Scientists

Corrections

G000038878

Page	Line	
28	4	PROGRAM AddressLabel (output);
30	7	... 'x10' : 6...
	10	... 'x10' : 6 ...
34	14	... 'x10' : col3 ...
	17	write ('milli' : col1, 'm' : col2, 'x10' : col3 ...
46	13	... cu m/s' : 20);
	15	... rcm + hcm * i : 8,
59	4	... cu m/s' : 20);
	8	... rcm + hcm * i : 8,
65	–1	V1 := 0.5 * A * T1S;
69	21	... 'L' : 10);
71	–3,–2,–1	N = 10
		Total = 409.60
		Mean = 40.9600
77	28	... {Findhighest}
92	–7,–6	... 0.5 * h * ((E ... currentp/L));
93	13	reports := round (TS / h / imax);
97	6	... : S}
109	–3	... course code',
110	11	... 4 error(s)
133	9	product, firstproduct : 0 .. maxint;
	16	readln(product); firstproduct := product;
136	–11	*insert*: VAR i : 1 .. maxint;
	–8	END; {HistogramofCurrent}
139	–10	*insert*: pi = 3.141592;
141	–18	*insert*: pi = 3.141592;
145	–8	writeln(i : 4, x : 10 : 6);
165	–6	*replace by*: order (a,8); 8 is not a variable
168	14	... : 0..59;
	–11,–10,–9	*replace by*:
		if S {is about to tick over i.e.} = 59 then begin
		if M {is about to tick over i.e.} = 59
		then H := next (H, 1, 12);
		M := next (M, 0, 59);
		end;
		S := next (S, 0, 59);
169	19	... 5 + 6 + 8 + 2 ...
190	–5,–4	{Uses global constants: L, n, reports}
191	23	writeln('x = ', ...);
	24	*delete*
204	–14	*delete*
205	18,19	Type in day, month and year : 22 2 1990
209	–3	... until ch <> ' '; readln (inp);
214	19,20	readln (num); writeln ('Enter the ', num : 1, ...
215	7	... ave)) : 1 ...
218	–10	... raintable[m], 10);
250	22	... per second',
251	2	*delete*
	14	END; {ModuleHasLanded}
257	16	channelerror := checkint <> ...
280	–7	... {f := f + temp}
282	–11	cadd (f, f, temp);

(Continued)

Approach to numerical methods

Numerical methods are an essential part of the toolbox of a scientist or engineer interested in getting the most out of a computer. In many cases, with modern computer libraries, it may be possible simply to use a package to solve the numerical part of a physical problem. Nevertheless, as a programmer, one still has to have an elementary knowledge of the kinds of methods that exist, and some idea of how they work.

We have chosen to include a selection of methods and examples as the discussion on Pascal unfolds. They provide excellent case studies and they reinforce the idea that a computer is a really useful tool. Moreover, it is hoped that by making numerical methods easy for students, they will not be seen as a dry or obscure adjunct to scientific programming, but rather as part and parcel of the programming process.

Standards

Pascal is blessed with an internationally accepted standard – ISO 7185 and BS 6192. This has enhanced its portability, but has restricted its ability to adapt to advances in hardware. In three areas in particular, the standard language falls short of what a modern programmer would need. These are connecting up to files, string handling and graphics.

Every Pascal implementation **has** to provide a means for Pascal files to be connected to those of the operating system, and this is not covered by the standard. We have therefore adopted the one most widely used (an extension of reset); mentioned the others, and tried to minimise the effect on portability by keeping these statements in special places.

There is enough to study in standard Pascal without having to branch into intricate string handling problems. Thus we have for the most part avoided the string extensions which are common in most implementations. The place where a string is essential is in the naming of a file, for use in the previously mentioned extension.

To reinforce our approach to staying within the standard, we ran the programs in the book on a variety of computers and Pascal systems, including IBM PC-AT and IBM PS/2 with Turbo Pascal 4, Apple Macintosh SE with TML Pascal, Masscomp and Orion with UNIX and Oregon Pascal, and IBM 3090 with VM/CMS and VS-Pascal. On occasion, we were transferring programs on e-mail internationally on a daily basis, running the programs on completely different systems without change!

Structure charts and pseudo-code

Programmers – even experienced ones – need a means of expressing a solution in diagrammatic form. With lines and arrows and boxes, one can express with greater clarity the interaction of the parts, and can make modifications and extensions with rapidity.

There are in existence many formalised diagrammatic notations – flow charts, structure charts, Nassi-Schneiderman diagrams, JSP, to name but a few. We have not espoused any one of these, but use instead a simple, informal notation to explain the complex parts of a solution, before proceeding on to the programming or coding phase. Pseudo-code is a natural part of this notation, and we endeavour to convince the reader of its usefulness by example.

Programming vs problem solving

It is no longer sufficient to teach coding – the means by which explicit algorithms are translated into statements in a programming language. The expectation of today's scientists and engineers is that the whole computing milieu will assist in the solution of day-to-day physical problems. In addition to explaining syntax and the construction of a well-formed program, the modern programming text book has to include techniques for problem-solving.

Pascal Precisely for Engineers and Scientists is indeed such a modern text book. Every worked problem – and there are now over 60 of them – is introduced with a typically inexact statement. This is then refined in the process of devising a solution. Where applicable, the appropriate numerical technique is selected, and then we proceed to algorithm development. As mentioned above, algorithms are illustrated with diagrams, and important techniques are discussed, highlighted, and identified for re-use later on. There are two special sections on the topic, where the techniques are summarised.

Range of problems

There are now over 60 worked examples in the book, nearly all of them resulting in complete listed programs. The numerical methods and the examples are listed in the contents for easy reference.

In choosing the problems, we have tried to maintain a balance between the classic computing examples which illustrate Pascal features so well (finding the HCF, sorting student marks) and a range of simple applications in the problem domain of our expected audience. Since the fields of science and engineering cover a very wide spectrum, we have chosen to concentrate on applications in elementary circuit analysis (finding steady-state charges, identifying the saturation point of an amplifier) and basic mechanics (springs and beams and accelerating trains). We have tried not to let the application intrude into the programming insight which it is meant to provide, and in most cases, the numerical problems should still be within the capabilities of the average reader.

Who the book is for

The book is intended for science or engineering students learning to program for the first time in Pascal. Students would normally be in their first year at a university or college, and be proficient in mathematics to a senior level. The book does not require mathematical manipulation: rather, it emphasises the translation of mathematics into programs. Thus the book would certainly be accessible for school pupils taking science in senior years. Because there is an emphasis on facts and examples, rather than long discussions, the book would also be suitable for experienced programmers or hobbyists who wish to pick up Pascal quickly.

The book is based on courses given to engineering and science students at first year university level since 1980 and we have included many of the class-tested examples and exercises from these courses.

Learning aids

There is a whole range of these! Specifically, the book offers:

- Helpful **hints** and reminders in the margins
- Succinct **summaries** at the end of each chapter
- Self-check **quizzes** for each chapter, with answers
- Over 60 worked **examples** with complete programs
- Six large **case studies** of real physical problems
- Over 100 set **problems** to suit a wide range of abilities and interests
- **Answers** at the back to a selection of the problems.

The theme of *Pascal Precisely for Engineers and Scientists* is learning by example, but it also serves the role of a reference text. The **forms** (syntax) which introduce each new feature are collected in an appendix, together with the well-known **bubble diagrams**. The appendices also include **lists** of keywords and predefined types, procedures and functions, and a brief account of Turbo Pascal.

Acknowledgements

Our thanks are due to our colleagues and students at the Universities of Southampton and the Witwatersrand, and the many international reviewers, for all their helpful comments and advice; to the members of the Addison-Wesley editorial and production teams, especially Tim Pitts, Stephen Bishop and Sheila Chatten, for their unfailing and very professional support; and to William and Michael for being so understanding about all our preoccupation with the book.

Judy M Bishop, Nigel T Bishop
Southampton, England
May 1990

Organisation of the book

The book is divided into ten chapters. Unlike many text books, we do not follow a simple step-by-step coverage from Pascal syntax. Instead, we present an integrated approach which combines control, data and methodology in each chapter. This enables meaningful programs to be written from the start, and reinforces the idea that computers are really useful tools. The large table overleaf gives in detail the topics covered – both the Pascal and the methodologies – and can be used to 'navigate' around the book, in conjunction with the contents and index. A summary of the table shows that the book falls neatly into three parts:

Chapters	Content
1 – 5	Most of Pascal, early numerical methods, methodologies for structured programming and modular decomposition.
6 – 7	Arrays, more numerical methods and five substantial case studies.
8 – 10	The data structuring facilities of Pascal, advanced topics and non-numerical methods.

Thus one would regard Chapters 1 to 5 as forming the core, Chapters 6 and 7 as reinforcing this with numerous applications, and Chapters 8 to 10 as advanced material.

The examples

Throughout the book, new concepts are illustrated with small copy-book examples in-line. Then each new feature is fully explored in a genuine

	Structure	Data	Control	Input/Ouput	Algorithm and Program Development	Numerical Methods	Programming Techniques
2	Program Procedures	subranges expressions const	for-loops	write writeln field widths	meaningful identifiers good layout top-down development self-containedness counting loops		
3	Begin-End	var integer real	assignment if-then-else	read readln	comments initialising divide and conquer global/local variables side effects controlling input cascading conditionals arithmetic accuracy	Predictor-corrector Fourier series	mean highest number swapping
4		char in	while-loops repeat-loops case-statement	text files	conditional looping trailer values for data keyed selection detect and react	Search method Newton-Raphson	highest common factor dialogue user interfaces histograms graphs
5	value and var parameters Functions	boolean			logical expressions procedural interfaces modular decomposition	Secant method Simpson's rule Shooting method	
6		type subranges (again) array			secure programming data decomposition	Least squares fit SOR method Gaussian elimination Linear boundary value problem	scalar product standard deviation
7					handling a project re-use of procedures		random numbers
8		enumerated string record set			state indicators sticking to a standard data abstraction debugging		complex numbers abstract data types
9		conformant arrays			generalisation		sorting linear search access tables
10		pointers		files			linked lists stacks queues non-linear lists

worked example. These 60 or so examples serve more than as simple illustrations of concepts: they are also case studies in problem-solving and programming methodology.   All except a few are structured into the problem-solving steps of:

Problem

Solution

Examples

Algorithm

Program

Testing

which follow the ideas explained in section 1.4. In some cases, these steps are repeated within an example, which emphasises that program development does not always result in the correct solution straight away!

The numerical methods

In the same way, we take an integrated approach to numerical methods. Many of these result in fairly simple programs, so instead of putting all the methods and accompanying examples at the end of the book, we introduce two or three per chapter as the Pascal constructs make them feasible.

Since this is a programming text book and not a numerical methods one, the emphasis is on describing the method to a level at which it can be converted into a program. Nevertheless, the background to the methods is covered, and mention is made of other methods in the category. As with the examples, we follow a structured approach to introducing methods, with the headings:

Rationale

Methods

Theory

Algorithm

Procedure

Thus we take a method, explain the engineering context in which it is useful, mention other similar methods, outline the theory, and develop it into an algorithm in the form of a pseudo-code chart. Most methods result in the development of a stand-alone procedure which is then used in the example that follows, and often in other examples later on.

There is more discussion, in section 1.5, on the place of numerical methods in introductory programming, and the way in which they are presented in this book.

Hints

Hints catch the eye.

A novel feature of *Pascal Precisely for Engineers and Scientists* is the use of hints in the margin to highlight important points or add an aside. The reader might be encouraged to add more of his or her own!

Summary, quiz and problems

Each chapter is rounded off with

- a summary of what went before,

- a quick 10-point quiz to test details, and

- a set of problems of varying levels of difficulty.

Some of the problems relate to ordinary every-day circumstances, others are couched in terms of engineering experience. Full answers for the quizzes are given at the back of the book, as well as answers or hints for a selection of the problems.

In several cases, a problem is developed through a sequence of chapters, with additions and modifications being posed as more Pascal constructs are learnt. The case studies are also opportunities for tackling extensions to existing programs, with each being followed by a set of guided problems.

Contents

1

Computers and programming

In this initial chapter we introduce computers and discuss the various tasks involved in problem solving, programming and algorithm development. Some of this material will be revision for those who have encountered computers before. We end with a discussion on the place of numerical methods in scientific computing.

1.1   Computers

What is a computer?   A straight answer might be

> A computer is an electronic machine.

but this does not tell us very much – no more than saying that a refrigerator is an electric machine. If we ask 'what is a refrigerator?', the answer would be

> A refrigerator is an electric machine for
> making and keeping things cold.

This defines the object in terms of the *function* that it performs – in this case, it is a built-in function to cool things. The difference between a computer and most other machines is that a computer is not confined to performing a specific built-in function. Functions are supplied by means of **programs**.

Let's try again: what is a computer?

> A computer is an electronic machine which can be programmed to perform a variety of functions.

What functions? Look around and you will see computers in most walks of life these days. If one had a brainstorming session in class and asked everyone to name one use of computers, the list could well be something like:

banking	airline bookings
controlling spaceships	controlling washing machines
solving equations	newspaper publishing
payrolls	controlling chemical plants
advising doctors	calculating engineering constraints
stock control in shops	marking examinations
playing games	monitoring heartbeats

and so on. Computers in general have a seemingly endless range of functions, but there are limits to what any one computer can do, and these limits are imposed by

- the **devices** to which the computer is connected, such as automatic money dispensers, cash registers, optical card readers, chemical equipment, volt meters, laser printers etc.;

- the **hardware** of the computer, whether it is extensive or minimal, fast or slow;

- the **software** that is provided in the form of programs.

Thus, any one computer cannot perform any function – it must be suited to the task in terms of its hardware, and it must have the appropriate devices and software.

Classes of computers

There are many terms in computing which are used to describe classes of computers, both in terms of their hardware, or in terms of the functions they are capable of performing.   What follows is a guide to the most common computer jargon.

Mainframes
Mainframe computers are usually large in terms of their memory and the number of devices that can be connected to them. They are usually very fast, and are used by hundreds or thousands of people in big organisations. A mainframe computer can be located in one city, and by using **tele-communications** via land lines or satellite, it can receive and transmit data to and from **remote** sites or devices in other cities. Examples of such computers would be those used by banks, with their automatic tellers all over the country, or by a university, with **terminals** all over the campus.
  Large machines are **multiprogrammed**, in that they can deal with several

functions and many users seemingly all at once. Of course, there is still only one computer, but it is so fast that it can share its time between tasks, without humans noticing this sharing process – at least most of the time. When one does notice degradation in the visible performance at any one device connected to a mainframe (such as a wait before a balance slip is printed) then it means that the computer could well be getting congested, with too many things to do.

There are two different kinds of large machines, depending on the tasks that they mainly perform. By far the largest number of computers in the world are concerned with **information processing** (formerly **data processing** or DP), and the applications they are involved in tend to use very large amounts of information stored in a **database**. For example, a bank keeps a database of all its accounts, their owners' names and addresses, recent transactions, balances and so on. The other kind of mainframe is used for very complex and lengthy calculations such as weather prediction or nuclear physics research. These computers are extremely fast at numerical computations and tend to be called **supercomputers.**

Minicomputers and microcomputers

Throughout the 1970s and 1980s, computer hardware has been getting smaller and cheaper, thus bringing computers within the range of individuals, for their businesses, home organisation or pleasure. **Minicomputers** were the first of the affordable computers and they tended to be used by 10 to 20 people, performing much the same tasks as a mainframe, but on a smaller scale. They were thus often found in small businesses or university departments.

Next came the **microcomputers**, which were distinct in that they were intended to be used by one person at a time – enter the **personal computer**. Personal computers meant an explosion in usable, friendly software, with video games, word processors, and spreadsheets being the most popular. Nowadays, microcomputers often have very sophisticated devices for performing graphics, high quality typesetting or even speech synthesis.

Following on from the micros are the **supermicros** or **workstations**, which have hardware that rivals that of many mainframes, but that are still meant to be used by only a few people. Their function is to provide the increased power demanded by the more sophisticated applications in research and software development, such as expert systems or image processing.

Microprocessors

Mainframes, minis and micros are quite visible – one can walk into an office or computer room and see the metal cabinets containing the electronic machinery. Probably far more numerous are the computers which reside inside other machinery – often known as **microprocessors** or even just **chips**. Such a computer is manufactured with its software built in, and this would consist of a dedicated program for performing a specific task, such as controlling a washing machine or an arcade game.

Microprocessors are relatively cheap to manufacture, but they are not intended for use by people directly. They are embedded in the machine they control and essentially form part of it. The software for embedded computers is developed on some other, larger, computer, and then may be **down-loaded** to the chip. It could well be that the chip in a household machine or a car is the same as one in a microcomputer – the difference is that the microcomputer has additional devices that enable it to communicate directly with people, and to be reprogrammed to carry out new tasks.

Networks
Computers of different makes and capabilities can be connected together to provide communication or to enhance the capabilities of one by using the facilities of another. Networks can be created within a small area such as a building or a campus where the physical connections between the machines can be made relatively easily (these are known as **local area networks** or LANs), or, on a larger scale, computers can be connected right around the world, provided a common **network protocol** is observed during communication.

The beauty of networks for the ordinary user is that communication is often initially via a telephone, so that very little special equipment is needed. Of course, it is not legal to gain access to another computer unless one has permission, and this is the area of concern of **computer security**.

1.2   Hardware and software

The machinery of a computer is known as the **hardware**. When learning to program, one is most often faced with the hardware of a microcomputer, for use by one person at a time, or a terminal connected to a mainframe being used by many people. We shall describe a microcomputer here, since it includes all the important computer components. The situation for a terminal would be similar, but some of the devices of the computer may be in other rooms. The diagram that follows shows a typical microcomputer.

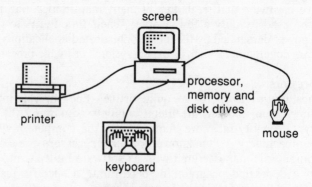

A typical microcomputer

While the arrangement of the boxes may vary, virtually every microcomputer will have a keyboard, screen, processor, memory, disk drive(s) and access to a printer. The mouse is optional, but is becoming increasingly popular. Let us look at each component in turn.

1. **Keyboard.** The keyboard enables one to type in instructions, programs and data to the computer. It resembles a typewriter, but has many more keys. The keyboard is an **input** device.

2. **Screen.** The screen enables one to see what is typed on the keyboard, and is also used by the computer for presenting results, messages, etc. Screens usually allow 80 characters across, and some 20–24 lines down. The screen is an **output** device.

3. **Processor.** The processor performs the actual work of the computer, calculating or processing data according to instructions, and producing results. Processor throughput can be measured in Mips (millions of instructions per second) and typically a microcomputer might run at 0.5 to 1 Mips. This figure will depend on the underlying speed of the computer's clock which is measured in Megahertz (MHz), with typical clock rates being 4.7 or 16MHz.

4. **Memory.** While it is working, the processor keeps the current program and much of the data and results in its memory. Memory is usually volatile in that the contents are erased when the power is switched off. Memory is measured in terms of **bytes** consisting of 8 binary digits (**bits**) and may in addition be organised in units called **words** which may be 16 or 32 bits long. Typically a microcomputer will have 1Mbyte (where M stands for Mega or $1\,048\,576 = 2^{20}$), but may have several Mbytes. Some memory is termed RAM (**randomly accessible memory**) and can be used freely by a program; other memory known as ROM (**read-only memory**) is used by software provided with the computer and cannot be overwritten.

5. **Disk drives.** In order for programs and data to be reusable, they must be stored on some permanent medium. Most computers have a sealed disk called a **hard disk** on which system programs as well as user programs can be kept. Hard disks vary in size, but for a microcomputer, a capacity of 40Mbytes is reasonable. Hard disks cannot be removed, and so for transporting and backing-up information, we also need to have a removable disk. These are called **floppy disks** or **diskettes**. Normally the user would remove the floppy disk at the end of the session and keep it safely until it is needed again. Floppies come in several physical sizes – 3.5 inch, 5.25 inch and 8 inch – and drives are built for one size only. The amount of information that can be stored on a floppy disk depends on the density and quality of the magnetic covering and may be from 800Kbytes to over 1 Mbyte.

6.   **Printer.** Printers produce the **hard copy** of programs or results that can be taken away and studied. The printer may be connected directly to a microcomputer, or it may be shared by several in which case there would be a switch box, possibly manually operated, to link the printer to a particular machine. Three types of printer are popular. In order of increasing cost they are:

- **matrix printers** which give reasonable quality printing, and are versatile in being able to output reasonable selections of fonts and graphics;

- **daisywheel printers** which resemble typewriters and produce typewriter quality output, but have a limited range of typefaces and cannot produce graphical output;

- **laser printers** which can produce output of nearly typeset quality, complete with font changes and graphics.

This book was printed on a laser printer using output from a microcomputer.

7.   **Mouse.** A mouse is a pointing device which acts as an assistant to the keyboard. It enables parts of the screen and the instructions that manipulate it to be selected more easily. To operate a mouse, one rolls it around on a flat tabletop, and the motion is reflected on the screen. When the correct place is found, a button on the mouse is clicked, to indicate that the computer can go ahead and perform the selected operation. Some mice have one button, some have two or even three.

Software

As **hardware** is the name for the electronic components discussed above, so **software** is the name for the programs that reside in the computer. In addition to hardware, computers also possess resident software, and additional software can be obtained and written. The figure below gives an impression of the different layers of software.

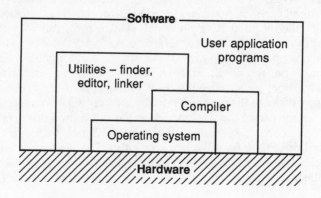

The main piece of resident software in a computer is its **operating system** which controls all the peripherals and provides an interface to the user. It generally handles access to the utilities, which can include an editor, a filer (or finder), and to the compiler.

The **editor** is a program that enables one to type in a program, store it on a disk file, edit it, and add to it at will. The **filer** is there to keep track of all the names and properties of the files and disks being used. On a multiprogramming system, further components of the operating system keep track of the amount of time and resources consumed by each user. Sometimes these are budgeted to users, and one has to take care to keep within one's allotted budget since the system could deny access if a budget has been exceeded.

A system may have several **compilers**, one for each computer language. The compiler's task is to translate a program into a form that the computer can then execute. In the process, it checks the program for incorrect spelling, grammar and usage and reports any errors to the user.

As you gain practical experience with using a computer, you will become familiar with the features for your particular computer. Although operating systems for different machines are superficially different, underneath they all provide the same sorts of functions, and after a while it becomes relatively easy to move from one computer to another.

1.3 Problem solving and programming

As we have already discussed, the crucial difference between computers and other machines is that computers can be **programmed**. What is a program?

> A program is a set of ordered instructions which can be understood by the computer.

The purpose of the program is to provide a new capability to the computer – a capability to solve a new problem. The process of developing the program is called **programming** but in reality it involves all the skills relevant to **problem solving** as well.

In the context of programming, problem solving involves several stages, each with its own particular difficulties and skills. The stages are:

- defining the problem,
- outlining a solution,
- developing an algorithm,
- programming the algorithm,
- testing the program,
- documenting the solution,
- maintenance.

Problem definition

The first step is naturally to define the problem. This is suprisingly difficult in practice. Problems that are intended for solution by a computer can be phrased at any level from the wishful:

'Theatre reservations are too slow in this town.'

to the specific:

'What is the standard deviation of the following 100 numbers?'

The purpose of the problem definition phase is to pin down the problem more exactly. To do this, we try to define what the **data** will look like, and what the expected **results** will be. It is often useful to work through an example with the person who set the problem, thus bringing to light any misconceptions or misunderstandings.

For example, suppose one is asked to arrange a file of student records 'in order'. The questions to be asked would include the following:

- What is the basis for the ordering – surnames or student numbers or years and then surnames, or whatever?

- Must the old file be replaced by the new one, or must it remain?

Despite the importance of this phase of problem solving, it is nevertheless the case that a problem can seldom be completely defined *a priori*. There will always be aspects which only become clear as a solution is being worked out, and this is quite acceptable. It is actually better to leave some questions open until more information is available, rather than to make pre-emptive assumptions which may spoil the solution at a later stage.

Outlining a solution

The very first question to be asked is 'Do we need a computer at all?' There are times when using a computer is not appropriate, although it seems attractive at first. For example, deciding to put one's car mileage, consumption and service record on a computer could turn out to be more of a nuisance than an aid because the computer is not available in the car, where most of the questions about its state will probably be asked. It would be better to stick with a log book and calculator.

However, given that a computerised solution is required, it is necessary at this stage to set up the parameters within which the solution must work. Must the solution be fast? Are answers required on a terminal? Must results be stored on disk as well? In fact, is all the necessary equipment available? For example, if we need to print a graph of a function, it will make quite a difference to the solution whether we have a graph plotter connected, or whether we have to simulate plotting by printing dots on a printer.

At this stage, too, one should be thinking of past solutions. Has this problem been solved before, or even something very like it? Time can be saved by reusing tried and tested methods, rather that starting from scratch with a solution. If the problem is in a particular domain, such as mathematics or biology, we should make sure that we have all the essential equations and methods worked out, and be aware of any constraints that apply to the numbers and arithmetic involved. As we shall see later on, computers have bounds on their arithmetic capabilities, and as a result errors can creep in.

Algorithms

It is at the algorithm stage that the logical thought-processes must start, and the outline of a solution be worked out into a step-by-step method. Algorithms have been around since long before computers were first thought of and are visible in many walks of life. For example, in cooking, one might find the following recipe for meringues:

Full treatment of algorithms in the next section.

> Beat the egg whites until stiff. You will know that
> they have been beaten enough, if they don't fall out
> when the bowl is turned over.

This is an unhelpful algorithm, since the test for completion will not allow the process to continue!

In general, algorithms in computer programming must have certain properties, if they are to be used as starting points for a program. These properties all relate to preciseness and are: unambiguous, finite, brief, self-checking and deterministic. An algorithm for summing positive and negative numbers together and separately would be:

Summing three ways

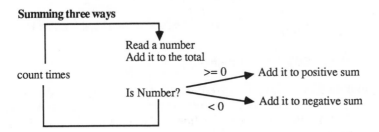

How to achieve good algorithms, and how to write then down, merits several sections on its own, and we shall take up the topic properly in the next section, and again in Chapter 5. Moreover, this whole book is a case study in algorithm development: there are over 60 worked examples where a problem is taken through a draft solution to an algorithm, and from there to a program which is tested on the computer.

Programming

Now we have to refine the algorithm and write it down in a programming language. There are many, many such languages in use throughout the world, but relatively few that are available on all kinds of computers. These are known as the **high-level languages**, and include Pascal, Ada, FORTRAN, COBOL, BASIC, C, LISP, Prolog and Modula-2. These languages are also **general purpose** in that they can, by and large, be used to solve a wide range of problems. They do have their special areas of application, though, with COBOL being business-oriented, FORTRAN being for scientific use, and Prolog being very good for artificial intelligence.

The choice of which language to use for a particular application will depend on what is available, and whether it has any specific features that give it an edge over others. For learning to program, educators usually choose a language that is **modern, easy to understand** and has **good protection against mistakes**. Pascal fulfils all these goals. It was devised in 1970 by a Swiss professor, Niklaus Wirth, and is now used throughout the world in universities and colleges as a first teaching language.

Named after Blaise Pascal, (1623–1662) the French mathematician and philosopher.

Part of a Pascal program that implements the algorithm depicted above is:

```
PROCEDURE Summation3;
VAR
  number  : real;
  i          : 1..10000; {say}
BEGIN
  Total := 0;
  PosTotal := 0;
  NegTotal := 0;
  FOR i := 1 to count do begin
    read (number);
    Total := Total + number;
    if number > 0 then PosTotal := PosTotal + number
                       else NegTotal := NegTotal + number;
  END {for};
  readln;
END; {Summation3}
```

The program is written in a stylised, yet fairly readable, English. Each step in the program is written on a new line, and the lines are indented to achieve certain effects. For example, the lines between the FOR and END {for} constitute a loop, and this is emphasised by the indentation.

High-level languages are **machine-independent** in that they can be run on any computer for which a compiler is available. Every computer also has its own specific **machine language** which it can execute directly, and which will differ from machine to machine. Programming is not usually done at this level, though sometimes it is necessary to use a symbolic form of the machine language, known as **assembly language** or just **assembler**.

Programming languages fulfil many of the properties of algorithms mentioned above, but there are good and bad ways of using them, just as there are good and bad ways of using English. One of the goals of this book is to teach the correct way of using a programming language, so that the resulting program is both efficiently executable by the computer and easily understandable by humans.

Testing

Once a program has been written down in a programming language, it has to be submitted to the computer in some way, **compiled** into that computer's machine language and then executed. On the way, things may go wrong, and steps may need to be repeated. This is all summed up in the following diagram.

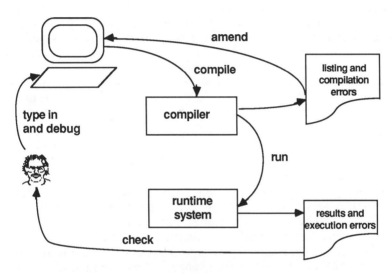

Life cycle of a program

The programmer takes his sheets of paper to a computer keyboard and types in the program. The program, now known as **source** is sent to the compiler, which checks its grammar or syntax. If anything is wrong, a list of **compilation** errors will be produced, or the errors could be indicated as they occur. The errors must be attended to by changing the program, and then the source is resubmitted to the compiler.

This process continues until there are no more errors. The program can then be **run**, which is done by a **runtime system** which is either part of Pascal or part of the computer's operating system. The program will produce results, and it may also produce **execution errors**. In either case, the results must be carefully scrutinised, a process which is usually better done away from the computer in peace and quiet. If the program is not executing correctly, then the necessary changes must be made, and the process begun again. Unfortunately, it is sometimes unclear what is causing an error, in which case, more information must be gained by putting additional instructions in the program. This process is known as **debugging**. Once a program runs without errors and produces the correct results, it can be released for production use. In the case of student programs, this usually implies handing it in for marking.

The debugging process is illustrated in many of the worked examples in this book, and particularly in example 6.1.

Documentation

When a program is running, it can provide instructions to the user as to what it expects in the way of data or other responses. However, it is not always possible to provide all information about the operation of a program in this way, and it is then necessary to write a **product manual** or **user's guide** to go with it. Such a document should be written primarily in the terminology of the problem domain, not in computer terms.

On the other hand, there is also a need for a **system manual** or **implementor's guide** which does go into the technical details of the program, and can be used particularly by people who may need to modify the program later.

Maintenance

Finally, the program is up and running, and like any piece of equipment, it needs to be maintained. It is not that parts of the program might 'wear out', but that the environment might change, such as a new kind of disk being added, or even a new processor. It is also true that requirements change over time, and because programs are so adaptable, people have come to expect an instant reaction to any desire for change. Thus programs are modified, expanded, speeded-up or otherwise fiddled with all the time, and this **maintenance** is a large part of any company's software budget.

As a student, you will be involved in relatively little maintenance, because once a program works, you move on to the next assignment. Nevertheless, it is worth remembering that the care that is put into writing clear programs and documentation to go with them will reduce the effort required to maintain such programs in the future. The six case studies in this book are specifically designed to exercise this part of computing, as each is followed by suggested improvements and extensions.

1.4   Algorithm development

The development of a good algorithm is central to the process of transforming an engineering problem into a computer program which solves it. Unfortunately, there is no science of algorithms that can be studied formally: much has to be learnt by experience and practice. Nevertheless, there are a few key techniques which we can follow, and which will guide us in the early stages of setting down methods in an orderly way.

We shall illustrate these techniques by considering the example of finding the sum of all the positive numbers in a given list of 20.

Notations

The first issue we must settle is the notation for writing down an algorithm. There are many notations, some proprietary, some informal and some more suited for business data processing. In the scientific community, the most widely used notations are **flow charts** and **pseudo-code.**

Consider the example of summing 20 numbers. A flow chart to do this would be:

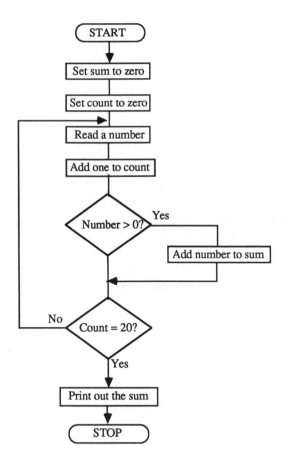

Flow charts have found their way into everyday life, and by their familiarity, are reasonably easy to read. Their disadvantages, though, are numerous. They are complicated to draw, and almost impossible to amend; they tend to encourage too much detail immediately, and, most of all, they do not foster the algorithm techniques which good programming practice now promotes. The above flow chart is already more detailed than the corresponding Pascal program would be.

The other popular alternative is pseudo-code, which is a stylised English more akin to modern programming. The same example in a pseudo-code would be:

(1) Set sum to zero
(2) Do 20 times
  (2.1) Read a number
  (2.2) If it is positive, add it to sum
(3) Print the sum

Pseudo-code treats algorithms at a higher level than flow charts. It employs indented levels to indicate structure and grouping, and enables us to see the algorithm at different levels of detail. The disadvantage of pseudo-code is that it loses the visual impact that lines and boxes convey.

Pseudo-code charts

In this book, we have chosen to use both charts and pseudo-code in an informal notation called **pseudo-code charts**. The form of a pseudo-code chart is as simple as possible, making them very easy to draw on paper, freehand.

The chart starts off with a **title** which indicates the overall intention of the algorithm. Thereafter, instructions are given in plain, though abbreviated, English, and lines are used to show alternative and repetitive paths. In our notation, the above algorithm becomes:

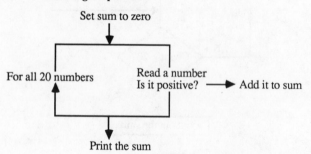

The box indicates that the instructions must be repeated: the action is given on the right hand side, and the information about how many times it must be done, on the left hand side. The question 'Is it positive?' is followed by an arrow that indicates what should be done in this case. After this choice has been taken, we proceed on and around the chart.

The advantage of an informal notation such as this is that an algorithm can be expressed in greater or lesser detail: we are not restricted to the kinds of instructions that we write down. Some may be at a very high level, such as 'Solve the first equation for x', whereas others are almost atomic actions, such as 'Set sum to zero'. In all other ways, the charts combine the advantages of the other two methods with few of the disadvantages.

Top-down development

Having settled on a notation, we can now discuss some of the algorithm development techniques we shall need in the chapters that follow. The first is as old as the hills – or at least as old as Caesar's invasion of Gaul – and is termed **top-down development**. It involves viewing a problem in its entirety, and then breaking it up into **sub-problems**. We then solve the sub-problems in the same way, just by breaking them up, until such time as we reach a sub-problem that can be solved by an existing technique, or by a simple sequence of instructions. (Caesar called this **divide-and-conquer**).

So, if we were taking our previous example from the top down, we would start off thus:

> **Summing the positives**
>> Set sum to zero
>> Read and add the positive numbers
>> Print the sum

The first and last instructions are already as simple as we can make them, but the middle one can be tackled further, giving

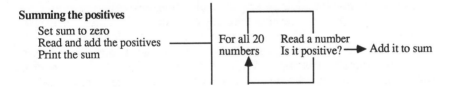

The line-and-bar notation indicates a refinement of the instruction 'Read and add positives'. Since we do the refinement step by step, this process is also known as **step-wise refinement**.

The six case studies in the book, as well as examples 3.7, 5.7 and 8.7 illustrate this process particularly well.

Structured programming

Within the field of computer programming, there was a revolution in the 1970s, as computer scientists sought to convert people from programming according to flow charts into something less error-prone. The key to new methodology, which was known as **structured programming**, was the use of a restricted set of constructs, which in themselves were simple, safe, and yet powerful. The three constructs are called:

- sequencing
- selection
- repetition.

Sequencing acknowledges that computers follow instructions in an ordered sequence, so that in the absence of any other information, sequencing prevails. Pascal features that support sequencing are the assignment (section 3.2), input-output (sections 2.4, 3.3, 4.4, 10.4) and the begin-end statements (section 3.4).

Selection enables choices to be made, based either on some **condition** or on a **key value**. The idea is that the actions associated with a choice form a closed sequence in themselves, and when they are completed, control returns automatically to after the choice. This is why in our pseudo-code chart we show the following:

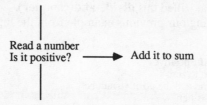

and do not bother to draw a line from 'Add it to sum' back to the main stream. Pascal statements which implement selection are the if-then-else (section 3.4) and the case-statement (section 4.3).

Repetition involves doing a sequence of actions several times, with either a count or a condition governing the number of the repetitions. Once again, the important point is that the sequence to be repeated forms a whole, and may not be split up, except by another of the structured constructs. We say this even in our small example. Within the repeated read-add cycle, there are two paths: the one has a read and a question, the other has a read, question and add. The distinction between the two is based on a selection construct in a proper way. Pascal features that implement repetition are the for-loop (section 2.5), the while and repeat-loops (section 4.2) and recursion (section 9.4).

Given the good languages we have these days, it is perhaps hard to imagine what the bad old days were like. The problem was related to the association of a label with certain instructions in a program, coupled with an ability to pass control to any statement willy-nilly. The opportunities for errors were legion. For example, the correct Pascal programming constructs derived from the algorithm above would be:

```
sum := 0;
```

```
for count := 1 to 20 do begin
  read(number);
  if number > 0 then sum := sum + number;
end;
write(sum);
```

Programmed with labels and the **goto** statement, this becomes very involved:

```
sum := 0;
count := 0;
1 : read(number);
if number > 0 then goto 2;
goto 3
2 : sum := sum + number;
3 : count := count + 1;
if count < 20 then goto 1;
write(sum);
```

If, for example, the *goto* 3 statement was omitted, the program would do completely the wrong thing. Yet the unstructured nature of the statements makes it difficult to spot such omissions.

Pascal was specifically designed to foster structured programming, and this book aims to reinforce these ideas by good example throughout.

Modular decomposition

Techniques of algorithm development are intimately entwined with good programming practice. Where structured programming helps in the lower levels of programming, a technique called **modular decomposition** assists in the higher levels.

Suppose we have a large, complex problem to solve, and in fact several people – maybe twenty or even a hundred, involved in the project. We would start by dividing up the tasks – but where do we draw the boundaries? How do we decide which sub-problems go together, and which depend on the results from others? A complex problem may well not devolve into a simple hierarchical structure as explained in the discussion under top-down development.

The key here is to decompose the problem into modules based on **interfaces**, whilst keeping the interaction between the modules to a minimum. We start with the different sorts of data in the solution and consider the operations that will be needed to manipulate them. For each sort of data, we parcel it up with its operations into a **module**. The module then decides on which parts of the data and operations it will export to the rest of the program, and reserves for itself those that it does not deem to be of public concern.

In this way, we keep interfaces to a minimum, and lessen the chances of confusion and errors. Even in our little summing example, we can see the benefits of modular decomposition. Suppose this algorithm forms part of a very much larger system. We would set the interface up to be only that data that was necessary to be seen outside – the **black box** approach. Thus the interface could be defined as

PROCEDURE PositiveSums (var sum : integer);

The program that used this black box would therefore only be concerned with the data in the sum: it would not have to know anything about number or count, which remain private to the workings of the algorithm.

Pascal features that support modular decomposition are procedures (sections 2.4, 5.4, 9.3), functions (section 5.3) and parameters (sections 5.2, 9.2, 9.3) .

Generalisation

An essential technique for launching an algorithm into the wide world of a programming project is to ensure that it is sufficiently general to be used in all the necessary cases. Take our example. We stipulated that 20 numbers would be read: what if there were 10 instead, or 400? Looking at the algorithm, it is clear that it will not change if there are more or fewer numbers. Thus we can generalise it to handle n numbers, making this part of the interface, i.e.

PROCEDURE PositiveSums (n : integer; var sum : integer);

Generalisation is supported in Pascal by means of parameters (sections 5.2, 9.2, 9.3).

Bottom-up and re-usable programming

It would be incorrect to believe that top-down is the only way to develop algorithms. We can also start at the opposite end and look for the small problems that can be easily solved. These can form building blocks for the problems higher up. It is all a question of scale: we developed the 'Summing the positives' algorithm from the top down, but within a wider picture, it could be part of a bottom-up process to develop tools for later use. In practice, a little bit of both is required – top-down and bottom-up.

The important spin-off from bottom-up development is that algorithms can be re-used in many different projects. This is certainly a theme of this book. Many of the algorithms developed in the early chapters form essential tools for more complex problems later on. In all cases, we have taken care to express the algorithms with clear interfaces so that they are self-contained, and can be re-used as is.

In scientific and engineering programming, it is likely that there will be a library of such components available on the computer. The skill then will be in reading the library's catalogue, in selecting the correct algorithm and in ensuring that the interfaces fit together properly.

Data abstraction

Modern thinking is that proper attention to the structure of data in a program is as important as attention to the control constructs. Indeed, we have seen above that the vital technique of modular decomposition depends on the way in which the data is viewed in a program.

In fact, in scientific and engineering problems, there is not the diversity of data that one finds in the system programming or data processing environments. Most often, the data is numeric, and structure is confined to vectors, matrices and tables. Nevertheless, knowledge of data structuring techniques is an essential part of any programmer's repertoire. Pascal has a rich choice of such techniques, and these are covered in Chapters 8 and 10. Their use is well illustrated in examples 5.7, 8.4, 8.6, 8.7 and case study 6.

1.5   Scientific computing

The advent of computers in the 1940s and 1950s was largely due to the efforts of scientists at the time who needed to solve more and more problems to a greater degree of accuracy. In order to use the computer, scientists had to express their mathematical models and solutions in numerical form. The branch of study which they relied on is called numerical analysis, and from it we have the numerical methods which are the mainstay of any computationally oriented engineer or scientist.

A **numerical method** is an expression of a mathematical solution in a form which produces numerical answers, rather than symbolic ones. Mathematicians typically manipulate symbols and produce symbolic answers. Engineers are concerned, in addition, with the physical properties of the mathematics, fitting actual values to equations, and expecting numbers as results.

The mathematical techniques that can be expressed numerically include:

- differentiation
- integration
- finding roots of equations
- solving differential equations
- solving simultaneous equations
- curve fitting and interpolation
- matrix manipulation.

Thus we can differentiate x^2 symbolically to give $2x$, but we can also apply a numerical technique which for a given value of x will produce the appropriate value for the differential. The value of the numerical methods is that they can be applied in cases where the symbolic answer is hard to find.

The above list contains techniques which are now very well understood and many can be explained at a simple algorithmic level. They therefore provide an excellent vehicle for the novice programmer to practice new-found skills.

In this book we shall present one or maybe two methods in most of the above categories, and then follow this with an example of their application, drawn from a real engineering problem.

An example

For example, in Chapter 3 we present a simple differential equation for the current variation in an LR circuit, viz.

$$\frac{dI}{dt} = \frac{E}{L} - \frac{R}{L} I$$

and show how it can be solved using a predictor-corrector algorithm, illustrated by the following pseudo-code chart:

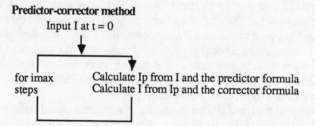

and the part of the program that would implement this algorithm are:

```
PROCEDURE PredictorCorrector;
  VAR
    i : 1..maxint;
    currentp : real;
  BEGIN
    FOR i := 1 to imax do begin
      currentp := current + h * (E/L – R * current/L);
      current := current + 0.5 * h * (E/L – R*current/L)+
                 (E/L – R*currentp/L);
      t := t + h;
    END;
  END; {PredictorCorrector}
```

What about understanding formulae?

The formulae involved in both the methods themselves and in their applications can look quite intimidating. Nevertheless, it is a programmer's job to be able to interpret formulae, and to present them in a form acceptable to the computer. With sights set on learning to program, it is not essential that the meaning of the formulae be understood. Such understanding will add to the fulfilment that programming a problem brings, but the methods and examples should still be accessible to those who are not familiar with the particular branch of engineering or science under discussion.

Graphics

The ability to express results graphically is one of the most attractive features of today's computers. Even in very simple terms, we can use diagrams to present a vivid realisation of lists of numbers.

For example, the output from the predictor-corrector algorithm mentioned above would normally be a table of the values of time, t, and current, I. But with very little effort we can enhance the table with a histogram showing explicitly the current value as follows:

t	I	
0.00	0.0000	
0.10	0.3625	* * * *
0.20	0.6593	* * * * * *
0.30	0.9023	* * * * * * * * *
0.40	1.1013	* * * * * * * * * *
0.50	1.2642	* * * * * * * * * * * *
0.60	1.3976	* * * * * * * * * * * * *
0.70	1.5068	* * * * * * * * * * * * * *
0.80	1.5962	* * * * * * * * * * * * * * *
0.90	1.6694	* * * * * * * * * * * * * * * *
1.00	1.7293	* * * * * * * * * * * * * * * * *

The advent of good graphical hardware is a 1980's phenomenon, and Pascal is a language from the early 1970's. Pascal therefore does not have features which enable one to go much further than simple histograms. However, most Pascal implementations do have ways of accessing graphics via a package, and this is discussed briefly in Chapter 4.

The use of graphics in real problems is shown in examples 4.8, 4.9, 6.5 and case study 4. It is also mentioned in several of the problems at the end of the chapters.

Packages

Numerical analysis is one of the more mature branches of computing and as such, is fortunate in having a wealth of techniques which are already written up as programs, or more precisely, as **packages**. The practising engineer or scientist who wishes to use a numerical technique as part of the solution to a problem will in many cases find the package he needs in the computer's library. As some of the methods are fairly complex, this is an obvious advantage.

In this book, we are primarily concerned with mastering the rudiments of programming in a particular language, and cannot at the same time reflect real-world practices exactly. Nevertheless, wherever possible, we have expressed the methods as self-contained modules, with tightly-controlled interfaces, and have shown how they can be used and re-used in different circumstances in different programs, without change.

Examples where this is done extensively are the predictor-corrector method, which is used in example 3.9 and again in case study 1; the SOR method, which is used in program example 6.6 and case study 2; and the secant method which is used in example 5.8 and case study 1.

Finding out more

This book does not intend to do more than present a selection of good numerical methods that have a wide applicability in science and engineering. To find out about more methods, and about their derivation and limitations, the reader will need to consult a text book specifically on numerical methods or numerical analysis.

Summary

☐   The functions of a computer are provided by **programs** and are constrained by the available **hardware**, **software** and **devices**.

☐   Different classes of computers have different capabilities, operate at different speeds, and are suitable for different applications.

☐   A simple computer comprises a processor, memory, disk drives, screen, keyboard, printer and mouse.

☐   Problem solving involves several well-defined steps, and leads to a solution which can be phrased as a program in a language such as Pascal.

☐   Programs need to be carefully designed, written, tested, documented and maintained.

☐   Scientific and engineering problems can be solved using numerical methods which can be expressed as computer programs.

Self-check quiz

1.   What limits the capabilities of a particular computer?
2.   What is meant by multiprogramming?
3.   Explain the difference between the terms
   - microcomputer
   - microprocessor
   - personal computer

- chip?
4. In what units is the speed of computers measured?
5. What is the difference between RAM and ROM?
6. What is the function of a compiler?
7. List five desirable properties of algorithms.
8. What is a machine language?
9. What is meant by a compilation error? By an execution error?
10. List some of the components of a system's documentation.

Problems

1.1   List the input devices and output devices for the computer you are familiar with.
1.2   What is the clock speed of the computer you are using?
1.3   How much memory does your computer have?
1.4   What is the capacity of the disks you are using?
1.5   Would this text book (including all the spaces) fit on your disk, assuming one printed character per byte of memory?
1.6   List all the software that you encountered when getting your first Pascal program running on your computer.
1.7   List all the computer applications that you come into contact with in the course of an ordinary week.
1.8   Decide on two very different algorithms for directing a stranger from the building you are in to the bus station.
1.9   What algorithms do you come into contact with in an ordinary day? Do they match up to the criteria listed in this chapter?
1.10 Have you ever been on the wrong end of a computer error? If so, could you tell whether the mistake was in the program or in the data that was fed in?

2

Beginning with Pascal

2.1 Programs
2.2 Output with write and writeln
2.3 Expressions with simple arithmetic
2.4 Structuring with procedures
2.5 Repetition with counting loops

Our first introduction to Pascal emphasises the constructs for organising a program in a structured way, and for obtaining satisfying amounts of output with a few simple statements. After covering the Pascal notation for writing formulae and printing out results, we concentrate on two important Pascal features: procedures and loops. The eight worked examples give an illustrative introduction to problem solving and show how we can take a problem through the steps of defining a solution, outlining an algorithm, translating it into a program, and testing it out.

2.1 Programs

A Pascal program consists of

- **declarations** which describe the objects of a program – its constants, types, variables, functions and procedures;

- **statements** which provide the step-by-step algorithm, making use of the objects.

The **objects** in a program are associated with the data that the program is intended to manipulate. Objects need **identifiers** by which the statements can refer to them. In keeping with the properties of algorithms, the statements are executed in sequence, one after the other. Some statements are specifically designed to alter this sequence, and are sometimes known as **control statements**, because they alter the flow of control of the program.

A program that is solving a real problem will also usually require input and produce output:

- **input** is the actual information or data that the program will process;
- **output** forms the results of the program's endeavours.

The data and results are considered to be in **files**. Files are held on a device such as a disk, and the particular files required by a program can be specified for each run of the program.

The form of a program

These elements are combined in the program in the following form:

Program

```
PROGRAM name (files);
   declarations
BEGIN
   statements
END.
```

The plain words such as PROGRAM, BEGIN and END are Pascal **keywords** which indicate the structure of the program. The words in italics describe parts of the program that must be supplied by the programmer. The program name is compulsory, but the files, declarations and statements are optional. Thus the following is a valid Pascal program which does nothing.

```
PROGRAM DoNothing;
   BEGIN
   END.
```

There are many kinds of declarations and many kinds of statements. Throughout this book we shall be introducing the various declarations and statements in easy stages, until the whole language is covered. We start in this chapter by looking at statements for writing, then we look at the declaration and use of procedures, and the statement for a counting loop.

2.2   Output with write and writeln

The information that a program produces as the result of its computations is generally known as **output**. The process of producing output is variously called outputting, printing or writing.

The form for the Pascal statements to print a piece of text are:

Output statements

```
write (list of items ) ;
writeln (list of items) ;
writeln;
```

where the list of items in parentheses consists of values to be printed, and the items are separated by commas. First we look at printing strings, and then at printing numbers.

A **string** is any sequence of characters enclosed in apostrophes, for example

'Resistance in ohms'   '£'   '$5.95 per lot'   'User''s Guide'

To include an apostrophe itself in a string, it is given twice, as in the last example. A character is the name given to a string of length one.

A **writeln statement** prints out the list of items and ends the line of print. Thus the statements

To include an apostrophe in a string, type it twice.

```
writeln ('James Stevenson');
writeln ('Civil Engineering');
writeln ('Greater University');
```

will cause the following to be written out:

James Stevenson
Civil Engineering
Greater University

*In examples, Pascal statements are given in plain type, and the resulting output in **bold**.*

The **write statement** works in a similar way except that it does not end the line of print, so that a subsequent write or writeln will continue to print on the same line from the last point reached.

The list of items is optional for a writeln statement and, if it appears on its own, then it will finish off the current line. This can be used to obtain a blank line, as in

```
writeln ('James Stevenson');
writeln ('Civil Engineering');
writeln ('Greater University');
writeln;
writeln ('------------------------');
```

which would give as output

James Stevenson
Civil Engineering
Greater University

Example 2.1   Printing a label

Our first program writes out a name and address for a label. The program
is:

```
PROGRAM Label (output);
  BEGIN
    writeln ('-----------------------------');
    writeln ('|                           |');
    writeln ('|    James Stevenson        |');
    writeln ('|    Civil Engineering      |');
    writeln ('|    Greater University     |');
    writeln ('|                           |');
    writeln ('-----------------------------');
  END.
```

The program name clearly indicates what the program is to do. The word
output after the program name indicates that the program is going to make
use of an output file to do some writing. The keyword BEGIN indicates the
start of the statements. After the keyword END, there is a full stop. The
output produced by this program would be:

```
-----------------------------
|                           |
|    James Stevenson        |
|    Civil Engineering      |
|    Greater University     |
|                           |
-----------------------------
```

Notice that we can use dashes, bars and other such symbols for effect, in the
same way as one would on a typewriter. There are many such printing
tricks, and computers are particularly good at them. Further examples in
this chapter illustrate some more.

Layout

How the program is written down, in terms of lines and spaces, does not have
an effect on how the output appears. Only what is inside the apostrophes is
actually written out. When writing strings, there is no gap caused by splitting
them up into different items or into different write statements, nor do blank
lines in the program have any effect. Therefore the following statements,
although unconventional, will cause the second line of the label to be printed
as before.

```
        write ('Civil');writeln  (' Engineer',
'ing');
```

The point is that the instructions given to the computer do not have to be in any special layout. We usually write them neatly one underneath each other, and we shall also use **indenting** to make groups of statements stand out, but there is no formal rule that says this should be so.

Other points about the form of the program which we can make right now are:

- more than one statement can be written on a line;

- statements can be split over several lines;

- statements are separated by semicolons.

The effect of this last point is that a semicolon is placed at the end of virtually every statement.

The layout of a program is irrelevant to the computer, but is very important to the human reader.

Field widths

An item to be printed can be followed by a colon and an indication of the number of spaces in which the item is to appear. This is useful for lining things up. If we wanted to write names of different lengths in columns then we could use:

```
writeln ('Resonant frequency':20, 'hertz':15);
writeln ('Inductance':20, 'henries':15);
writeln ('Capacitance':20, 'farads':15);
```

Resonant frequency	**hertz**
Inductance	**henries**
Capacitance	**farads**

Field widths can be used for making columns and gaps.

This feature is particularly useful for getting gaps of the correct size, using the string with a single space in it, instead of counting out the spaces explicitly. So

```
write (' ':10);
```

will write 10 spaces.

Example 2.2   SI Prefix table

We can write a program to print a double table of the power values of SI unit prefixes, using field widths to make the columns neatly. We choose columns of 8, 5 and 6 (total 19) for the prefix, abbreviation and value respectively. The powers of ten will be written using two lines, and making use of the column widths to line up the power correctly.

```
PROGRAM SIUnits (output);
   BEGIN
      writeln('Table of SI Unit Prefixes and Abbreviations');
```

```
writeln('=================================');
writeln;
writeln(' ':19, '–12':3,' ':25, '3');
write('pico':8, 'p':5, 'x10':6,' ':9);
writeln('kilo':8, 'K':5, 'x10':6);

writeln(' ':19, '–6':3,' ':25, '6');
write('micro':8, 'u':5, 'x10:6,' ':9);
writeln('mega':8,'M':5, 'x10':6);

writeln(' ':19, '–3':3,' ':25, '9');
write('milli':8, 'm':5, 'x10':6,' ':9);
writeln('giga':8,'G':5, 'x10':6);
```

        END.

which would produce output as:

Table of SI Unit Prefixes and Abbreviations
==================================

pico	p	$\text{x}10^{-12}$	kilo	K	$\text{x}10^{3}$
micro	u	$\text{x}10^{-6}$	mega	M	$\text{x}10^{6}$
milli	m	$\text{x}10^{-3}$	giga	G	$\text{x}10^{9}$

2.3   Expressions with simple arithmetic

The two programs developed in the last two sections used the write and writeln statements to print **strings**. It is also possible to print **numbers** and, indeed, to print the results of calculations. For example, to print the cube of 23 less 54, we would have

        writeln (23 * 23 * 23 – 54);

which would print out

        12113

Such calculations are called **expressions** in Pascal. The way in which expressions are written in computer languages is slightly different to the normal way of writing them in mathematics. The two main differences are

Computer languages use * for multiply and / for divide

- that multiplication is indicated by an asterisk *
- division is indicated by a slash /.

So, to convert 15°C to Fahrenheit, using the formula $\frac{9t}{5} + 32$ we would write writeln ((15 * 9 / 5) + 32);

which would print out

5.900000E+01

Integers and reals

The output from the temperature conversion is somewhat disconcerting: why is it printed with an E (presumably standing for an exponent to base 10), rather than just 59? The answer is in the **types** and their **operators**. Pascal distinguishes between **integer** numbers and **real** numbers. The integers represent whole numbers and the reals permit fractional parts, but **also include the integers**. For integers, we have the operators

+	addition
−	subtraction
*	multiplication

Pascal distinguishes between **Integer** numbers and **real** numbers.

(plus two others which we shall leave to Section 3.5). But the result of dividing two numbers is not defined for integers, so the fourth operator

/	division

gives an answer which is a real number, even if the operands are integers.

There is no Pascal operator for raising a value to a power, or for expressing roots. These must be done in a rather long-winded way using **functions**. For the time being we introduce only the functions for squaring and square-rooting, i.e.

x^2	sqr (x)
$\sqrt{x}$	sqrt (x)

Special functions for an exponent of 2 or 1/2.

These functions can be used as values themselves, so that the fourth root of x would be written *sqrt(sqrt(x))*. The rest of the functions are covered in section 3.6.

Real numbers span a wide range of values, and by default, Pascal prints them in scientific format, with one figure before the decimal point, and the resulting decimal exponent after an E. This is clearly messy for simple results, and there are two ways of overriding it:

1. Use field widths.

2. Convert the real back to an integer.

We shall consider the first one here, and leave the second to section 3.5.

Field widths for numbers

Pascal has defaults for writing out numbers, which are usually:

Integers	12 figures,
Reals	scientific form with 6 decimal places,

In both cases, the numbers are written flush to the right. To change either default, we can indicate a **field width** which defines the size of the gap in which the number is to be written. The field width comes after the expression, preceded by a colon. One field width can be specified for integers, and one or two for reals. The effects are as follows:

Integer, one field width	print the number in that width,
Real, one field width	print the number in that width, using scientific form
Real, two field widths	print the number in the gap given by the first width, with the decimal places given by the second width.

Pascal overrides field widths that are too small.

If the overall width given is too small, Pascal overrides it and prints the number in as big a space as needed. If the decimal places are too few, the number is suitably rounded.

In the following examples, ~ is used to indicate a space, to show how the field widths actually affect the output:

A field width of 1 writes the number flush on the left.

writeln (21 * 4);	~ ~ ~ ~ ~ ~ ~ ~ ~ ~ 84
writeln (21 * 4 : 2);	84
writeln (21 * 4 : 7);	~ ~ ~ ~ ~ 84
writeln (21 * 4 : 1);	84
writeln (−21 / 4);	−5.250000E+00
writeln (−21 / 4 : 7);	−5.3E+00
writeln (−21 / 4 : 6 : 2);	~ −5.25
writeln (−21 / 4 : 6 : 1);	~ ~ −5.3
writeln (−21 / 4 : 4 : 2);	−5.25
writeln (−21 / 4 : 4 : 0);	~ ~ −5

You should experiment with your Pascal system, to see exactly how it reacts to different conditions.

Numbers and strings can be written in the same write statements, so for example, we might have:

```
writeln('Today''s temperature will be 15 celsius, that''s ',
    15*9/5+32:2:0, 'fahrenheit.');
```

Today's temperature will be 15 celsius, that's 59 fahrenheit.

A decimal width of 0 prints a real as an integer.

Named constants

In science and engineering, many values acquire names. For example, 3.141592 is known as *pi*, and *g* is $9.8m/s^2$. Giving quantities names makes them easier to remember and use. Pascal acknowledges this advantage by allowing values to be assigned to names.

Constants are declared directly under the program statement in a special section which has the form:

Constant declaration

```
CONST
    identifier = value;
    identifier = value;

    . . .

    identifier = value;
```

It is helpful to follow a constant declaration with a comment on its units, where applicable. The comment is enclosed in curly brackets. Comments are there to explain parts of the program, but are not executed when the program runs. Examples of constant declarations are: *More on comments in section 3.1.*

```
CONST
    pi          = 3.141592;
    g           = 9.8;       {m/s/s}
    litrespergal = 4.546;
    kmpermile   = 1.609;
    speedlimit  = 90;        {km/hour}
    kilo        = 1000;
    taxrate     = 10;        {%}
```

Once the declaration has been made, the name of the constant can be used wherever the number is required. The name should convey more information than a plain number, and if the value has to change, then the change need only be made once – in the declaration. If, for example, the tax rate were to be raised to 15%, then only this one declaration would need to be altered, not all occurrences of the number 10. Since there may be occurrences of the number 10 which are not related to *taxrate,* confusion is also avoided. *Named constants aid readability and make program changes easier.*

Example 2.3 SI Prefix table with constants

Even a simple example like the Table of Prefixes (example 2.2) can be improved with constants. We can define each column width as a constant, and add on gaps when needed. The resulting program is:

```
PROGRAM SIUnits (output);
    CONST
        col1 = 8;
```

```
                              col2 = 5;
                              col3 = 6;
                              gap = 9;
                              super1 = 19;  {col1 + col2 + col3}
                              super2 = 25;  {super1 + gap − 3}
                           BEGIN
                              writeln('Table of SI Unit Prefixes and Abbreviations');
                              writeln('===================================');
                              writeln;
                              writeln(' ':super1, '−12':3, ' ':super2, '3');
                              write('pico':col1, 'p':col2, 'x10':col3, ' ':gap);
                              writeln('kilo':col1, 'K':col2, 'x10':col3);

                              writeln(' ':super1, '−6':3,' ':super2, '6');
                              write('micro':col1, 'u':col2, 'x10:col3, ' ':gap);
                              writeln('mega':col1, 'M':col2, 'x10':col3);

                              writeln(' ':super1, '−3':3,' ':super2, '9');
                              write('milli':8:col1, 'm':col2, 'x10:col3, ' ':gap);
                              writeln('giga':col1, 'G':col2, 'x10':col3);

                           END.
```

Achieving
flexibility.

The new program will be easy to change: by just altering the constants in the heading, we can adjust the columns for a new format.

Precedence

Pascal uses the normal arithmetic precedence for operators, i.e. * and / will take precedence over + and −, but because everything is written on a single line, parentheses are needed more often than in mathematics in order to ensure the correct precedence. For example, consider the following Pascal equivalents for common formulae:

$\sqrt{b^2 - 4ac}$	sqrt(sqr(b) − 4 * a * c)
$\frac{1}{2}\,mv^2$	0.5 * m * sqr(v)
$\sqrt{2gE\left(\dfrac{1}{W_1} + \dfrac{1}{W_2}\right)}$	sqrt (2 * g * E * (1 / W1 + 1 / W2))
$\dfrac{L_1 + L_2 + \sqrt{M}}{L_1 + L_2 - 2M}$	(L1 + L2 + sqrt(M)) / (L1 + L2 − 2 * M)
$\dfrac{1}{2\pi\sqrt{LC}}$	1/ (2 * pi * sqrt(L * C))

One important point to note is that the operators / and * have the same precedence and are evaluated left to right, so that

Multiplication is not done before division.

$$a\,/\,b\,{}^*\,c \quad \text{is} \quad \frac{ac}{b} \quad\quad \text{not} \quad \frac{a}{bc}$$

Example 2.4 Effective resistance

| Problem |

In a particular circuit, there are three resistances connected in parallel as follows:

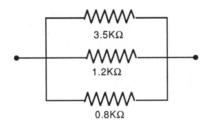

3.5KΩ

1.2KΩ

0.8KΩ

We want to calculate the effective resistance through this section of the circuit.

| Solution |

The formula for the effective resistance, R, of n resistors in parallel is

$$\frac{1}{R} = \frac{1}{r_1} + \frac{1}{r_2} + \ldots + \frac{1}{r_n}$$

Using this, R itself is found by dividing 1 by the result of the calculation on the right hand side.

| Program |

We can write a program with this as an expression, using the three values in the diagram above.

```
PROGRAM EffectiveResistance (output);
  BEGIN
    writeln('For three resistors connected in parallel');
    writeln;
    writeln('       |------- 3.5 Kohms -------|');
    writeln('------ |------- 1.2 Kohms -------| -------');
    writeln('       |------- 0.8 Kohms -------|');
    writeln;
    writeln('The effective resistance is ',
            1/ (1/3.5 + 1/1.2 + 1/0.8):1:4, 'Kohms');
  END.
```

Strings that are too long for a line of program must be broken up into smaller strings.

| Testing |

Running the program produces the following output:

For three resistors connected in parallel

```
         |------- 3.5 Kohms ------|
------- |------- 1.2 Kohms ------| -------
         |------- 0.8 Kohms ------|
```

The effective resistance is 0.4221 Kohms

2.4   Structuring with procedures

Programs can
be subdivided
into
procedures.

A **procedure** is a group of declarations and statements which is given a name and may be called upon by this name to perform a particular action. A procedure is therefore just like a program – it could in fact be called a **subprogram**. The simple form of a procedure declaration is:

Simple procedure declaration

```
PROCEDURE name;
  declarations
  BEGIN
    statements
  END; {name}
```

The difference between this form and that for a program is essentially in the last line, where the END is followed by a semicolon, not a full stop, and the name of the procedure is repeated in curly brackets after it. (The name at the end is optional, but conventional, and is used consistently thoughout this book.) An example of a procedure would therefore be

```
PROCEDURE square;
  BEGIN
    writeln ('-----------');
    writeln ('|          |');
    writeln ('|          |');
    writeln ('|          |');
    writeln ('-----------');
  END; {square}
```

Creating a procedure like this is a **declaration**. The name *square* is declared to be the action of performing the given statements.

Having been declared in the declaration part of a program, a procedure can be **called** by mentioning its name thus

Simple procedure call

```
name ;
```

So for example, to print a square, all we need to say is

```
square;
```

the effect of which will be to print

This constitutes a **statement**. When a call statement is executed, the procedure is entered and its statements are performed until its END is reached, whereupon execution passes back to the statement after the call.

Defining procedures in this way will enable us to cut down on repetition, but it also provides a means of creating a structure for a program, and the name of a procedure can be carefully chosen to reflect the action it performs, thus enhancing the readability of the program.

Example 2.5   Architect's impressions

Problem   An architect wishes to print symbols such as a house, a tree and a church, in a design drawing.

Solution   A solution would be to use a computer to print them, as we have been doing. (Another solution would be to use pencil and paper, but that would spoil this as a programming example!)

Algorithm   First of all, we look to see if there are any existing algorithms or bits of program that we can use. So far, we have a program that prints a label: if we excluded the names inside, we would have the effect of printing a rectangle. Similarly, we could devise statements to print a triangle such as

Using a bit of imagination and adapting the size of the label to be a rectangle or a square, we can construct a house, a tree and a church from these components.

(although we have cheated in omitting the bottom line of the triangle in the case of the house and church).

In order to describe the creation of these shapes, we use a notation which consists of a mixture of English and lines. Working from the top down, we start off with a description of the overall solution as

> **Architect's Impressions**
> Print a house
> Print a tree
> Print a church

Then each line can be refined in turn. If we wish to show more than one level of refinement on a digram, we use the line-and-bar symbol. So the house is defined as printing a triangle and square, and the printing of a square is further refined, as shown in the chart.

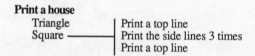

The church is similar, with the addition of the cross and the use of a rectangle. Finally there is the tree:

> **Tree**
> Triangle
> Print a top line
> Print a double bar twice

There is a lot of repetition here, which is especially noticeable with the triangle, which is used in all three shapes. So we shall use procedures as a means of packaging up statements to print the individual components. They can then be used in the different symbols, without writing out all the statements again.

Program

```
PROGRAM Shapes (output);

  PROCEDURE square;
    BEGIN
      writeln ('----------');
      writeln ('|        |');
      writeln ('|        |');
      writeln ('|        |');
      writeln ('----------');
    END; {square}

  PROCEDURE rectangle;
    BEGIN
      writeln ('------------------------');
      writeln ('|                      |');
      writeln ('|                      |');
      writeln ('|                      |');
      writeln ('------------------------');
    END; {rectangle}

  PROCEDURE triangle;
    BEGIN
      writeln ('   /\   ');
      writeln ('  /  \  ');
      writeln (' /    \ ');
    END; {triangle}

  BEGIN
    writeln ('****** Architect''s Impressions ******');
    writeln;

    writeln ('A house');
    writeln;
    triangle;
    square;
    writeln;  writeln;

    writeln ('A tree');
    writeln;
    triangle;
    writeln ('------');
    writeln ('  | |  ');
    writeln ('  | |  ');
    writeln; writeln;

    writeln ('A church');
    writeln;
    writeln ('   +');
    triangle;
    rectangle;
    writeln; writeln;
  END.
```

Procedures
must be
defined before
they are used.

There are a few points to note about this fairly substantial program. The
procedures come first because they are declarations. Then the program itself
begins by printing out an introductory string. This is a good idea, because
the appearance of such a message will confirm that the program has begun to
run. Then each shape has been given a name, and a few blank lines have been
added between shapes.

| Testing | The program can be run, and it will produce the following
output, as expected.

A program
should
introduce itself.

****** **Architect's Impressions** ******

A house

A tree

A church

Step-wise refinement

The most important advantage of procedures is their ability to assist in the problem solving process. A solution becomes more manageable when it is divided up into smaller pieces. Each of these can be viewed as a procedure, with a name which reflects its function. Then the work of each procedure can be further broken down, with another layer of procedures to solve the subproblems. This is known as the process of **step-wise refinement** and is an important problem-solving technique.

Procedures are vital to the problem solving process.

A program that is written in this way gives more information to the reader as to its function and its operation than one that consists of a single long sequence of statements.

There are other tangible advantages to procedures. If a procedure is carefully written, it may well be feasible to copy it for use in another program that requires the same functionality. Such a procedure is called **reusable**. Within a single program, procedures can also reduce repetition, thus making a program more compact. The smaller the program, the less memory it uses, and in certain circumstances memory may be at a premium. Thus procedures contribute to **space efficiency**. Shorter programs, provided they are neatly laid out, are generally easier to read than longer ones, and procedures contribute substantially to the **readability** of a program.

Procedures reduce repetition and encourage reuseability.

2.5   Repetition with counting loops

Computers, like all machines, are very good at doing the same thing over and over again. In a program, such repetition can be formulated as a **loop**. There are two kinds of loops possible in Pascal – **counting** loops and **conditional** loops. In this section we look at how counting loops are achieved; the conditional ones are introduced in section 4.2.

In order to get on with programming quickly, this section adopts a 'just do it this way' approach for the declarations that have to be associated with loops. The full discussion of how and why these work is given at the start of the next chapter.

The form of a counting loop

A counting loop is specified in two parts, the loop variable declaration and the corresponding for-statement.

There is more about declarations in the next chapter.

Loop variable declaration

> VAR *loop variable : lower.. upper*

For-statement

```
FOR loop variable := lower to upper DO BEGIN
    statements
END;
```

As before, the plain words form the template, and the ones in italics have to be appropriately filled in for an actual loop. The VAR declaration introduces a **loop variable** which is intended to operate between the values specified for *lower* and *upper*. These values may be numbers or single characters, for example, the following would be valid loop declarations:

VAR i : 1..10;

VAR letter : 'a' .. 'z';

Additional possibilities for loop variables are discussed in Chapter 6.

The keyword FOR introduces the loop and states that the loop variable will start at *lower* and finish at *upper*. The keywords DO BEGIN introduce the **loop body** which consists of statements finishing off with the keyword END. Notice that the END is aligned with the FOR and the statements in the body will be indented. As some variation on the position of the other keywords is possible, some text books place the BEGIN on a separate line underneath the FOR. The present formulation is, however, a neat one and is used throughout this book. In addition, we believe that too many capital letters in a program makes it hard to read, so often we only put the first keyword on a line in capitals: in the above form, *to* is not in capitals for this reason. Because of the introductory keyword, these loops are also known as **for-loops**.

The way in which loops are laid out is a matter of taste.

The action of the loop is to repeat the statements for each successive value of the loop variable. As a first example, the following declaration and statement will cause five labels to be printed, each followed by two blank lines. We assume the existence of the *rectangle* procedure as defined earlier.

```
VAR counter : 1..5;

FOR counter := 1 to 5 do begin
    rectangle;
    writeln;
    writeln;
END;
```

Simpler loops

If there is only one statement in the loop body then the keywords BEGIN and END can be omitted. For example, consider how to compress the writing out of the three lines comprising the vertical sides of a square. Using a loop, we could have:

```
VAR  line : 1..3;

FOR line := 1 to 3 do
   writeln ('|            |');
```

The effect of this would be to start the loop variable *line* at 1, write the string, go around the loop, set *line* to 2, write the string again, go around, set *line* to 3, and write the string a third time. At this point the values indicated for *line* have been exhausted, and the loop ends.

Named constants can also be used as loop bounds. Using named constants, we could generalise the above loop to print a number of lines which is specified in the declarations, i.e.

```
CONST
   depth = 3;
VAR  line : 1.. depth;

FOR line := 1 to depth do
   writeln ('|            |');
```

Named constants help to generalise loops.

Using the loop variable

The loop variable serves to record the current iteration of a loop and its values can be used in various ways:

- in a write statement;
- in simple arithmetic;
- as part of the bounds of another loop.

Together, these three facilities make looping much more interesting. In order to focus on the looping operations themselves, we shall explore a few examples of loops of this sort. The examples are given as fragments of a Pascal program: it is assumed that the declarations and statements will slot into the appropriate parts of a full program.

Printing sequences

To print out the first ten even numbers, we can have a loop going from one to ten, and then write out double the loop variable, as in

```
VAR number : 1..10;

FOR number := 1 to 10 do
   write(number * 2);
writeln;
```

which will produce

2   4   6   8   10   12   14   16   18   20

To print the odd numbers requires a bit of thought. If *number * 2* is an even number, then *number * 2 + 1* or *number * 2 – 1* is an odd number. Choosing one of these expressions, we have

```
VAR number : 0..9;

FOR number := 0 to 9 do
  write(number * 2 + 1);
writeln;
```

which will produce

1   3   5   7   9   11   13   15   17   19

A loop variable over characters can be used to print the alphabet, as in

Loops can be used for characters too.

```
VAR  letter : 'A' .. 'M';

FOR letter := 'A' .. 'M' do
  write(letter, ' ');
```

which would produce

A B C D E F G H I J K L M

Loop variables cannot be real numbers, but they can be used in expressions which produce real numbers. For example, to print 100 times the reciprocal of the numbers between *min* and *max*, to 6 decimal places, we would have:

Loops for real numbers must be done via integers.

```
CONST
  min = 100;
  max = 105;

VAR
  r : 100 .. 105;

FOR r := 100 to 120 do
  writeln(r, 100 / r : 8:6);
```

giving

```
100    1.000000
101    0.990099
102    0.980392
103    0.970874
104    0.961538
105    0.952381
```

Example 2.6 Flow of liquid in a pipe

Problem   An engineer is responsible for recommending certain sizes of pipes for a new plant. The radius of the pipes can vary between 10cm and 50cm, in intervals of 5cm. The flow of liquid in the pipe is constant at 2m/s. The decision as to the sizes of pipe required will be made on the basis of volume of liquid flowing out of the pipe, measured in cubic metres per second. Graphically, we have:

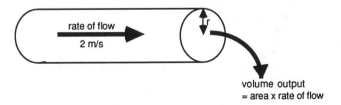

Solution   The volume is given by the area of the pipe's cross-section multiplied by the rate of flow. We can write a program to loop through the possible radius sizes, calculating the volume and printing it out.

Algorithm   The loop is to go from 10cm to 50cm, in multiples of 5cm. If we start r at 10, then we are looking at calculating the volume for radii

$$10,$$
$$10 + 5$$
$$10 + 15$$
$$\ldots$$
$$10 + 40$$

This can be rewritten as $r + ih$, where $r = 10$, $h = 5$ and i goes from 0 to 8. Thus to print out the radii, we would use the sequence-printing loop:

```
FOR i := 0 to 8 do
    writeln (10 + i * 5, );
```

However, we must not forget to convert the radius given in centimetres to metres by dividing r and h by 100 when calculating the volume. To ensure that we keep track of these values, we declare them, and pi, as named constants, i.e.

Remember to get the units right.

```
CONST
    rcm = 10;      rm = 0.1;
    hcm = 5;       hm = 0.05;
    pi = 3.141592;
```

The column width for the tabulation can best be worked out from the headings required, giving 12 for the radius and 16 for the volume.

Program

Flow is declared in the program as it is printed in the introduction.

These are declared here because they are only used in this procedure.

```
PROGRAM LiquidFlow (output);
  CONST
  flow = 2;  {m/s}

  PROCEDURE Printtable;
  CONST
    rcm = 10;   rm = 0.1;
    hcm = 5;    hm = 0.05;
    pi = 3.141592;
  VAR
    i : 0 .. 8;
  BEGIN
    writeln('Radius in cm':12, 'Volume in cu m/s':16);
    FOR i := 0 to 8 do
      writeln( rcm + hcm * i:12,
               pi * sqr(rm + hm * i) * flow:16:4);
  END; {Printtable}

BEGIN
  writeln('***** Volume of liquid flowing from pipes *****');
  writeln;
  writeln('Flow rate is constant at ', flow:1,' m/s');
  writeln;
  Printtable;
END.
```

(There is another version of this program shown in section 3.1).

Testing

The output from the program will be as follows:

***** Volume of liquid flowing from pipes *****

Flow rate is constant at 2 m/s

Radius in cm	Volume in cu m/s
10	0.0628
15	0.1414
20	0.2513
25	0.3927
30	0.5655
35	0.7697
40	1.0053
45	1.2723
50	1.5708

Nested loops

A for-loop is a statement. Therefore it can appear wherever a statement can appear, and one of these places is within a loop itself. This possibility leads to so-called **nested loops**, illustrated in the next example.

Example 2.7   Landscape features

| Problem | In addition to the church, house and tree, the architect wishes to show landscape, such as hillocks and mountains. These are represented by filled in shapes as in

```
        **                              ***
       ****                        *********
      ******                    ***************
     ********                 ******************
    *********               *********************
   ***********            ***********************
     Mountain                      Hillock
```

| Solution | We note that the each of these shapes consists of rows, where each row has the number of stars corresponding to its vertical position. In the case of the mountain, row 1 has 2 stars, row 2 has 4, row 3 has 6 and so on. In order to position the stars in the correct place, we note that the rest of a rectangle drawn around the mountain is spaces, so that in any one row, there is a corresponding number of spaces.

The hillock follows the same pattern, except that the ratio of spaces to stars can be based on a sine curve, rather than on a straight line.

| Algorithm | If we were to print the right side only of the mountain, i.e.

```
*
**
***
****
*****
******
```

we could use nested loops, as described by the following algorithm.

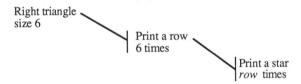

Although we have used 6 as the fixed height of the mountain, it would obviously be more general to declare this a named constant.

| Program | This translates into the following procedure.

```
PROCEDURE RightTriangle;
  CONST
    height = 6;
  VAR
    row, star : 1..height;

  BEGIN
    FOR row := 1 to height do begin
      FOR star := 1 to row do
        write('*');
      writeln;
    END;
  END; {RightTriangle}
```

Establishing the limits on fairly complex loops. Now consider the full mountain. On each row, there is one less space than the row number, i.e. in row 1 there are 5, in row 2 there are 4, and so on. Once we have reached the correct place to start the stars, we print double the number, to get both sides of the mountain. Thus the loops to print the full mountain are:

```
PROCEDURE Mountain;
  CONST
    height = 6;
  VAR
    row, piece : 1..height;

  BEGIN
    FOR row := 1 to height do begin
      FOR piece := row + 1 to height do
        write (' ');
      FOR piece := 1 to row do
        write('**');
      writeln;
    END;
  END {Mountain};
```

Considering the hillock, we see that we need to calculate a value of x for given values of y between 1 and 0, but scaled by 5. This requires an arcsin function, which we have not yet introduced, and would also require us to run a loop backwards, from 5 to 0. This aspect is picked up after example 2.8.

This example has shown us how nested loops can be used to good effect, and how the loop variables can be used in controlling inner loops.

Skipping the body of a loop

When loop bounds consist of expressions, it may happen that when evaluated, the lower bound may already exceed the upper one. In this case, the loop body is not executed at all. In the above example, the first nested loop

Loop bodies can be skipped.

    FOR piece := row + 1 to height do . . .

will be in this situation when *row* is equal to *height*. No spaces are written for this row, which is exactly what was intended.

Example 2.8   Table of square roots

| Problem | We wish to print a table of square roots for numbers between 1 and 100, so that the whole table fits nicely on the screen. |

| Solution | We can use the function *sqrt(i)* inside a write statement to print out the square root of the number *i*. We need to think about |

How to plan a table.

how to arrange the layout of the table. A standard computer screen has lines 80 characters long. Allowing for 4 decimal places for the square root, the minimum field widths for the number will be 3 and for the root 6, and we need to add on a bit for space in between the numbers, as in

    ~~~~ 80 ~~~ 8.1234 ~~~~~ 81 ~~ 8.2345 ~~~~ 82 ~~ 8.3456 ...

Thus 16 characters will be ample for each pair, giving 5 pairs per line. For the 100 numbers, this gives 20 lines, which will fit nicely on a screen. We can then use nested loops to get the desired effect.

| Algorithm | We can tackle the solution from the top. Assuming that we know how to print one line, we can set up a loop to print 20 |

lines. Printing one line can be put in a procedure, *printline*, with its own loop and loop variable, say *i*. The expression for printing a number on that line will be

    i + line*5 ,

assuming that *i* starts at 0 and goes on to 19. (Check this out by hand.)

One issue is the exact field widths for the numbers, and the size of the gaps in between. Instead of printing a gap, we can add the gap onto the field width for the numbers, giving :6 for the number and :8:4 for its root. This has the added advantage of giving a bit of space for larger numbers, should the program be adapted to print from 1 to 1000, say.

Create column gaps by adding space to field widths.

We can also use the field width for strings feature, to set the column headings to line up on the same widths. This can be done in a separate *initialise* procedure, which also prints the table heading.

Program

```
PROGRAM SquareRoots (output);
VAR  line : 0 .. 19;

  PROCEDURE initialise;
   VAR i : 1..5;
   BEGIN
    writeln ('Table of square roots of numbers 1 to 100');
    writeln ('===================================');
    writeln;
    FOR i := 1 to 5 do
      write (' No.':6, ' Root':8);
    writeln;
   END; {initialise}

  PROCEDURE printline;
   VAR i : 1..5;
   BEGIN
    FOR i := 1 to 5 do
      write ((i + line * 5) : 6, (sqrt (i + line * 5 )) :8:4);
    writeln;
   END; {printline}

BEGIN
  initialise;
  FOR line := 0 to 19 do
    printline;
END.
```

Testing

Running the program confirms that it does produce the required effect, and the right answers. Here is an extract:

Table of square roots of numbers 1 to 100

===================================

No.	Root	No.	Root	No.	Root	No.	Root	No.	Root
1	1.0000	2	1.4142	3	1.7321	4	2.0000	5	2.2361
6	2.4495	7	2.6458	8	2.8284	9	3.0000	10	3.1623
11	3.3166	12	3.4641	13	3.6056	14	3.7417	15	3.8730
16	4.0000	17	4.1231	18	4.2426	19	4.3589	20	4.4721
21	4.5826	22	4.6904	23	4.7958	24	4.8990	25	5.0000
26	5.0990	27	5.1962	28	5.2915	29	5.3852	30	5.4772

...

Counting backwards

Pascal has a further looping option, that of counting backwards. This is seldom needed and is indicated by replacing the *to* in the for-statement by the keyword *downto*. Thus to print the sequence

10 9 8 7 6 5 4 3 2 1 0 –1 –2 –3 –4 –5 –6

we could say

```
VAR n : 10 .. –6;

FOR n := 10 downto –6 do
   write(n);
```

A nice example of counting backwards is found in the song 'One man went to mow', which is discussed in the answers to one of the problems below.

Summary

- ☐ Programs consist of declarations and statements.
- ☐ Output is performed through the write and writeln statements.
- ☐ Layout of statements is important for readability.
- ☐ Expressions use the operators + (addition), – (subtraction), * (multiplication), / (division), with ( ) parentheses to override the usual precedences.
- ☐ Pascal distinguishes between integer and real numbers: division using / always produces a real number.
- ☐ The default field widths and forms for printing numbers can be overridden.
- ☐ Procedures are groups of statements that serve a common purpose and can be called upon from other places in the program.
- ☐ Statements can be repeated by grouping them in a counting or for-loop.
- ☐ Counting loops consist of a loop variable declaration and a FOR statement.
- ☐ The loop variable specifies the range of the corresponding loop.
- ☐ The loop variable can be printed out from inside the loop, or used in simple arithmetic.
- ☐ If the lower bound of a loop exceeds the upper, then the body of the loop is not performed at all.
- ☐ Loop variables can be used to count backwards if DOWNTO is specified.
- ☐ A loop variable must be declared in the procedure that uses it.

Self-check quiz

1. What is the difference between a write statement and a writeln statement?
2. Spot the errors in the following program.

```
PROGRAM Messy (input, output);

VARIABLE loop : 1..5;

PROCEDURE Tops;
  writeln ('Tops');
END; {Tops}

BEGIN
  FOR loop = 1 .. 10 do begin
    write('Programming is ');
    Tops;
    writeln (!);
  end;
END;
```

3. Can a program have two loop variables of the same name?
4. Write the following expression in Pascal:

$$\frac{x^2 - 1}{\sqrt{x - 2}}$$

5. Which would appear first in a program listing – the declaration of a procedure or the call of it?
6. The following procedure is meant to print out the five times table. What will it actually print out? Correct it in two different ways.

```
PROCEDURE Fivetimes;
  VAR multiple : 1..12;
  BEGIN
    for multiple := 1 to 12 do
      write('5 times ');
      write(multiple);
      write('is');
      writeln (5*multiple);
  END; {Fivetimes}
```

7. How many stars would be printed by

```
FOR star := 10 downto 5 do write('*');
```

8. Write a for-loop to print the sequence **–13 –5 3 11 19 27 35** .
9. What would be printed by the following statement

```
writeln (13/4 : 8:3,  13/4 : 8:0,  13/4: 8);
```

10. Write statements to print out the first four powers and roots of π to 6 decimal places.

Problems

2.1   A firm of engineers is interested in knowing the area of different shapes with the same basic measurement. Specifically, they would like to compare the area of a square, circle, equilateral triangle and rhombus (angle 45°) with the measurement r used as follows:

Write a program to print these values (in m^2) for a range of values of r from 1 to 20 metres. *Hint*: the area of a circle is πr^2, of an equilateral triangle $\frac{\sqrt{3}}{4}r^2$, and of the rhombus $\frac{r^2}{\sqrt{2}}$.

2.2   Write a program which prints out the first 10 terms in the series

$$\sum \frac{1}{i^2} = 1 + \frac{1}{2^2} + \frac{1}{3^2} + \ldots$$

2.3   A circuit has two resistors connected in parallel. We wish to investigate the effective resistance of the two components for values between 1 and 20 ohms each. Write a program to print a table of the effective resistances, with the values for the first resistor down the side and the values for the second across the top. *Hint*: The formula for the effective resistance is given in example 2.4.

2.4   A firm wishes to manufacture hollow aluminium balls made from various thicknesses of aluminium. Print a table of the amount of aluminium needed for balls with radii from 10cm to 30cm and thicknesses from 1mm to 5mm. Choose suitable intervals in each case. *Hint*: the volume of a sphere is given by the formula $\frac{4}{3}\pi r^3$.

2.5   Raising to a power x^y can be done by a loop, provided y is an integer. Using nested loops with x and y, write a program to print out a table of x to the power y for y up to 5 and x up to as high as your computer will go in integers. Then convert x to a real number by multiplying by 1.0 and see how high you can go.

2.6   Given the following program, what output does it produce?

```
PROGRAM Mystery (output);
  VAR i : 1..2;

  PROCEDURE splodge;
    VAR line : 1..4;
    BEGIN
      FOR line := 1 to 4 do
        writeln ('*********');
    END; {splodge}

  BEGIN
    FOR i := 1 to 2 do begin
      splodge;
      writeln ('    |  |');
      writeln ('    |  |');
      writeln ('    |  |');
      splodge;
      writeln;
    END;
  END.
```

2.7   Write a program which uses loops to print out the song 'One man went to mow'. Use digits rather than words for the numbers, as in

1 man went to mow, went to mow a meadow,
1 man and his dog, went to mow a meadow.

2 men went to mow, went to mow a meadow,
2 men, 1 man and his dog, went to mow a meadow.

3 men went to mow, went to mow a meadow,
3 men, 2 men, 1 man and his dog, went to mow a meadow.

2.8   Write a program which uses for-statements and write statements to produce the
       following triangle:

```
1
2  2
3  3  3
4  4  4  4
5  5  5  5  5
```

2.9   Adapt the program in the previous problem to print the triangle so that the numbers
       are centred, as below. Adapt it again to print the triangle upside down.

```
      1
    2   2
  3   3   3
4   4   4   4
```

2.10   Perform a thorough investigation of the behaviour of your Pascal system in printing
       integer and real numbers using field widths.

2.11   A car speedometer is connected to the transmission and by assuming a constant tyre
       circumference, transforms the number of revolutions per second of the drive shaft
       into kilometres per hour. However, the circumference of the tyre will

       • decrease as the tread wears away,

       • increase as the tyre becomes hot, and

       • vary with the amount of air inside it.

       For a car with a speedometer calibrated for a 60cm diameter tyre, the true road speed
       is given by $t(s,c) = s(1 + c/100)$ when the speedometer shows speed s and the actual
       tyre diameter is $60 + c\%$ cm.
           Write a program which tabulates the function $t(s,c)$ for speeds $s = 30, 35, \ldots$
       115, 120 and tyre change factors $c = -10, -8, \ldots 8, 10$.

2.12   There is a special tax on cars in Zanyland which is presently at the following rate:

Net price	Rate
< D5000	15%
D5000 – D10000	D1000 (flat rate)
>D10000	10%

       Write a program which prints out the net price, tax and gross price for cars with net
       prices between D2500 and D12500 in steps of D500.

3

Changing and choosing

This chapter starts by systematically going through the details of the concepts introduced so far. Three new statements are added – for assigning, reading, and selecting alternative paths – and the types integer and real are completely defined with all their properties. We also show applications of the first two numerical methods: solving differential equations using a predictor-corrector algorithm and approximating periodic functions with a Fourier series. The limitations of computer arithmetic are mentioned, with examples.

3.1   Basic syntax

When viewed as a typed document, a Pascal program consists of

- identifiers,
- keywords,
- comments,
- punctuation,
- spaces and blank lines.

Keywords, identifiers and comments have their own simple rules, which will be discussed below. The punctuation allowed in Pascal is a mixture of ordinary marks such as comma, semicolon and parentheses, and arithmetic symbols such as + and /.

Avoid 'screen creep' by keeping statements compact.

Spaces and blank lines are important in aiding the readability of a Pascal program, and should be used freely. One word of caution – if a program has many blank lines, or has statements spread out over several lines, then the amount of information that can be displayed on a screen is limited, and it may be hard to understand a program that is presented in small fragments. In this book, we tend to use blank lines between procedures, and to keep statements fairly compact. Other books use other conventions, such as always putting BEGIN on a new line. The resulting spread over several pages of what could be a short program does not really aid readability.

Upper and lower case are the same in Pascal.

Pascal programs are usually typed in small letters or **lower case** but free use can be made of capital letters (known as **upper case**) for emphasis. Some Pascal systems have built into them **pretty printers** which will reformat your program into a fixed style of indenting and mixture of cases, while some systems insist on lower-case letters only. We shall assume that you can control how your programs are written, and we shall adopt a neat, consistent style for laying them out.

Develop a neat style of layout, and stick to it.

Keywords

There are 35 words in Pascal which have special meanings and are reserved for use as **keywords**. (See Appendix A for a full list.) Some of these are:

PROGRAM	PROCEDURE
BEGIN	to
END	do
FOR	VAR
IF	then

Keywords are reserved and cannot be used as names in a program.

Keywords can be written in small letters or in capitals, depending upon which looks better at the time. The convention we use is that the first keyword on a line, such as PROCEDURE or FOR, is written in capitals, while other less important words such as *to* and *of* can stay in small letters. Other text books have different conventions, sometimes putting all keywords in capitals, or using bold or italics for this effect. The point is that Pascal doesn't care about case, so that all the following are valid versions of a keyword:

PROCEDURE	Procedure
procedure	**procedure**
procedure	

Two of Pascal's keywords – CONST and VAR – are abbreviations. They introduce the constant and variable sections of the declarations, and must be used in this abbreviated form. However, other keywords cannot be abbreviated. For example, PROC cannot be used for PROCEDURE.

Identifiers

The terms 'name', 'word' and 'identifier' have been used rather loosely up to now to describe sequences of letters. The proper Pascal term is **identifier**, and there is a precise definition of what constitutes an identifier:

An **identifier** is a sequence of letters and digits that
- starts with a letter,
- treats the lower- and upper-case letters as equivalent,
- does not have the same spelling as any keyword.

Thus identifiers may not include spaces. This restriction becomes important when identifiers are formed from phrases rather than from single nouns or verbs. A convention often used is to employ the second property and put a capital letter at the start of each English word, thus serving to break up an otherwise confusing jumble of letters. For example, we could write

ReduceToOne   rather than   *reducetoone* .

Bearing all this in mind, which of the following are valid identifiers?

ReduceToOne	LastLimit
TRIANGULAR	rectangle
R1	Planck'sConstant
FirstResistance	MI5
1stvalue	Hello!
X	end
water-level	Number of lines

Pascal identifiers may not contain spaces.

Capitals are useful for breaking up long identifiers.

The following ones are invalid, for the reasons given:

1stvalue	cannot start with a digit
Hello!	! is not a letter or digit
end	END (and hence end) is a keyword
water-level	- is not a letter or digit
Number of lines	spaces are not letters or digits
Planck'sConstant	cannot have an apostrophe

Mistakes in the formation of identifiers are detected by the compiler, but most compilers will simply give one of two messages such as

Invalid identifier
Identifier already exists

without any explanation as to what exactly is wrong. The most common mistakes are using a keyword or starting an identifier with a digit. However, after a few weeks of programming, the rules become second nature.

Predefined identifiers

Pascal has certain identifiers which are predefined for all programs, but are not keywords. Some we have seen are:

integer
write
writeln

Integer and writeln are **not** keywords and should not be in capitals.

and others will be introduced later. The point about these identifiers is that they should be regarded as keywords from the point of view of not defining them as something else. If we declared the word *write* as a loop variable, say, then the original meaning of *write* would be lost, and trying to use it for writing would fail. Once again, conforming to this restriction should become natural after a while.

Comments

Although Pascal is a precise language, parts of programs can sometimes be a bit cryptic. To make these parts easier to understand, comments can be added.

> A **comment** is any text enclosed in { }, except curly brackets themselves.

Apart from explaining what is going on, comments are also used to amplify the bare syntax of Pascal in various ways. We have already seen this usage in explaining the units of constants and in the practice of following the end of a procedure with its name. Consider the program from example 2.5, which has been suitably amplified with seven different sorts of comments.

Underlining
Header

Author and date

Declaration
reference
Units

```
PROGRAM LiquidFlow (output);
{------------------}
{ A program to tabulate the volume of liquid flowing
  through pipes of varying diameters.  The rate of flow
  is constant.
                          Written by J M Bishop, April 1990}

CONST
  flow = 2;  {m/s}

PROCEDURE Printtable;
{-------------}
  {Uses flow, declared in the program}
  CONST
    rcm = 10;     {radius in cm}
    rm = 0.1;     {radius in metres}
    hcm = 5;      {increment for each new pipe, in cm}
    hm = 0.05;    {ditto in m}
    pi = 3.141592;
```

```
VAR
  i : 0 .. 8;

BEGIN
  writeln('Radius in cm':12, 'Volume in cu m/s':16);
  FOR i := 0 to 8 do
    {hcm * i gives the next increment to add to the base size}      Explanation
    {The radius is calculated in cm, the volume in cu m/s}

    writeln( rcm + hcm * i:12,
             pi * sqr(rm + hm * i) * flow:16:4);
  END; {Printtable}                                                 Procedure end

BEGIN
  writeln('***** Volume of liquid flowing from pipes *****');
  writeln;
  writeln('Flow rate is constant at ', flow:1,' m/s');
  writeln;
  Printtable;
END.
```

The program certainly looks good and most of the comments are useful. In the programs that follow, we shall normally omit the header and author comments, and keep the explanations sparing: our aim is to amplify the Pascal, not to duplicate it. Each programmer should develop an individual commenting style which suits the needs of the project being undertaken. Often commenting style is a matter of policy, and serves to give programs a uniform apprearance. This can make them easier to read for those in a group.

Syntax

In Chapter 2, we introduced the *form* of various parts of a program with three such forms being given – for the program itself, for a procedure and for a counting loop. To recall, the form for a for-loop is

All the forms are collected together in an Appendix.

For-statement

```
FOR loopid := lower to upper do begin
  statements
END;
```

These forms are ways of describing the **syntax** of Pascal. The syntax defines exactly which words are needed in what order to achieve a desired effect. In the notation we have used for the syntax, the plain words are those that *have* to be there, forming a **template**, while the words in italics represent syntactical elements that are filled in each time.

There are other more formal ways of representing syntax, one of which uses so-called 'bubble diagrams'. In this notation, the counting loop would be described as:

See the
Appendix for
the full bubble
diagrams.

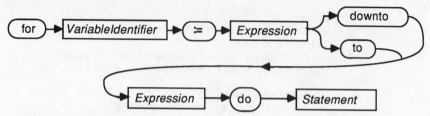

Such diagrams are useful when writing a compiler or resolving difficult syntactical points, but for the purposes of learning the language, the template approach is adequate. The complete collected forms and bubble diagrams are given as appendices.

Semantics

Whereas syntax gives the form of the Pascal construct, the semantics tells us how it works, or what it means. In most cases, it is sufficient to describe the semantics in clear English. Consider, for example, the description of the for-statement from section 2.4:

Semantics of a
for-loop.

> The action of the loop is to repeat the statements
> for each successive value of the loop variable.

This is followed by examples and further details of the special cases that may occur. In keeping with the tutorial style followed in this book, the semantics are discussed in the text and summarised at the end of each chapter. For a more succinct description of semantics, one should consult the Pascal Standard.

3.2 Variables and assignment

A Pascal program, as we saw before, consists of declarations and statements. The purpose of the declarations is to associate identifiers with the objects that are going to be used in the statements. There are five kinds of declaration, each of which is introduced by a special keyword, viz:

CONST   PROCEDURE
TYPE   FUNCTION
VAR

The first three introduce constant, type and variable declarations, and must appear in that order. The other two can be repeated as many times as necessary in order to define each procedure and function. In this section we look at constant and variable declarations; type declarations and procedures and functions are covered in later chapters.

More on types in Chapter 6; more on procedures in Chapters 5 and 8.

Variables

The Pascal programs in Chapter 2 were fairly rudimentary in that they did certain things without much change. Changes did come about through for-loops where the loop variable acquired different values as the loop progressed, and these values could actually be used to alter the effect of other statements. This idea of different values being represented by the same identifier at different stages in the execution of a program is generalised in the concept of a **variable**.

Variables record the changing state of a program.

> A **variable** denotes a value that may change during execution. Every variable has associated with it an identifier and a type. The type determines the range of values of the variable and governs how the variable may be used.

Variables are declared in var-declarations. After the keyword VAR, any number of variables may be declared, with their associated types. The form is

Variable declaration

```
VAR
    identifiers : type;
    identifiers : type;
        . . .
    identifiers : type;
```

If there is more than one identifier for a type, then they are separated by commas. The type may be one of the five predefined types, which are

```
integer              real
boolean              char
text
```

or a user-defined type, as described in Chapter 8. If the type is integer or char (for character), then we can indicate the actual range of values needed

Subranges
make variable
declarations
more specific.

instead, using a **subrange** as follows:

Subrange type

> *lower .. upper*

Thus instead of specifying

> VAR height : integer;

we try to be specific, as in:

> VAR
>   height : 0 .. 5; {metres}

It is a good idea to use a comment to give any other useful information such as physical units, currencies and so on.

For this chapter, we shall only deal with integers and reals. Within this limitation, examples of declarations are:

Line up the
types, and don't
forget the units!

> VAR
>   side   : 1..3;
>   line   : 1..10;
>   temperature   : −50..160;   {in degrees celsius}
>   frequency   : 50 .. 500;   {kilohertz}
>   x, y, z   : real;   {unknowns}
>   salary   : real;   {3000 to 30000, approx}

It is worthwhile keeping declarations neat and tidy, with the identifiers, types and comments lined up.

Assignment

Having declared a variable, we can now use an assignment to give it a value. The assignment statement has the form

Assignment statement

> *variable := expression ;*

The effect of an assignment statement is to evaluate the expression and to assign the resulting value to the variable indicated by the identifier. The symbol which indicates the assignment is read 'becomes'. Thus we can write

> temperature := 24;

and read it '*temperature* becomes 24'. The value of the expression is 24, and this is assigned to the variable *temperature*. In the next sequence

        salary := 20000;
        salary := salary + 500;

salary is assigned the value 20000, and this is then used to calculate the new salary value for the same variable by adding 500.

Assignment is not the same as equality.

Example 3.1 Swapping

| Problem | The values in two variables need to be interchanged. |

| Solution | Write some assignment statements. |

| Algorithm | Suppose the variables are called *x* and *y*. A first stab at an answer might be: |

        x := y;
        y := x;

What happens here? If *x* has the value 5 and *y* has the value 9, then a trace reveals:

statement	x	y
	5	9
x := y;	9	9
y := x;	9	9

The result is incorrect. The problem occurs in the first statement, when the value of *y* is put in *x* causing the original value of *x* to be lost. In order for the swap to work correctly, the value of *x* must first be copied, so that it can subsequently be used for setting up *y*. To do this, an additional variable is needed. Since it is only of temporary use, it will be called *temp*. The correct sequence of statements is:

Swapping needs a temporary resting place.

        temp := x;
        x := y;
        y := temp;

and the trace would be (with ~ indicating undefined as yet)

statement	x	y	temp
	5	9	~
temp := x;	5	9	5
x := y;	9	9	5
y := temp;	9	5	5

Initialising

Remember to initialise all variables.

When variables are declared, no value is specified for them. Thus variables must always be initialised by the program before being used. This point is illustrated in the traces above, where variables which had not been touched had tildes (~) to indicate that they were undefined. Inadvertently using a variable that has not been initialised is a common source of errors in a program, and something that should be continually guarded against. The importance of remembering this property is brought out in the examples in the next section.

Example 3.2   Accelerating train

| Problem | A train starts with an acceleration of 0.5 m/s², which decreases uniformly to zero in 2 minutes. It then travels with uniform speed for 3 minutes, after which it is brought to rest by the brakes with a constant deceleration of 1 m/s². This is shown in the diagram:

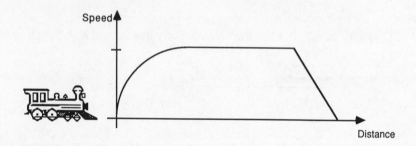

We want to find out how far the train travelled in km.

| Solution | Although we have been given precise figures for this journey, the problem could well come up again with different values, so we shall generalise, and refer to the various times, distances, velocities and accelerations as follows:

A, R The acceleration and deceleration rates.

$T_1 V_1 D_1$ The time, velocity and distance achieved at the point when acceleration stops.

$T_2 D_2$ The time, and distance achieved at the point when deceleration starts.

D_3 The distance achieved when deceleration stops.

Given this, we can use the usual motion equations to get to the velocity and distance over the period of acceleration as

$$V_1 = \frac{A\,T_1}{2}$$

$$D_1 = \frac{A\,T_2{}^2}{3}$$

The distance D_2 covered at constant speed depends on the velocity reached, and is simply $V_1 T_2$. For the final distance of deceleration, we have

$$D_3 = \frac{V_2{}^2}{2R}$$

| Algorithm | Armed with these equations, we simply have to calculate the three distances and add them up. Using Pascal identifiers corresponding to those defined above, the algorithm would be

> **Train travel**
> Calculate V1 and D1 with t = 120
> Calculate D2 based on V1.
> Calculate D3 based on V2 and R.
> The distance is D1 + D2 + D3.

Because D_2 depends on V_1, and just to make things clearer, we declare variables for each of the distances and do the calculations step by step.

| Program |

```
PROGRAM TrainTravel (output);
  CONST
    A = 0.5;      {m/s/s}
    R = 1.0;      {m/s/s}
    T1 = 2;       {min}
    T2 = 3;       {min}
    kilo = 1000;

  VAR
    D, D1, D2, D3  : real; {metres}
    V1             : real; {m/s}
    T1s, T2s       : real; {seconds}

  BEGIN
    writeln('****** Train travel ******');
    writeln;
    writeln(A:3:1,' m/s/s for ',T1:1,' mins, ');
    writeln('constant speed for ',T2:1, ' mins, ');
    writeln(' and ',R:3:1, ' m/s/s to rest');
    writeln;
    T1s := T1 * 60;
    T2s := T2 * 60;
    V1 := 0.5 * A * T1;
```

Constants cannot have expressions so T1s and T2s must be variables.

sqr(T1s) could
have been
used instead of
T1s * T1s.

```
D1 := (A * T1s * T1s) / 3;
D2 := V1 * T2s;
D3 := V1 * V1 / (2 * R);
D := (D1 + D2 + D3) / kilo;
writeln ('The journey covers ', D:1:1, ' km');
END.
```

| Testing |

Running the program gives:

****** Train travel ******

**0.5 m/s/s for 2 mins,
constant speed for 3 mins,
and 1.0 m/s/s to rest**

The journey covers 8.3 km

We can verify by calculation that the answer is correct.

Global and local variables

The variables that are declared at the program level are termed **global** and
are available for use by all procedures within the program. If these
procedures change a variable in error – perhaps because different people
were writing different procedures – then errors will occur that will be
difficult to trace. A procedure that changes a global variable is said to have a
side effect, and side effects are generally a bad thing. Thus we would like to
keep our procedures **self-contained** and limit, if not entirely avoid,
side effects.

Side effects are
bad.

At present we have not learnt enough about Pascal to eliminate
side effects, but we can keep them to a minimum by declaring variables
specifically in the procedures that need them, rather than all together at the
start of a program. These variables are called **local** variables, and one can
rely upon them being altered only by the statements within the procedure
itself.

Making
interfaces plain.

In Chapter 5 we shall look at features which will enable us to make our
procedures entirely self-contained, and to limit all communication between
procedures to a defined interface, rather than to assignments to globals.
Meanwhile, we shall adopt the practice of always indicating, by means of a
comment, any references by a procedure to global variables.

3.3 Input with read and readln

A program will most often need to acquire values for its variables from the
outside world. For example, in the train travel example it would be more
convenient to have the various accelerations and periods typed into the
program, rather than set as constants. Such values form the **data** for the

program and could consist of tables stored on disk, replies to questions or just lists of values to be typed in. Values for variables are acquired by means of the read and readln statements.

The form of read and readln statements

The three general forms of these statements are:

Input statements

```
read (list of variables);
readln (list of variables);
readln;
```

The list of variables consists of identifiers separated by commas, as in

```
read(salary, temperature, x);
```

Data must be supplied which conforms with the types required. Thus for this statement, suitable data would be

```
20000   23   603.24
```

The read statement picks off values to put into each variable in its list, and is quite happy to skip over spaces and blank lines when looking for a number. It will not usually skip over anything else, so that, using the ordinary read statement, we cannot put other information between numbers, such as

```
20000 dollars    70 degrees C    603.24
```

The readln statement works just like the read statement except that when it has filled up all its variables, it looks for the end of line, skipping everything in its path. This can be used to accommodate information such as that above. If we have the statements as data

Numbers should be separated by a space or the end of a line.

```
readln(salary);
readln(temperature);
readln(x);

20000 dollars
70 degrees C
603.24
```

then all will be well. Having read each number, Pascal will skip the rest of the line as desired.

Example 3.3   Resonant frequency

| **Problem** | A simple inductance/capacitance circuit has been set up and we wish to calculate the inductance required to resonate with a |

given capacitance at a given frequency. Diagrammatically, we have:

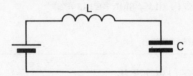

| **Solution** | The formula for the inductance L is $L = \dfrac{1}{\omega^2 C}$. |

We can write a program which asks the user to type in the required values for ω and C and prints out the answer. Better still, we could ask for a range of values of C, and print out a table of answers.

| **Algorithm** | A simple for-loop will do for the printing out of the table. Requesting and reading the values requires a write or writeln |

followed by a read or readln. There is a question as to which to use, and unfortunately, the answer depends on the computer system you are using. With standard Pascal, one could do it like this:

Ways of synchronising a write and read.

```
write('Capacitance in nanofarads, C: '); readln(C);
```

Capacitance in nanofarads, C: 1.5 <return>

Because there is a readln statement, the return key must be pressed after the number – this is a useful discipline. Some Pascal systems, however, do not permit input until after output of a line has finished. In this case, one would have to use:

```
writeln ('Capacitance in nanofarads, C: '); readln(C);
```

Capacitance in nanofarads, C:
1.5 <return>

We shall adopt the first method. We shall also not indicate the <return> in sample outputs: it must be assumed that the last data item on every line is terminated in this way. So we might have:

```
write('Start and end capacitance in nanofarads, C1 C2: ');
readln(C1,C2);
```

Start and end capacitance in nanofarads, C1 C2: 1.5   2.5

Finally, we must get our units right: the resonant frequency will be in megaradians per second and the capacitance in nanofarads, so some multiplying will need to be done to get the answer in henries. In fact, if we do a test calculation, we find that the answers will be in the range of microhenries, so we should adjust the formula accordingly. Notice that the scientific forms 1E6 and 1E–12 are useful in this context.

| Program |

Input is now also mentioned in the program header.

```
PROGRAM ResonantFrequency (input, output);
  CONST
    pi = 3.141592;

  VAR
    C, C1, C2  : 0..1000;  {nanofarads}
    f               : real; {kilohertz}
    L               : real; {microhenries}

  BEGIN
    writeln('**** Resonant frequency in an LC network ****');
    writeln;
    write('Start and end capacitance in nanofarads, C1  C2: ');
    readln(C1, C2);
    write('Resonant frequency in Mrad/s, omega: ');
    readln(f);
    writeln('The inductance, L, is given in microhenries');
    writeln;
    writeln('C':6,'L':18);
    FOR C := C1 to C2 do begin
      L := 1E6 / (4 * sqr(pi) * sqr(f * 10E6) * C * 1E-12);
      writeln(C:6, L:12:4);
    end;
  END.
```

| Testing | The following would be sample run of the program.

**** Resonant frequency in an LC network ****

Start and end capacitance in nanofarads, C1 C2: 25 30
Frequency in Mrad/s: 3
The inductance, L, is given in microhenries

C	L
25	1.1258
26	1.0825
27	1.0424
28	1.0052
29	0.9705
30	0.9382

How do we know the answers are correct? We can work out the formula using a calculator for a few values of C and confirm that the program gives the same answers.

Signalling the end of data

Many problems (for example the next one) will require large quantities of data items to be read in. The issue is how to know when the end of the data has been reached. There are actually four ways:

1. state in advance how many items there must be;

2. precede the data by a count of how many items there actually are;

3. put a special terminating value at the end of the items;

4. make use of an end-of-file property to mark the end of the items.

The first two methods are applicable to counting loops, since they rely on the number of numbers being known before reading starts. In the next two methods the number of numbers is not relevant, rather the reading stops when a certain condition is achieved. These two are applicable to conditional loops, and are discussed in section 4.2.

Of the two methods for counting loops, the second is more general, since the same program will be able to read in 10 numbers, or 55 or 1800, with just the data being changed. This is illustrated in the next example.

Example 3.4   Computing the mean

Problem The mean of some numbers is often needed in calculations. We would like to construct a procedure to read in the numbers and calculate the sum and mean.

Solution It is quite straightforward to read the numbers into a program, adding each one in turn to a total. This can then be divided by however many were read, to give the mean. We shall use method 2 above, and precede the numbers with a count of how many there will be.

Algorithm The algorithm is fairly simple, but has one important feature: the total must be initialised to zero before adding commences.

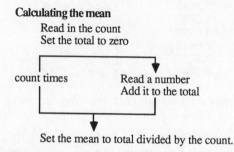

Calculating the mean
Read in the count
Set the total to zero

count times   Read a number
                   Add it to the total

Set the mean to total divided by the count.

When reading in the count, we take care to give some idea as to the amount of numbers we are expecting.

The program is structured in procedures, with *Summation* possibly being useful in other programs later on. In order to emphasise that *Summation* uses global variables, we list them in a comment at the start of the procedure. In Chapter 5, we shall see how this can be formalised in Pascal.

```
PROGRAM  ComputingtheMean (input, output);
VAR
  count  : 1..10000; {say}
  total    : real;

  PROCEDURE Initialise;
  BEGIN
    writeln ('****** Computing the Mean ******');
    write ('How many numbers (up to 10000)? ');          Tell the user
    readln (count);                                       any limits built
    writeln('Type in the ',count:1,' numbers ending with return');  into the
  END; {Initialise}                                       program.

  PROCEDURE Summation;
    {Makes use of global variable    : count             Identifying the
       and returns global variable    : total}           globals used.
    VAR
      i    : 1 .. 10000;
      number : real;
    BEGIN
      total := 0;
      FOR i := 1 to count do begin
        read(number);
        total := total + number;
      END;
      readln;
    END; {Summation}

BEGIN
  Initialise;
  Summation;
  writeln;
  writeln ('N = ':8, count:8);
  writeln ('Total = ':8, total:8:2);
  writeln ('Mean = ':8, total / count:8:4);
END.
```

Running the program would produce:

```
****** Computing the Mean ******
How many numbers (up to 10000)? 10
Type in the 10 numbers
7 65 65.1 40 90.5 12 55 52 20 3
N =    8
Total =   402.60
Mean =  50.3250
```

For every readln
in the program,
the user must
press return.
The way in which the dialogue between the program and the user is set up is very important, and is discussed again in Chapter 4. This program follows a fairly simple pattern of requiring the return key to be pressed after the count and after the last of the numbers: more returns are optional, but the program will require at least these two, because of the readlns at these points.

Notice, too, the output formatting for the answers: it is usually a good idea to line up results in some way.

3.4 Selection with if-then-else

Two methods of changing the values of variables have been covered so far, that is assignment and reading in. We now consider how to check the values in variables, and choose alternative actions based on the result of the check. Pascal has two **selection** statements known as the **if-statement** and the **case-statement**. The first is covered here, and the second in section 4.3.

Form of the if-statement

The general form of the if-statement is

If-statement

```
IF condition THEN statement
        ELSE statement;
```

where a condition, in its simplest form, consists of a comparison between two items or expressions of the same type, using one of the following six operations:

More conditions
appear in
section 4.1 on
booleans.

=	equals
<>	not equals
<	less than
<=	less than or equals
>	greater than
>=	greater than or equals

Examples of simple conditions are:

```
voltage < 0.01
speed > speedlimit
age <= 16
year = 1066
day <> 29
initial = 'J'
```

In the if-statement we refer to the statement following the *then* as the **then-part** and similarly to the statement following the *else* as the **else-part**. The whole if-statement is executed as follows. First, the condition is evaluated. If this result is true, then the then-part is executed, and the else-part is skipped. If the result is false the then-part is skipped and the else-part is executed. A simple example would be:

```
if number >= 0 then writeln('Positive')
             else writeln('Negative');
```

In the general form of the if-statement, the else-part is given in italics. This means that it is optional and the statement can be used in an *if-then* version. For example,

```
if linecount = 24 then wait;
```

A consequence of this option is that if the else-part is present, the statement before the keyword ELSE must not have a semicolon at the end. The reason for this is to enable Pascal to distinguish between if-then and if-then-else statements.

There must be no semicolon before an ELSE.

Example 3.5   Summing three ways

| Problem | A list of numbers needs to be summed, and separate sums kept of the positive and negative numbers as well. |

| Solution | Start with the *Summation* procedure from the previous example. Add in two new totalling variables, and use an if-statement to cause values to be added to one or the other. Leave out the mean bit. |

| Algorithm | The loop in algorithm form is

Summing three ways

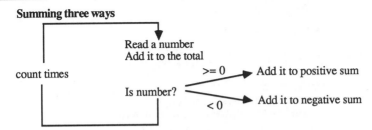

| Program | The program uses procedures as before.

```
PROGRAM ThreeSums (input, output);
   VAR
      count          : 1..10000; {say}
      Total, PosTotal,
```

```
                        NegTotal        : real;

                    PROCEDURE Initialise;
                      BEGIN
                        writeln('*******Three sums *****');
                        write('How many numbers (1..10000)? ');
                        readln(count);
                        writeln('Type in the ',count:1,' numbers ending with return.');
                      END; {Initialise}

                    PROCEDURE Summation3;
                      {Use global variable        : count
                       returns global variables   : Total, PosTotal and NegTotal}
                      VAR
                        number  : real;
                        i         : 1..10000; {say}
                      BEGIN
                        Total := 0;
                        PosTotal := 0;
                        NegTotal := 0;
                        FOR i := 1 to count do begin
                          read (number);
                          Total := Total + number;
                          if number > 0 then PosTotal := PosTotal + number
                                        else NegTotal := NegTotal + number;
                        END;
                        readln;
                      END; {Summation3}

                    PROCEDURE Finalise;
                      BEGIN
                        writeln('Total = ':20, Total:10:4);
                        writeln('Positive total = ':20, PosTotal:10:4);
                        writeln ('Negative total = ':20, NegTotal:10:4);
                      END; {Finalise}

                    BEGIN
                      Initialise;
                      Summation3;
                      Finalise;
                    END.
```

| Testing | A complete run would look like this: |

```
***** Three sums *****
How many numbers (1..10000)? 12
Type in the 12 numbers ending with a return
  65.5     34      −22      90       19
  87      −15.2     0      100      6.1
  −1       77
Total =        440.4000
Positive total =        478.6000
Negative total is =     −38.2000
```

Compound statements

There may be times when several statements are needed in the then- or else-parts of an if-statement. These must be enclosed in *begin-end*, as was done with for-loops. Such a group of statements enclosed in *begin-end* is called a **compound statement**, and may be used in place of a statement. The form of a compound statement is therefore:

Compound statement

```
BEGIN
   statements
END ;
```

Suppose that in the *Threesums* program, it is also required to know how many positive and negative numbers were read. Then two more counters are needed, and, to each part of the if-statement, an extra statement is added to do the counting. Thus the if-statement would become:

Begin-end is a versatile grouping construct.

```
if number >= 0 then  begin
    PosTotal := PosTotal + number;
    PosCount := PosCount + 1;
  end
  else begin
    NegTotal := NegTotal + number;
    NegCount := NegCount + 1;
  end;
```

Successive else-ifs

Sometimes, there are more than two possibilities that need to be considered. One way in which this is done is by **successive else-ifs**. The condition of the first if-statement eliminates one case, leaving the rest to the else-part. The else-part in its turn introduces another if-statement which selects out another condition and leaves the rest to its else-part, and so on. This is illustrated nicely in an example that prints out a class of pass for various ranges of marks, thus:

```
if marks >= 75 then writeln('First') else
if marks >= 70 then writeln('Upper second') else
if marks >= 60 then writeln('Lower second') else
if marks >= 50 then writeln('Third') else
                writeln('Fail');
```

Notice a few points about this statement:

- The conditions are carefully ordered, so that each eliminates a certain range of marks. Thus the line that writes out a third class for anything over 50 will only be reached when it has already been established that the mark is under 60.

- The last class, fail, is given for all the rest of the marks, and does not need a condition.

- Layout of successive if-statements is important, and should try to reflect the pattern of conditions as much as possible.

Careful layout of control constructs aids readability. A secondary consideration is that the most frequently occurring conditions should be checked first. If it is more likely that people will fail, then it will be marginally more efficient to arrange the order of the conditions thus:

```
if mark < 50 then    writeln('Fail') else
if mark < 60 then    writeln('Third') else
if mark < 70 then    writeln('Lower second') else
if mark < 75 then    writeln('Upper second') else
                     writeln('First');
```

Example 3.6 The highest number

Problem Find the largest value in a sequence of numbers.

Solution A program can read in the numbers one at a time, remembering the highest so far, and updating this if necessary. We note that negative numbers should be catered for as well.

Algorithm development by induction. **Algorithm** This is a very interesting algorithm, because it is based on induction. We start by assuming that we have found the highest of n numbers. Then the $n + 1$th number is read. To find the highest of the $n + 1$ numbers, all that needs to be done is to compare the new number to the highest so far, and if it is higher, to replace the highest. This process can then be repeated for as long as required.

The question is, how does the process start? Well, the highest number of a sequence that is one long must be just that number. So we start by reading in one number, make it the highest and proceed from there. The algorithm is:

Finding the highest

Read a value for the highest, to start

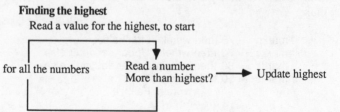

Program

```
PROGRAM Highestvalue (input,output);
  CONST
    max = 10000;
  VAR
    highest   : real;
    n         : 0 .. max;

  PROCEDURE Initialise;
    BEGIN
      writeln('*****  Finding the highest number *****');
      write('How many numbers (1 to ', max:1, ')? ');
      readln (n);
      writeln('Type in the ',n:1,' numbers followed by a return');
    END; {Initialise}

  PROCEDURE Findhighest;
    {Use global variable       : n
     returns global variable   : highest}
    VAR
      i   : 0 .. max;
      number  : real;
    BEGIN
      read(highest);
      for i := 2 to n do begin
        read(number);
        if number > highest then highest := number;
      end;
      readln;
    END; {Findhighest};

  BEGIN
    Initialise;
    Findhighest;
    writeln('The highest number is ', highest:1:2);
  END.
```

Testing   A typical run gives:

```
***** Finding the highest number *****
How many numbers (1 to 10000)? 12
Type in the 12 numbers followed by a return
14  17.8  19.3  0.5  12  34  98  54.6  4.4  0.2  65 55
The highest number is 98.00
```

It is a good idea to test such an algorithm with the first number being the highest, then with the last, and then with one in the middle. Another test would be to have all the numbers except one equal. This is left up to the reader.

3.5 Type integer

Variables, constants, expressions and functions all have **types** in Pascal, and the type governs exactly how they can be used. For the moment, we shall consider only the two numerical types, integer and real. More types and type mechanisms are introduced in succeeding chapters.

Integer values

Integers are used for counting – one of the computer's most common tasks. The integer type in Pascal is applicable to all those items that are inherently whole numbers such as a year, number of children, and counters of all sorts.

In mathematical terms, the integer numbers extend infinitely on either side of zero; on a computer, they are bounded by the storage allocated to hold them. Typically, this will restrict the range to

$$-2\,147\,483\,648 \quad \text{to} \quad +2\,147\,483\,647$$

On some older computers, the space set aside for integers gives a very much smaller range of

$$-32\,768 \quad \text{to} \quad +32\,767$$

Don't assume that integers can be very large.

It may well be that when programming on such a machine, larger numbers are needed, in which case a solution may be to switch to real numbers.

Whatever the range that is available, Pascal provides a predefined constant called *maxint* which gives the value of the largest integer. Thus on any machine, one can discover the range by simply printing out *maxint*, as in

```
writeln('Maxint is ', maxint);
```

Literals are the symbols used to express the values of a given type. For integers, the literals are formed from digits optionally preceded by a sign of plus or minus. Pascal is, however, strict about how numbers are written, and in particular, there cannot be spaces or commas in them to separate the thousands. The following are all valid Pascal integers:

```
1000000  –16567      80
```

whereas the following are not:

```
1,000,000 –16 567     80c
```

Integer operators and functions

Integer literals, constants, variables and functions can be formed into integer expressions using any of the three operators + (plus) – (minus) and * (multiply). There are also two more that permit integer division, giving the quotient and remainder respectively. These are:

x div y	divide *x* by *y* and discard the remainder
x mod y	remainder after *x* is divided by *y*

Mod is not defined if *y* is negative and, of course, both *mod* and *div* are undefined if *y* is zero. Some examples will clarify this.

17 div 6	= 2	17 mod 6	= 5
6 div 17	= 0	6 mod 17	= 6
18 div 6	= 3	18 mod 6	= 0
−13 div 2	= −6	13 mod −3	= undefined

Mod and *div* are frequently used to break an integer up into its digits. If we know that a number has three digits, then the leftmost digit can be extracted by taking *n div 100* (i.e. how many hundreds are there?), and the rightmost digit is found with *n mod 10* (i.e. What remains after dividing by 10?). In Pascal, this would be

```
VAR
  n                  : 000 .. 999;
  units, tens, hundreds : 0 .. 9;

  units := n mod 10;
  tens  := (n div 10) mod 10;
  hundreds := n div 100;
```

The relational operators such as = and < (introduced in the previous section) can also be used between integers.

There are four predefined functions which operate on integers and return integers as their values. They are

abs(n)	absolute value of *n*
sqr(n)	square of *n* i.e. *n* * *n*
succ(n)	successor of *n* i.e. *n* + 1
pred(n)	predecessor of *n* i.e. *n* − 1

Division with / always yields a real number.

Although only the + − and * are defined between integers to produce integer results, a division operator / can be used between integers and it will produce a real result. There are also the two useful conversion functions

trunc(x)	smallest integer less than *x*
round(x)	nearest integer to *x*

These two functions take a real expression and produce an integer. *Trunc* cuts off (or truncates) the fractional part of the number, and returns the integer part. *Round* will round up or down to the nearest integer. Thus we have

trunc (6.3)	= 6	round (6.3)	= 6
trunc (6.8)	= 6	round (6.8)	= 7

Integer input and output

Integer values can be read and written using the usual four input/output statements, i.e. *read*, *readln*, *write* and *writeln*. We have already covered the details of reading and writing numbers in previous sections, so here we just summarise the points made:

1. For input, the number supplied as data must conform to the notation for literals and therefore may not contain commas, full stops or spaces.

2. The read and readln statements will skip any leading spaces, including blank lines, before the integer begins. However, they will not skip over any other characters.

3. Standard Pascal permits any non-digit to end a number but this flexibility is not usual in other languages and therefore not all Pascal systems implement it. It is best to restrict data design to numbers that are always terminated by spaces or ends-of-line.

4. An integer is written right-justified in a fixed space of about 12 characters unless a field width is given.

5. If the field width is not large enough, it is expanded. This fact is used to get left-justified numbers by using a field width of :1.

6. The field width may be any integer expression.

Example 3.7   Timetables in the 24h clock

Problem   A delivery firm has acquired a new fleet of vehicles which are able to travel 15% faster than the old vehicles (while still staying within the speed limit). They would like to print out new timetables automatically for their deliveries, based exactly on the old ones.

Solution   The old timetables looked like this:

Departs	Zone 1	Zone 2	Zone 3	Zone 4
0600	0610	0622	0654	0712
0630	0640	0752	0824	0844
0700	0711	0735		
0730	0742	0756		
0745	0800		etc.	
0800				
0810				

There is no pattern to the times, so the only way of making the conversion will be to read in each number in turn and print out the new time as 85% of the old. The question is how to do arithmetic on times.

Algorithm   Times consist of two parts – hours and minutes. The only way to do multiplication on a time is to convert it to either hours or minutes first, perform the calculation, then convert it back. The overall algorithm is:

Update timetables

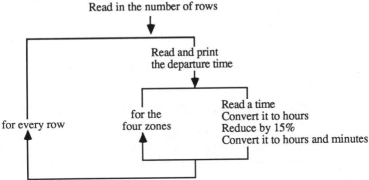

Notice that we don't convert the departure times, only the arrivals!

The first conversion involves splitting an integer into two parts, which we can do with the mod and div operators, as described earlier. The algorithm is:

Convert to real hours	**Example 0715**
Find hours from time div 60	7
Find minutes from time mod 60	15
Set realhours to hours + minutes / 60	7.25

Converting back, on the other hand, requires use of trunc and round to get the integer and fractional parts. The algorithm is:

Convert to hours and minutes	**Example 7.25**
Set hours to the integer part	7
Set minutes to 60 * fractional part	(7.25-7) * 60 = 15

Program Developing a program like this can best be done with procedures. We start with the 'top-level' as follows, using comments and procedure calls to indicate bits that need to be filled in later.

Example of top-down development.

```
PROGRAM NewTimetable (input, output);

{***Declarations here***}

BEGIN
  Initialise; {Print headings etc.}
  Getsizeoftable; {No. of rows}
  FOR r := 1 to noofrows do begin
    read (t);

    ConverttoRealHours;
```

```
            realhours := reduction * realhours;

            ConverttoHoursandMins;

            write(t);
        END;
    END.
```

Then we expand each of the procedures and at the same time, set up declarations. For example,

```
    PROCEDURE ConverttoHoursandMins;          Declarations
        BEGIN
            hours := trunc (realhours);            hours : 0..23;
            mins := round ((realhours – hours) * 60);   realhours : real;
        END;  {ConverttoHoursandMIns}           mins : 0..59;
```

The development of the rest of the program is left to the reader.

3.6   Type real

Real numbers are those that may have fractional parts, and are used for quantities where this is appropriate, such as prices, weights and measures and mathematical results. A real number does not have to have a fractional part, though, and the values of all the integer numbers are contained in the set of reals.

There are two ways of writing real numbers. Fixed point is the usual way, with a decimal point (not comma) being used. Examples of fixed point reals are:

$$3.141593 \qquad 0.18 \qquad 5.0 \qquad 0.000004 \qquad 10000000$$

Floating point numbers have a mantissa and exponent.

The second real form is one that splits the number into a fraction known as the **mantissa** and an **exponent**. This is known as **floating point** form. The purpose of the floating point is to be able to represent very large or very small numbers without having all the zeros. The exponent indicates a power of 10 by which the fraction must be modified. Since the power can be positive or negative, and there is no rule about how the split must be made, there can be many ways of representing a single number in floating point form. For example, consider the number forty million. In fixed point form it is 40000000.0, which is rather hard to read. In floating point form it can be written as 4E7 or 40E6. Similarly, for a very small fraction such as 0.000001, the floating point form could be 0.1E–5 or 1.0E–6.

When dealing with physical values measured in kilometres or nanoseconds or megabytes for example, keeping exponents to multiples of three helps to reflect the prefix conventions of SI units. Thus we would have:

5085 kilometres	5.085E6 metres
7 nanoseconds	7.0E–9 seconds
10 megawatts	10E6 watts

The range of values of a real number is very much larger than that of an integer. Since there are two parts to a real number – the fraction and exponent – the range is expressed in terms of the number of significant digits that can be accommodated and the highest value of the exponent. As with the integers, the range depends on the number of bits allocated to each part. Typically, reals will be stored in 64 bits, giving the following range:

- 16 digits of accuracy

- exponent from –38 to +38

If only 32 bits are used, then the exponent stays the same, but the number of significant digits in the fraction drops to a mere six. The effect of the limit on significant digits is that the following two numbers, if read in, would both be stored as the same value:

    12345678.12345678
    12345678.1234567812345

Further implications of floating point on computation are discussed below.

Because they cannot be exactly expressed in decimal notation, real variables cannot have lower and upper bounds that can be checked by the compiler, as is the case with integers. However, such information is useful to readers of the program and it is good practice to indicate the expected accuracy and range of each variable as a comment. Examples of real constant and variable declarations are:

Use comments to indicate real subranges.

```
CONST
   pi     = 3.141593;
   VAT    = 0.15;   {15%}

VAR
   second      : real;   {0.00 .. 59.99}
   capacitance : real;   { in microfarads}
   percentage  : real;   {0.0 .. 100.0}
   share       : real;   {0.00 .. 0.99}
   cost        : real;   {0 .. 100 000 000 dollars}
   temperature : real;   {– 40 .. 50 degrees C}
   x, y, z     : real;   {–1.000000E–15 .. 1.000000E15}
```

Real operators and functions

There are four operators for reals, i.e. $+ - * /$. The slash symbol is used for division. It is not applicable to integers in the sense that it does not produce an integer result. However, if / is applied to integers, Pascal will perform the division and produce a real result.

There are several standard functions that operate on real numbers. There are five mathematical functions:

abs (x)	$|x|$	absolute value
sqr(x)	x^2	square
sqrt(x)	$\sqrt{x}$	square root
ln(x)	$\log_e x$	natural logarithm
exp(x)	e^x	natural exponentiation

Remember: the trig. functions use radians not degrees.

and three trigonometric functions, for x given in radians (not degrees),

sin(x)	$\sin x$	sine in radians
cos(x)	$\cos x$	cosine in radians
arctan(x)	$\tan^{-1} x$	inverse tangent

See Chapter 5 for how to construct the rest of the trig. functions.

Pascal does not have a built in operator for raising something to a power. This is achieved by using the *ln* and *exp* functions as follows:

$$x^y \quad = \quad e^{\,y\,\ln(x)} \quad = \quad \exp(y * \ln(x))$$

However, if y is a small known integer, then it may be easier to simply use multiplication, as in

$$x^4 = \quad x * x * x * x$$

Note that it is not permissible to raise a negative number to a fractional power using *exp* and *ln* directly.

Real input and output

Real numbers of either form can be read in using read and readln, with the same convention as for integers that the number should end with a space or the end of a line. Real numbers can be written out in write and writeln statements, but in the absence of any formatting, they are written in floating point form. Most of the time, though, numbers will be required to be output in fixed point, in which case, two field widths must be given as described earlier in section 2.4.

Arithmetic accuracy

Since computer arithmetic is done in fixed-sized words there has to be some way of handling calculations that go outside the range of numbers provided. There are two possibilities:

Two problems with computer numbers.

- an approximate value is used and calculation continues;
- an error occurs and calculation is abandoned.

The first approach is used when there is a loss of precision in how the number is stored, and the second is used when the number actually goes outside the range. These two cases are now considered.

Rounding error

The fraction of a floating point number holds all the digits of precision available. Sometimes an operation may produce a number which has more digits than can be accommodated. Some digits will be lost, and this may affect subsequent calculations and the end result. This effect is known as rounding error.

To illustrate this effect, assume that there is a little computer with reals stored with

- 4 digits in the mantissa,
- 1 digit in the exponent.

First consider the problem of inexact division. The expression 10 / 3 * 3 should produce 10, but in fact may work out as

$$10 / 3 * 3 = 3.333$$
$$*3$$
$$= 9.999$$

Precision was irretrievably lost in the division. This is quite a common result and you should see if it happens on your computer. If the answer is printed in floating point form, the inaccuracy should be apparent; if printed in fixed point with a field width for the fraction smaller than the digits provided by the mantissa, then the number may be rounded and appear to be correct. Thus on the little computer with 4 digits in the mantissa,

writeln (10 / 3 * 3, 10 / 3 * 3 :8:1);

gives

.999E0   10.0

This phenomenon is the same no matter how large the mantissa.

The second problem occurs in large multiplications. If two four-digit numbers are multiplied, the result will have seven or eight digits, but still, on our little computer, only four can be stored. For example

$$60.08 * 4.134 = 248.37072$$
$$\text{cannot be represented}$$
$$= 248.4$$

Such effects become more noticeable with very large numbers. On this little computer with a 4-digit mantissa, we have

largest number	0.9999 E 9 or	999 900 000
second largest number	0.9998 E 9 or	999 800 000

In between these, there is nothing, so that any of the 100 000 missing values have to be represented by one of these. For example

999 934 628   is represented by   999 900 000
999 876 543   is represented by   999 900 000

When multiplying, see what happens:

73.56 * 1101 = 80 9<u>89.56</u>

                                  cannot be represented

             = 80 990

Overflow and underflow

These are error conditions where a number itself, rather than just its precision, is too large or too small. They apply to integers and reals.

The largest integer value is given by the constant *maxint*. It is not possible to create or store an integer value larger than this. The computer should catch such attempts and signal an error. More subtly, it is also not permissible to go out of range during a computation, even if the final result is within range. So, for example, the following expression cannot be evaluated:

maxint * 2 div 3

because twice the value of *maxint* cannot be represented, even as a temporary value. However, if the expression is rewritten in the following way, the evaluation becomes possible:

maxint div 3 * 2

Just switching to real arithmetic as in

maxint * 2 / 3

would not help because most Pascal systems will remain in integer mode as long as possible. Thus they will still treat the multiplication as an integer operator, and only switch to real when encountering the /. It is, however, always better to use integers if they are applicable, because rounding error problems are avoided. Moreover, real variables cannot be used in several places where integers are acceptable, for example as loop variables in for-statements or as key-expressions in case-statements.

At the other end of the scale, for floating point we have for our little 4-digit computer

smallest number   0.1000E–9 or 0.0000000001

Any value less than half of this will be stored as zero. This fact must be remembered when performing computations with very small numbers. Multiplication is especially vulnerable, as shown in this expression:

$$a / (b * c) \quad \text{where} \qquad \begin{array}{ll} a = 0.0000004 & \text{or } 0.4\text{E--}6 \\ b = 0.00001 & \text{or } 0.1\text{E--}4 \\ c = 0.000\,004 & \text{or } 0.4\text{E--}5 \end{array}$$

$b * c$ produces 0.4E–10 which is smaller than the smallest real, and therefore is represented as 0. As a result, the division will fail. As often happens, reordering an expression enables it to be evaluated more accurately. In this case, the equivalent form of $a / b / c$ will work. a / b gives 0.04, and this divided by c gives the answer of 10 000.

Example 3.8   Demonstration of rounding error

| Problem | Many formulae in calculus involve taking a limit as some

quantity (say h) tends to zero. One would suppose that making h smaller and smaller would lead to better and better results. However, because of rounding error, this is not so. We wish to illustrate this effect on more than one computer, if possible.

| Solution | Let us consider the square root function. The first two

derivitives of sqrt(x) can be estimated by the formula

$$\frac{d}{dx} \sqrt{x} = \frac{\sqrt{x+h} - \sqrt{x-h}}{2h}$$

$$\frac{d^2}{dx^2} \sqrt{x} = \frac{\sqrt{x+h} - 2\sqrt{x} + \sqrt{x-h}}{h^2}$$

with h tending to zero. We shall calculate these expressions for h starting at 0.1 and being divided by 10 at successive times round the loop. If we choose a value for x such as 1, we know in advance that the correct answers are 0.5 and –0.25. We can then ascertain when the answers are closest to these results. The algorithm is a straightforward for-loop, and we can go directly to the program.

| Program |

```
PROGRAM RoundingError (output);
  VAR
    x,h,
    deriv1,deriv2   : real;
    i               : 1..8;
  BEGIN
    h := 1;
```

```
x := 1;
writeln('**********Demonstration of rounding errors********');
writeln;
writeln ('Finite difference calculation of 1st and 2nd ');
writeln ('derivatives of sqrt(x) at x = 1');
writeln( 'Analytic answers are deriv1 = 0.5, deriv2 = –0.25');
writeln;
writeln(' h       deriv1              deriv2');
FOR i := 1 to 8 do begin
  h := h/10;
  deriv1 := (sqrt(x + h) – sqrt(x – h)) / (2 * h);
  deriv2 := (sqrt(x + h) + sqrt(x – h) – 2 * sqrt(x)) / (h * h);
  write('10e-', i:1,' ',deriv1,' ',deriv2);
  writeln;
END;
END.
```

Try this on your computer, too. | Testing | We tested the program on two computers. Computer A used 32 bit floating point numbers and Computer B had 64 bit floating numbers. On A, the program produced the following output:

**********Demonstration of rounding errors********

Finite difference calculation of 1st and 2nd derivatives of sqrt(x) at x = 1; analytic answers: deriv1 = 0.5, deriv2 = -0.25

h	deriv1	deriv2
10e-1	5.006278e-01	-2.507925e-01
10e-2	5.000085e-01	-2.503395e-01
10e-3	4.999936e-01	-2.384186e-01
10e-4	4.997850e-01	0.000000e+00
10e-5	5.006791e-01	0.000000e+00
10e-6	4.768372e-01	0.000000e+00
10e-7	8.940698e-01	0.000000e+00
10e-8	0.000000e+00	0.000000e+00

The most accurate results were obtained when h = 10e-2: thereafter things deteriorated rapidly. However, on Computer B, a different picture emerged. 64 bit floating point numbers were in use, giving a considerable accuracy, viz.

10e-1	5.0062775059818873700e-1	-2.5078537793346534440e-1
10e-2	5.0000625027345361520e-1	-2.5000781291018275150e-1
10e-3	5.0000006250002732660e-1	-2.5000007812503964590e-1
10e-4	5.0000000062500022480e-1	-2.5000000077914086300e-1
10e-5	5.0000000000625173700e-1	-2.5000000008525147260e-1
10e-6	5.0000000000009346860e-1	-2.4999989058083205150e-1
10e-7	4.9999999999974110300e-1	-2.5000617895343246750e-1
10e-8	4.9999999999974110300e-1	-2.4936649967166601990e-1
10e-9	4.9999999998076756500e-1	-2.1684043449710088680e-1
10e-10	5.0000000017050294520e-1	0.0000000000000000000e+0

The best estimate for the first derivative was at 10E-6 and for the second derivative at 10E-5. For very small h the estimates for the second derivative are completely useless.

3.7 Numerical methods using for-loops

In this text book, we are going to introduce numerical methods gradually, using them to exercise the programming techniques that we have just learnt. Many of the methods that are really useful to engineers do not require sophisticated programming skills, and can be mastered early on. We look at two in this section, and illustrate them with an example from circuit analysis.

Method 1   Solving a d.e. with a predictor-corrector

| Rationale | An important use of computing in science and engineering is the finding of approximate answers to problems in calculus that cannot be solved exactly. In the course of this book we shall be looking at several different types of such problems. The first we shall tackle is how to solve a differential equation. Simple differential equations (d.e.s) can be solved analytically, but as they become more complex, numerical techniques are necessary. An example of a first-order ordinary differential equation would be the formula for the velocity of an object falling under gravity through a fluid, for example water. This is:

$$\frac{dv}{dt} = g - \frac{kv^a}{m}$$

| Methods | Differential equations can be divided into **initial value problems** where information is given at only one value of x, and **boundary value problems**, where data is specified at both ends of a range of values for x. We shall consider here the theory for initial value problems and home in on a good method for solving one first order equation. Solutions to boundary value problems are discussed in Chapters 5 and 6.

| Theory | Consider the single first order differential equation

$$\frac{dy}{dx} = f(x, y)$$

with y given at some initial value of x. Suppose that we want to solve for y in the interval $0 \leq x \leq L$ and with the initial value of y at$(x=0) = y_0$.

The simplest and probably best known method for finding values of y for values of x is **Euler's Method.** We split the interval $[0..L]$ up into n equal subintervals as shown and let the length of each subinterval be $h = L / n$.

Leonhard Euler (1707–1783)

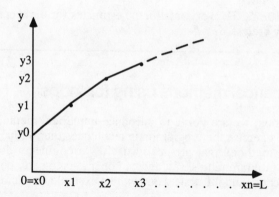

Then we successively estimate a value for y_{i+1} in terms of x_i, y_i. For Euler's method the formula is

$$y_{i+1} = y_i + h f(x_i, y_i)$$

Most methods are set in the same framework but differ in the above formula. Although well-known, Euler's method's poor accuracy means that it is rarely used in real life.

A more accurate method is the **predictor-corrector** method. Each step consists of two stages. First we use a **predictor** formula which gives a first estimate of the solution, i.e.

$$y_p = y + h f(x, y)$$

and then a **corrector** formula which uses y_p to obtain a better approximation, i.e.

$$y = y + \frac{1}{2} h \left(f(x, y) + f(x + h, y_p) \right)$$

This new value of y is fed back into the predictor, and the process repeated until the desired range of x-values has been covered. Other methods that will be found in texts on numerical methods are Runge-Kutta methods (discussed in problem 5.16), multistep methods, and various improvements to the basic predictor-corrector method.

| Algorithm | The algorithm for the predictor-corrector method is dominated by the loop over the interval of values for x. At each iteration, we need to compute the predictor value for y_{i+1}, compute the corrector value and then move on to the next subinterval. This is illustrated in the pseudo-code chart.

The algorithm can then be translated into a Pascal procedure. A generalised procedure is outside the scope of this chapter and is discussed in Chapter 5. In the example that follows, we implement the algorithm for a specific case.

Predictor-corrector algorithm

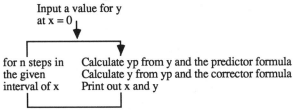

for n steps in the given interval of x	Calculate yp from y and the predictor formula Calculate y from yp and the corrector formula Print out x and y

Example 3.9   Current variation in an RL circuit

Problem	An electrical circuit consists of an inductance L, a resistance R and a constant power source E, as shown below.

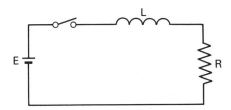

Initially the switch is open, and there is no current in the circuit. At time $t = 0$, the switch is closed and the current builds up. We want to know the variation in the current over the first 1s after the switch is closed.

Solution	Once the switch is closed, the voltage changes around the circuit must add up to zero, by Kirchhoff's Law. This gives:

$$L\frac{dI}{dt} + RI - E = 0$$

which gives the differential equation

$$\frac{dI}{dt} = \frac{E}{L} - \frac{R}{L}I$$

Taking this as $f(t, I)$, we can use the predictor-corrector method to solve the differential equation for I at various intervals for t up to 2s.

Algorithm	The algorithm starts by reading in initial values for the various parts of the circuit, and for h. Typically, h is taken as 0.01 and

we may need to find the value of I for times up to $t = 1$ (seconds). That means that 100 intermediate values are calculated. We would probably like to know some of these intermediate values, but not all of them.

We can use a nested loop, suppressing writing in the inner loop, and only printing values in the outer loop.

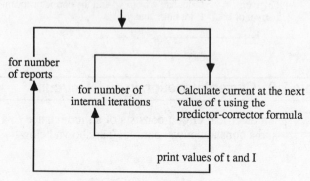

Current in RL circuit algorithm
Ask the user for the initial values

for number
of reports

for number of
internal iterations

Calculate current at the next
value of t using the
predictor-corrector formula

print values of t and I

| Program |

```
PROGRAM RLcurrent (input, output);
    {Illustrates the predictor-corrector method for solving
     a single first order differential equation}

VAR
    {See the procedure Initialise for the meaning
     and units of these variables}
    E, R, L,
    current, t, h    : real;
    reports,j,imax   : 1..maxint;

PROCEDURE PredictorCorrector;
    {Uses global variables       : imax, current, t, h for the method
               and                : E, L and R for the function
     Returns global variables     : t, current}

VAR
    i : 1..maxint;
    currentp : real;

BEGIN
    FOR i := 1 to imax do begin
        currentp := current + h * (E / L – R * current / L);
        current := current + 0.5 * h * (E / L – R * current / L) +
                    (E / L – R * currentp / L);
        t := t + h;
    END;
END; {PredictorCorrector}

PROCEDURE initialise;
    VAR TS : 0..maxint;  {seconds}
```

```
BEGIN
  writeln("***** Electrical current in an RL circuit *****');
  writeln ("***** Using predictor-corrector algorithm *****');
  writeln;
  writeln('Solves: dI / dt = E / L – RI / L ');
     writeln;
  write('Emf source in volts, E: ');  readln (E);
  write ('Inductance in henries, L:');  readln(L);
  write ('Resistance in ohms, R:' );  readln(R);
  write('Step length h:');  readln(h);
  write('Number of iterations before reporting:');  readln(imax);
  write('Stopping time in seconds, TS:');  readln(TS);
  reports := TS / h / imax;
  writeln;
  writeln('    t          I');
  t := 0;
  current := 0;
END; {Initialise}

BEGIN
  initialise;
  writeln(t:10:2,'    ',current:10:4);
  FOR j := 1 to reports do begin
    PredictorCorrector;
    writeln(t:10:2,'    ',current:10:4);
  END;
END.
```

| Testing |

For typical values, the program produces:

***** Electrical current in an RL circuit *****
***** Using predictor-corrector algorithm *****

Solves: dI / dt = E / L – RI / L

Emf source in volts, E: 20
Inductance in henries, L: 5
Resistance in ohms, R: 10
Step length h: 0.01
Number of iterations before reporting: 10
Stopping time in seconds, TS: 1
The current, I, is given in amps.

t	I
0.00	0.0000
0.10	0.3625
0.20	0.6593
0.30	0.9023
0.40	1.1013
0.50	1.2642
0.60	1.3976
0.70	1.5068
0.80	1.5962
0.90	1.6694
1.00	1.7293

How do we know the answers are correct? Analytically, the solution to the differential equation with initial condition $I = 0$ and $t = 0$ is $i = \dfrac{E}{R}\left(1 - e^{-Rt/l}\right)$ and we can easily check that the results from the program are correct.

Method 2   The Fourier series

| Rationale | There are many problems in engineering which depend on periodic functions, such as the loading of a beam or the steady state of the current in a circuit, the flow of heat through metals or of fluid through pipes. For example, the waveform of a cathode-ray oscilloscope sweep generator is given by

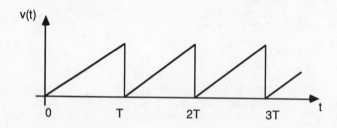

Named after Jean Baptiste Joseph Fourier (1768-1830).

where T is the fundamental period of the function. This sort of function can be approximated by a series of trigonometrical functions, known as a **Fourier series**. The value of the function at successive points can then be calculated by evaluating the series.

| Theory | Fourier showed that if $f(t)$ is periodic, then it can be expressed as

$$f(t) = a_v + \sum_{n=1}^{\infty} a_n \cos n\omega t + b_n \sin n\omega t$$

where a_v, a_n and b_n are Fourier coefficients and are calculated from $f(t)$ and ω is related by $\omega = \dfrac{T}{2\pi}$ to the fundamental period, T, of the function. For example, the simple square periodic wave function given by

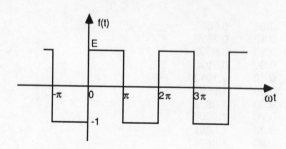

can be approximated by the Fourier series

$$f(t) = \frac{4E}{\pi} \left(\sin \omega t + \frac{1}{3} \sin 3\omega t + \frac{1}{5} \sin 5\omega t \ \dots \right)$$

Given the symmetry in the terms, this kind of formula should be easy to convert into a program. One problem would be how to sum to infinity. Clearly, we shall have to cut off somewhere. There is a way of calculating how many terms are needed, which depends on the accuracy required, and this is covered in the case study on the temperature in a plate in Chapter 7. We shall meanwhile choose some large number, such as 100, for the example that follows.

Example 3.10   Circuit with a sinusoidal voltage

Problem   The circuit in example 3.9 is to be supplied not with a constant power source, but one with a voltage that has the following waveform:

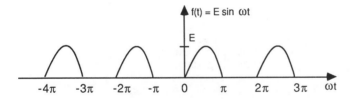

f(t) = E sin ωt

We want to examine the current in the circuit over the first two seconds this time.

Solution   Voltage with the above waveform can be approximated with a Fourier series:

$$v(t) = \frac{E}{\pi} + \frac{E}{2} \sin \omega t - \frac{2E}{\pi} \left(\frac{\cos 2\omega t}{2^2 - 1} + \frac{\cos 4\omega t}{4^2 - 1} + \frac{\cos 6\omega t}{6^2 - 1} + \dots \right)$$

The current in the circuit is given by:

$$I = \frac{V}{Z}$$

where

V is the voltage computed at $\omega t - \alpha$

α is the phase lag = $\arctan(L\omega / R)$

Z is the impedance given by $\sqrt{R^2 + L^2\omega^2}$

So we can write a program to calculate I for various values of t.

| Algorithm | This is a lot of formulae! Nevertheless, it is possible to break the problem down. We want to evaluate I at various values of t. |

This reduces to evaluating $v(t)$ and dividing by Z. Evaluating $v(t)$ consists of taking the first two terms and the multiplier, and then doing the series, which we shall call S, i.e.

$$v(t) = \frac{E}{\pi} + \frac{E}{2} \sin \omega t - \frac{2E}{\pi} S$$

Evaluating S is done in a loop for $i = 2,4,6\ldots$, adding up the terms $\dfrac{\cos i\omega t}{i^2 - 1}$

| Program |

```
PROGRAM SinusoidalVoltage (input, output);
  {Calculation of the current in an RL circuit
  with a half-wave rectified sinusoidal voltage}

  CONST pi = 3.141592;
  VAR
  t            : real; {seconds}
  j, reports   : 1.. 1000; {reports}
  omega        : real; {rad/s}
  alpha        : real; {phase lag}
  Z            : real; {impedence}
  current      : real; {amps}
  S            : real; {sum of Fourier terms}
  noterms      : integer; {no. of terms}
  h            : real; {time between reports}
  E,v          : real; {volts}
  L            : real; {inductance in henries}
  R            : real; {resistance in ohms}

  PROCEDURE Initialise;
    VAR TS : real;
    BEGIN
      writeln('***** Currrent in an RL circuit ******');
      writeln('Using a half-wave rectified sinusoidal voltage');
      writeln('approximated by a Fourier series');
      writeln;
      write('Voltage amplitude in volts, E: ');  readln(E);
      write('Periodic frequence in rad/s, omega: '); readln(omega);
      write('Inductance in henries, L :'); readln(L);
      write('Resistance in ohms, R: '); readln(R);
      write('Stopping time in seconds, TS: ');  readln(TS);
      write('Interval between reports: '); readln(h);
      write('How many Fourier terms? ');  readln(noterms);
      reports := trunc(TS / h);
      t := 0;
      alpha := arctan (L * omega / R);
      Z := sqrt(sqr(R) + sqr(L) * sqr(omega));
```

```
      writeln;
      writeln(' t              I');
   END; {Initialise}


PROCEDURE Fourierterms;
   {Uses global variables        : omega, t, alpha, noterms
    Returns global variable      : S
   VAR
     i : 0..1000;
   BEGIN
     S := 0;
     for i := 1 to noterms do
       S := S + cos(2 * i * (omega * t – alpha))/(sqr(2 * i) – 1);
   END;  {Fourierterms}


BEGIN
   Initialise;
   FOR j := 1 to reports do begin
     Fourierterms;
     v := E / pi + E * 0.5 * sin(omega * t – alpha) – 2 * E / pi * S;
     current := v / Z;
     t := t + h;
     writeln(t:5:2, current:18:4);
   END;
END.
```

| Testing |

We run the program for the same data values as the previous example.

***** Current in an RL circuit ******
Using a half-wave rectified sinusoidal voltage
approximated by a Fourier series

Voltage amplitude in volts, E: 20
Periodic frequence in rad/s, omega: 10
Inductance in henries, L :5
Resistance in ohms, R: 10
Stopping time in seconds, TS: 2
Interval between reports: 0.1
How many Fourier terms? : 100

t	I
0.10	0.0000
0.20	0.0000
0.30	0.2300
0.40	0.3916
0.50	0.1932
0.60	0.0000
0.70	0.0000
0.80	0.0000
0.90	0.1321
1.00	0.3821
1.10	0.2809
1.20	0.0000
1.30	0.0000

1.40	-0.0000
1.50	0.0237
1.60	0.3422
1.70	0.3462
1.80	0.0318
1.90	0.0000
2.00	-0.0000

The negative zero for some of the current values is suprising. It is evidence of a **truncation error** caused by evaluating a finite number of terms in the series, rather than all (infinity). If the program is run with fewer terms, more of the values will be presented as very small negative numbers, when they should be zero. Thus the Fourier series represents a good approximation of the actual function, but still only an approximation.

Self-check quiz

1. Given the following group of declarations, which ones would cause the compiler to report errors and why?

```
CONST
    max      = 10;
    K        = 1,000;
    initials = 'JFK'
    Prize    = D50;
    2ndPrize = D25;
VAR
    maximum   : 0..max;
    i, j, k   : integer;
    start, end : char;
```

2. State four ways of controlling the reading in of a variable number of data items.
3. Given the following statements and data, what will be printed out?

```
VAR                          Data:
    i, j, k : integer;       67   56
                             98   91
    read (i);                11   33
    readln;
    readln(j);
    readln(k);
    writeln(i,j,k);
```

4. The following set of statements is very inefficient. Why is this so? Rewrite them more efficiently.

```
if pre = 'm' then write('milli');
if pre = 'c' then write('centi');
if pre = 'K' then write('kilo');
```

5. The following piece of program is meant to swap the values in x and y if it is necessary, so that x lands up with the lower one. What will actually happen? Correct the program.

(Continues)

Summary

- [ ] An identifier consists of a sequence of letters and digits starting with a letter and not containing spaces. Pascal does not distinguish between upper- and lower-case letters.

- [ ] Pascal has 35 keywords (such as BEGIN and FOR) and several predefined identifiers (such as *integer* and *writeln*) which have special meanings and may not be re-declared as identifiers.

- [ ] Comments are enclosed in { } or (* *) and serve to amplify and explain the program.

- [ ] A variable denotes a value which may change during execution of the program. Each variable has a type which governs the values it may hold.

- [ ] An assignment statement gives a variable a (new) value.

- [ ] When reading numbers, the read statement will skip spaces before a number and may insist on a space or line end to finish a number.

- [ ] The if-then-else statement serves as a two-way selection mechanism, or as a single selection in the form of if-then, or as a multi-way selection with successive else-ifs.

- [ ] Then- and else-parts that consist of more than one statement must be grouped with BEGIN-END, forming a compound statement.

- [ ] Integers range over ± 2 thousand million on most computers. Real numbers can usually go up to $10^{\pm 38}$ with some 16 digits of accuracy.

- [ ] Real numbers use a floating point representation which gives flexibility on size and accuracy. This can cause problems with very large and very small numbers.

- [ ] The operators and functions for integers and reals are:

Type	Operators	Functions
Integer	+ – * div mod	*abs, sqr, succ, pred, trunc, round*
Real	+ – *	*abs, sqr, sqrt, ln, exp, sin, cos, arctan, trunc, round*

- [ ] Errors in programs can be caused by uninitialised variables, and by misuse of global variables.

- [ ] The predictor-corrector method can be used for finding the solution to differential equations.

- [ ] Periodic waveforms can be approximated by a Fourier series.

```
if x > y then
   temp := x;
   x := y;
   y := temp;
```

6. How would you write out the value of the smallest integer on your computer?
7. If *x* has the value 1948, what would be output by

   ```
   write (x, x:1, x mod 2:1,ord(odd(x)):1);
   ```

8. Under what conditions are the *mod* operator and the *exp, ln* and *arctan* functions not defined?
9. Given the constant declaration and corresponding write statement:

   ```
   CONST pi = 3.14159265;
   writeln(pi : 10:6);
   ```

   what would the output be, if the computer being used has 11 decimal digits of precision? What would it be on a computer with 4 digits of precision?
10. At a factory, the 24-hour day is divided into three shifts as follows:

Shift 1	from 00.00 to 07.59
Shift 2	from 08.00 to 15.59
Shift 3	from 16.00 to 23.59

    Write an assignment statement which calculates from the time (which is given as a real number) the length of the appropriate shift (which is an integer number).

Problems

3.1 A farmer wishes to build a fence around an irregular paddock. He has measured the position of the four corners as (x,y) distances in km relative to his house as follows:

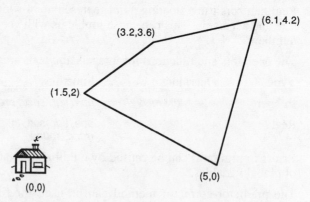

Write a program to print out the perimeter of the paddock, using the formula for the distance between two points as

$$\sqrt{(x_1 - x_2)^2 + (y_1 - y_2)^2}$$

3.2 Extend example 2.3 so that the resistance values are read in. Extend the program further to cater for a variable number of resistances in parallel between 2 and 5. The program should start off by asking for the number of resistors.

3.3   Consider the following inverting amplifier circuit, representing an ideal operational amplifier operating within its linear range.

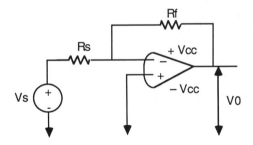

The terminal voltage v_0 is given by

$$v_0 = \frac{-R_f}{R_s} v_s$$

and the amplifier saturates when

$$\left| \frac{V_{CC}}{v_s} \right| > \frac{R_f}{R_s}$$

Write a program which reads in values for the two resistors R_f and R_s in KΩ, and the operational amplifier voltage V_{CC} in volts and calculates the range of input voltages v_s such that the amplifier does not saturate. For this range of inputs, print the output voltage v_0.

3.4   The classes of pass at Zanyland College have the following names, ranges and abbreviations : First 75%+ (I), Upper Second 70%+ (II–1), Lower Second 60%+ (II–2), Third 50%+ (III) and Fail 49%– (F). Write five procedures called *eye*, *one*, *two*, *dash* and *eff*, which respectively print out the symbols for I, 1, 2, – and F in large format, going sideways, for example, F is:

Now write a successive else-if sequence which uses these procedures to print out in large format the symbol for a given mark.

3.5   A street is lit by 4 lamps of 1000W each on lamp-posts 20m high and 50m apart, i.e.

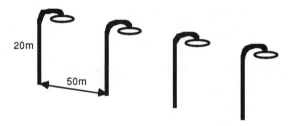

The intensity of illumination, in candelas, produced by a lamp of height h and power C at a point d from the post is given by

$$L = \frac{C\,h}{(h^2 + d^2)^{1.5}}$$

The level of illumination at any one point can therefore be found by adding up the contributions of each of the four lamps.

Write a program which calculates the intensity of illumination at 10 metre intervals under the lamps. *Hint*: Although specific values have been given for C, h and d, construct the program so that these values are read in, and test your program for various different sets of data.

3.6   The rainfall figures in mm are available for each day of the past four weeks. We want to know

- the total rainfall for each week,
- the wettest day of the 28,
- the driest week of the 4.

Write a program which will read in several sets of 28 rainfall figures and print out the three bits of information required. Sample data and results would be

Sample data	Sample results
3 0 0 7 8 21 0	39mm
0 1 1 0 0 0 4	6mm
9 6 7 0 0 0 0	24mm
0 0 0 0 0 0 1	1mm

The wettest day was day 6.
The driest week was week 4.

3.7   The natural logarithmic function $ln(x)$ can be approximated by the series

$$ln(1 + x) = x - \frac{x^2}{2} + \frac{x^3}{3} - \frac{x^4}{4} \dots$$

for $-1 < x < 1$. Write a program which computes the first 8 terms of the series and outputs the value of the function for values of x in a given interval and with a given step. In each case, print the corresponding value of the Pascal $ln(x)$ function. *Hint:* Use the odd function to determine the sign for each term.

3.8   The Zanyland Golf Course has nine holes. At each hole, a player is expected to be able to sink the ball in the hole in 1 to 5 shots. This gives a course average or **par** of 30. A player's score for the course is the sum of the numbers of shots for each hole. Depending on his past performance, a player is granted a **handicap** which is subtracted from his score to give his actual result for a game. Players are also interested in knowing whether they have scored under par or not. When players play together, the winner is the one with the lowest score. If the scoring of a golf game were computerised, sample input and output might be:

Player	Handicap	Shots per hole	Total	Result	Under Par?
1	6	1 3 6 2 1 4 3 2 4	26	20	yes
2	3	2 2 2 2 4 4 4 2 2	24	21	yes
3	2	4 5 4 3 4 1 3 5 4	33	31	no

The winner is player 1 with a handicapped result of 20

Write a program which

- reads in the shots per hole for several players,
- calculates each total score, handicapped score and par decision,
- determines the winning player and the winning score.

3.9 A sensitive drug cannot sustain a change in temperature of more that 30°C in a 24 hour period. The temperatures are monitored and recorded every 2 hours. Write a program the laboratory technician can run once a day to determine whether or not to throw the drug away.

3.10 The Zanyland Traffic Department wants to decide whether or not to mount a campaign against illegal parking. A number of traffic inspectors are sent to different zones in the city where parking time is restricted. The different zones have different time restrictions. Each of the traffic officers has to monitor any ten cars in their zone and record the actual time the vehicle was parked in the time restricted zone. If 50% or more of the cars were parked for a longer period than allowed, the traffic department will decide to launch a massive campaign. Write a program which

- reads in the number of zones,
- reads the time limit and actual parking-time for ten vehicles for each zone,
- determines the number of cars exceeding the time limit in each of the zones,
- decides whether a campaign should be mounted or not,
- identifies the zone where the situation is the worst.

Sample input and output might be:

Please enter the number of zones: 3

Area	Limit	Parking times	Over limit
1	60	20 40 70 35 45 78 34 56 73 5	3
2	45	62 47 68 40 53 62 120 8 15 72	7
3	30	66 32 41 89 7 25 29 33 54 17	6

A campaign must be mounted.
Concentrate on area 2

3.11 Rough graphs of trigonometric functions can be plotted on a screen or printer by having the x-axis running downwards and the y-axis across. The value of the function can be multiplied by some scaling factor (such as 30) and used to determine the number of spaces to be printed before the point. Write a simple Pascal program to print a graph of $\sin(x)$ or $\cos(x)$ between 0 and $\pi/2$. Then extend the program to put the x-axis in the centre of the page and print the graphs of the functions for -2π to 2π. (Remember that the Pascal trig. functions expect parameters in radians.)

3.12 The Fibonacci series consists of a series of numbers in which each number is the sum of the two preceding ones, i.e.

1 1 2 3 5 8 13 21 34 55 ...

Write a program to print the first 50 terms of the series. Adapt the program so that it prints out only every third number. What do you notice about the numbers?

3.13 Engineers in a plant have been trained to work in kilograms when measuring mass, but their clients and suppliers often wish to know know quantities in pounds (lbs) and ounces (oz). The engineers would like to a print out conversion tables to paste on little cards 20 lines deep. The output should be arranged in three columns to look like this:

kg	lbs oz	kg	lbs oz	kg	lbs oz
10.0	22 1	12.0	26 7	14.0	30 14
10.1	22 4	12.1	26 11	14.1	31 1
10.2	22 8	12.2	26 14	14.2	31 5
10.3	22 11	12.3	27 2	14.3	31 8

Write a program which reads in the starting kg value and prints out the appropriate card for 6kg from there on. *Hint*: The conversion factor is $1\text{kg} = 2.205\text{ lb}$.

3.14 The RL circuit discussed in examples 3.9 and 3.10 is to be supplied with a voltage having a simple square waveform which is approximated by the Fourier series

$$f(t) = \frac{4E}{\pi} \left(\sin \omega t + \frac{1}{3} \sin 3\omega t + \frac{1}{5} \sin 5\omega t \ \ldots \right)$$

Adapt the program in example 3.10 to print out the current for this new waveform.

3.15 The probability of two people in a group of n having the same birthday is

$$p(n) = 1 - \frac{365}{365} \times \frac{364}{365} \times \frac{363}{365} \ \ldots \ \frac{365 - n + 1}{365}$$

Write a program to evaluate and print this probability for groups of 2 to 60 people.

3.16 Write a procedure to implement Euler's method for solving a differential equation (section 6.5). Test the procedure in a program which solves current in an RL circuit problem of example 3.5. Compare the results with those obtained for the predictor-corrector method.

3.17 The velocity of an object starting from rest and falling under gravity through a fluid is given by the differential equation

$$m \frac{dv}{dt} = mg - kv^2$$

where

- m and v are the object's mass and velocity (take $m = 2\text{kg}$),
- t is time,
- g is the gravitational acceleration, taken as 9.8 ms^{-2},
- k is a constant depending on the object's size and shape and on the fluid (take $k = 100\text{Nm}^{-2}\text{s}^{-2}$).

Use the predictor-corrector method (example 3.5) to find the terminal velocity v_T.

3.18 Use the Euler procedure of problem 3.16 to solve the problem in 3.17, and compare the results obtained with those for the predictor-corrector method.

3.19 Use the Euler method and the predictor-corrector method to solve the following differential equations:

(a) Find $q(\pi)$ if $\frac{dq}{du} = q^2 \sin(u)$ with $q(0) = 0.2$

(b) Find $y(2)$ if $\frac{dy}{dt} = \sqrt{t(1 + y)}$ with $y(1) = -0.88888$.

Characters and loops

So far we have dealt mainly with numeric values. Much of computing is concerned with numbers, but certainly not all of it. Computers are also information processing machines, and information consists mainly of text, which in turn consists of characters. This chapter looks at the types character and text and considers ways in which they are processed by a Pascal program. We introduce three control statements – the while-loop, repeat-loop and case-statement – and discuss possibilities for directing graphics from a Pascal program. For numerical methods, we look at ways of finding roots of equations, starting with the simple but crude search method, and moving on to the really useful Newton-Raphson method.

4.1 Characters

The character type in Pascal is called *char.* We shall examine the properties of *char* as we did for integers and reals.

Character values

There are usually 128 different character symbols that one can use in a program. These include the letters, digits, punctuation symbols, arithmetic operators and various other special control characters. The latter cause things to happen, such as feeding a page of paper or ringing a bell. The particular range of values depends on the underlying character set of the computer, which is most often the ASCII set. This set includes

ASCII stands for
American
Standard
Codes for
Information
Interchange.

A B C D ...
a b c d ...
0 1 2 3 ...
. , ; : ? ! % ( ) + − = / * @ $ ...

For a full list of characters, consult the manual for your particular Pascal system.

A character literal is written within single quotes (or apostrophes), e.g. 'A' or '+'. A quote itself is written twice, within its own quotes, i.e. "".

Character input and output is straightforward. Characters can appear in read and write statements, interspersed with numbers and strings. If *ch* and *sign* are character variables and *amount* is an integer, then we can have statements such as

```
read(ch);
writeln('The balance is ', sign, amount:1);
```

which would produce the output

The balance is −300

Characters are
right-justified in
their fields.

The length of a character is one. If a field width is specified in the write statement, the character will be right-justified in the appropriate number of spaces. For example, we might have the statement and output:

```
writeln ('Jones', 'A':10);
```

Jones~ ~ ~ ~ ~ ~ ~ ~ ~ A

Character operators and functions

The six relational operators are defined for characters, i.e.

$$= \quad <> \quad < \quad > \quad <= \quad >=$$

There is no
inbuilt ordering
between letters
and digits.

The ordering achieved by the relational operators is based on the underlying character set, and may well differ from computer to computer. Therefore we cannot rely on any group of characters, say the letters, always coming before, say, the digits. However, we can assume that the letters themselves are in the correct alphabetic order and that the digits 0 to 9 are also in sequence.

A loop variable of a for-statement can be of type character, as can the key of a case-statement (see section 4.3). For example, consider the excerpt

```
{Printing all characters between two that are given}
read(first, last);
if first < last
```

```
then
    for ch := first to last do write(ch)
else
    for ch := last to first do write(ch);
```

Given *OK* as data, it will write out **KLMNO**.

There is also a special operator for set membership, *in*, which can be put to good use with characters. It is discussed at the end of the section.

There are four predefined functions for characters namely

succ(ch)	the next characters after *ch* (c.f. +1 for integers)
pred(ch)	the character before *ch* (c.f. −1 for integers)
ord(ch)	the ordinal value of *ch* in the underlying character set
chr(n)	the character whose ordinal value is *n.*

There are natural error conditions associated with these functions. If there are 128 possible characters with ordinal values from 0 to 127, then *pred(0)* and *succ(127)* are undefined, as is the *chr* of any number outside this range.

As an example of the use of *ord*, consider how to convert a capital letter to a small one. Subtracting the ordinal value of the first capital letter – 'A' – from the given character's ordinal value gives us an ordinal value for that character starting at 0. Then if we add the ordinal value of the first lower-case 'a', and convert the value back to a character, it will be in the range of the lower-case letters. The full Pascal formula is:

Converting between capital and small letters.

```
smallch := chr(ord(ch) − ord('A') + ord('a'));
```

We can test this out on the ASCII set where *ord('A')* is 65 and *ord('a')* is 97. Then given *ch* is 'S', we have

```
smallch  = chr(83 − 65 + 97)  =  chr(115)  = 's'
```

The important point to note is that we do not have to know the ordinal values of 'A' and 'a' in order to do the conversion, nor do we need to know whether the capitals come before the smalls in the character set. The above formula is completely general. This conversion formula fits nicely into a function, which is covered later in section 5.2. For now, we shall just use it in a statement:

```
if ch in ['A'..'Z'] then ch := chr(ord(ch) − ord('A') + ord('a'));
```

Notice that it is important to check whether the character is a capital before converting it.

Example 4.1   Printing the character set

The *ord* and *chr* functions can be used to discover the ordering of the characters on a computer. Assuming that there are 128 characters, the following program will print them out, together with their ordinal values.

```
PROGRAM CharacterSet (output);
  VAR i : 0 .. 127;
  BEGIN
    for i := 0 to 127 do write(i:4, chr(i):2);
  END.
```

Running this program, one notices that funny things happen on the screen at first – this is because special characters such as DEL, LF, BEL, etc. are being printed. To omit these characters, the loop can start at 32 or so.

Exercise
Alter the program to print out the characters in neat columns across the page.

The in-operator

The in-operator gives set membership.

Characters form natural subsets. For example, there is the set of digits, the set of capital letters, the set of vowels, and so on. In Pascal, we can construct sets of characters and use the *in* operator to check whether a value is in a given set.

A set is constructed from a list of items and ranges of items, enclosed in square brackets. The ranges are expressed as starting value and ending value either side of double dots. For example, typical sets are:

```
['A', 'E', 'I', 'O', 'U', 'a', 'e', 'i', 'o', 'u']
['0'..'9']
['+', '–', '0'..'9', '.', 'E']
```

More about sets in Chapter 8.

There is more about sets in Chapter 8, but note here that we can also construct sets of integers, and that the elements of a set must all be of the same type. Thus we cannot mix character literals and integer literals in the same set.

To use the in-operator for expression *e* and set *s,* we have

```
e in s
```

When checking for something not in a set, we have to use the somewhat clumsy notation

```
not (e in s)
```

Example 4.2   Validating course codes

| Problem | Course codes at Zanyland University have a precise form: 4 capital letters followed immediately by 3 digits and terminated |

by a space. As a first step in validating that student registrations have been typed in correctly into the computer database, we want a procedure that checks the above rule.

| Solution | The procedure can be written to perform the check, and put with a small program that can read possible course codes and validate them.

| Algorithm | The algorithm is straightforward. We have to check a sequence of eight characters where the first four must be capital letters, the next three must be digits and the eighth must be a space. If an error occurs at any stage, we want to note the fact, but carry on checking to see how many errors there are. So we declare an integer variable *error*, initially set to zero, and every time a rule is broken, we increase its value by one. After all the characters have been read, the course code is correct provided that *error* is still zero.

| Program |

```
PROGRAM ValidateCourseCode(input,output);
VAR
  error : 0..99;

PROCEDURE check;
  {Returns global variable    : error}
  CONST
    space = ' ';
  VAR
    i : 1 ..4;
    ch : char;
  BEGIN
    error := 0;
    FOR i := 1 to 4 do begin
      read(ch);
      IF not (ch in ['A'..'Z'])
        then error := error + 1;
    END;
    FOR i := 1 to 3 do begin
      read(ch);
      IF not (ch in ['0'..'9'])
        then error := error + 1;
    END;
    read(ch);
    IF ch <> space
      then error := error + 1;
    END; {check}

BEGIN
  writeln('********Course Code validation********');
  writeln;
  writeln ('Type a possible course code, '
          'followed by a space and return.');
  error := 0;
```

```
          Check;
          readln;
          IF error = 0
            then writeln('Course code correct')
            else writeln('Course code incorrect: ',error:2,' error(s)');
       END.
```

| Testing | A typical run might be:

> ******* **Course code validation** *******
> **Type a possible course code, followed by a space and return.**
> CM104
> **Course code incorrect: 1 error(s)**

Interactive programs

The program guides the user.

An **interactive program** is one that is run with the user sitting in front of a terminal and entering data as necessary. This is how most programs are run these days, and even large programs will start off with a bit of dialogue before starting on their computations. In interactive mode, it is the computer program, rather than the user, that is in control all the time. The program decides what needs to be read, and what will be written. The only way the user can alter the course of the program is by responding to set questions. In particular, the user can't just ask the program 'What should I do next?' or 'How do you want your data?'. It is the responsibility of the programmer to provide all the necessary information to guide the user and to anticipate any problems. To do this fully, more Pascal is necessary, so the issue will be taken up again at the end of the next section. Meanwhile, we can look at some basic techniques of dialogue.

Dialogue

Dialogue with a user via a terminal should be precise, but friendly. Instructions should be quite clear, yet should not take up too much space. The reason for this is that it is not helpful if the instructions disappear off the top of the screen before the user has had time to respond to them. There are many ways of issuing instructions and choice depends on personal taste, but the following list of guidelines is a good start.

Five hints on good dialogue.

1. A program should introduce itself, so that the user knows it has started running. If there are different versions of a program, the version name or number should appear in the introduction. Examples are:

    > ****** **Summing numbers** ******
    > ****** **Summing numbers (Version 2 – with dialogue)** ******

2. Data can be requested by a prompt being written out on the screen first. If the answer expected is a single item, then a *write-readln* sequence

enables the answer to be written on the same line as the prompt. The user enters the reply ending up with a return. As an example,

```
write('How many numbers (1..10000)? ');
readln(count);
```

would produce

How many numbers (1..10000)? 7

The return has two functions: it serves to terminate the number (a space would too) and it preserves the neatness of the dialogue. To coordinate the statements with the intended data format therefore, we recommend a *readln* rather than a *read* at this point.

3. If a limit applies on the value to be read, then this should be made quite plain, as in the above example. It is equally helpful if the fact that there is no limit is communicated, as in example 4.3.

4. Bulk data should not be subject to individual requests. Thus if a list of items is required, there need not be a prompt for each item, just one for the list. Certainly, large amounts of data should be input with read, not readln.

5. One of the most common pieces of dialogue is a request from the program for permission to continue. The answer required is a yes or no. Typically, this is abbreviated to Y or N, but the program should also permit y or n as answers. The condition for continuing can be expressed in a conditional using set membership as in:

```
VAR reply : char;

write('More data? ');  readln(reply);
if ch in ['Y', 'y'] then {proceed}
```

4.2 Conditional loops with while and repeat

This text started off by introducing loops in order to emphasise the power of programming in handling repetitive tasks in a simple way. The loops that have been used up to now have all had a common property – their duration was explicit. By looking at the starting and finishing values of the for statement, the number of times the loop would execute could be calculated. However, not all solutions can be formulated in such precise terms. For example, when reading data, it is not always possible to know in advance how much data there will be, or when the person supplying the data will wish to stop. Thus we need the concept of a **conditional loop** – one that will stop according to some conditions. Specifically, these conditions need not necessarily be defined in terms of a fixed number of iterations.

The form of conditional loops

Conditional loops are phrased in terms of while or repeat statements. A general form of a loop using the while statement is:

While statement

> *Initialise the conditions*
> WHILE *conditions* DO BEGIN
> *Statements to perform the loop*
> *and change the conditions*
> END;

While-loops check the condition at the beginning.

After statements to initialise variables involved in the conditions, the loop itself starts by checking the conditions. If they evaluate to true, the body of the while-statement is entered and executed. When the END is reached, control goes around again to the WHILE and the conditions are checked again. This process is repeated until the test of the conditions evaluates to false, at which point the looping stops, and control is passed to the statement following the END.

The general form of the repeat statement is similar, as shown overleaf. The repeat loop starts off by going through its body at least once before checking the conditions. This can sometimes be a desirable property, but in general the while-statement is more useful.

Repeat statement

> *Initialise the conditions*
> REPEAT
> *Statements to perform the loop*
> *and change the conditions*
> UNTIL *conditions;*

Repeat loops check the condition at the end.

Notice that the repeat statement is the only one in Pascal that does not need a BEGIN-END around a group of statements. Putting them in would not invalidate the statement, but it would look peculiar to experienced Pascal programmers, and is therefore not a good idea.

The two very important points about conditional loops are that

Remember these!

- the conditions must be initialised;
- the conditions must change during the loop.

If the conditions are not initialised, then the loop will be working on incorrect or even undefined information. If they are not altered during the loop, then there will be no chance of them changing and causing the loop to end.

Simpler forms

The general form of a while loop can be simplified in two ways. If only one statement forms the body of the loop, then the BEGIN-END can (but doesn't have to) be omitted. It is unusual for both processing and changing to be possible in a single statement, but we shall see examples of it later. Most conditional loops will consist of several statements and will need the BEGIN-END.

The other simplification is more common, in that only a single condition may apply to the loop, not several as implied in the general form. A condition is expressed as a boolean expression and this may be as simple as a single variable. Very often the conditions start with *not*, as we shall see.

Before going on to a problem, consider some small illustrative examples of conditional loops, bearing in mind the importance of formulating them correctly. In order to convey the sense of the looping process, some of the examples make use of procedures, which do as their names suggest.

Developing a conditional loop

The first example simulates trying to find a pair from a drawerful of mixed coloured socks.

How to formulate a loop correctly.

```
PickaSock;
PickAnotherSock;
WHILE not  aPair DO BEGIN
   DiscardaSock;
   PickAnotherSock;
END;
```

The loop is initialised by having two socks in hand: this is essential so that the check for a pair can be correctly performed. The loop is correctly formulated in that the condition will change each time round, as a new sock is selected. There are, however, two crucial flaws in the loop.

Suppose a pair is never found. The condition is not met so the loop continues, but the operation *PickAnotherSock* will eventually fail, and the whole operation will crash. The other problem is similar – suppose there were no socks in the drawer to start with. In this case, neither of the initialising statements can be performed, and the program as it stands will not be able to execute. These two situations can be summed up as

- guard against not being able to begin;
- guard against never ending.

The remedy is to provide additional conditions as the guards. In this case, we need to know if sufficient socks (i.e. at least two) exist to be able to test for a pair, and then we need to know when the drawer becomes empty. Both conditions are based on the number of socks in the drawer, and we assume that this figure can be provided in some way. The corrected version of the loop then becomes:

```
IF NumberofSocksinDrawer >= 2 then begin
  PickaSock;
  PickAnotherSock;
END;

WHILE (NumberofSocksinDrawer > 0) and not aPair  DO BEGIN
  DiscardaSock;
  PickAnotherSock;
END;

{At this point, a pair may or may not have been found}
```

Follow-up
actions to a
conditional
loop.
There is one final consideration with any conditional loop. If there is more than one part to the condition governing the loop, it may be necessary to know at the end which part caused the loop to stop. In the example, it seems sensible to be able to decide whether the search was successful or not. This is called a **follow-up action**, and is performed by re-checking some of the conditions, as in

```
IF aPair then writeln('Got a pair of socks')
        else writeln('Bad luck, no pair found.');
```

Notice that when conditions are connected (as they often are), one must be careful as to which is tested. In this case, it would not have been correct to test for empty as in

```
IF empty then writeln ('Bad luck, no pair found.')
        else writeln ('Got a pair of socks');
```

since the pair could have been found on the very last time round the loop. The drawer would also be empty, but that is irrelevant for this purpose.

Exercise
Write the necessary if-then-else statements to report on whether a pair was found or not, whether the drawer was empty initially, or whether it became empty during the search.

Example 4.3   Highest common factor (HCF)

| Problem | We wish to find the highest common factor (HCF) of two numbers. |

| Solution |

One possible solution would be to find all the factors of each number and then compare both lists for the highest one. Fortunately, there is a quicker way!

Suppose a and b are the numbers, a is larger than b and their HCF is f. Then $a - b$ and b will also have an HCF of f. If we use this fact, repeatedly replacing the larger of the two numbers by their difference, until the two numbers are the same, then this figure will be the HCF, even if it is 1.

| Algorithm |

The above discussion can be be expressed in the following algorithm.

A simple but elegant algorithm.

Highest Common Factor

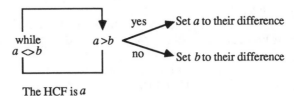

| Examples |

a	b	$\lvert a - b \rvert$
65	39	26
26	39	13
13	26	13
13	13	HCF

a	b	$\lvert a - b \rvert$
99	66	33
33	66	33
33	33	HCF

| Program |

```
PROGRAM HCF (input, output);
  VAR
    a, b : 0 .. maxint;
  BEGIN
    writeln('****** Finding the HCF ******');
    write('What are the two numbers? ');
    readln(a, b);
    WHILE a <> b do
      if a > b then a := a – b
               else b := b – a;
    writeln('The HCF is ', a);
  END.
```

Conditional loops and input data

The next example deals with input data: we wish to read numbers until a certain target number is found, and then stop. The loop is:

```
read(target);
read(number);
WHILE number <> target do
  read(number);
```

Here we have a case of a single statement in the loop body. Reading is special in that it involves processing data, and it also changes the value of variables. Thus a read performs the dual function of the body of a loop and changing the conditions.

Now consider the two guards mentioned above: the loop may not be able to start if no data exists, and it may never end if the target does not appear. Both of these relate to an **end of data** condition, which we shall assume for the moment is maintained in a boolean function called *endofdata*. Assuming that at least the target can be read, then the loop is re-phrased as

Protecting a
read statement.

```
read(target);
if not endofdata then read(number);
WHILE not endofdata and (target <> number) do
  read(number);
```

The lesson here is that read statements should always be protected, whether by conditions in if-statements or in while-statements.

If knowing the reason for stopping is important then the following statement would be reasonable:

```
IF number = target  then writeln('Found ',target:1)
                     else writeln(target:1, ' is not there.');
```

Reasonable, but not strictly correct: if there was no data at all, then nothing is ever read into number, and so this question cannot be asked. This indicates that the case of no data must be handled and got rid of quite separately from the normal case. The correct statements to do this are given next.

Trailer values

The condition for end of data could be formulated in several ways. One way would be to use the built-in functions, which are discussed in section 4.4. Another way is to have a **terminator value** which is supplied by the user as the last item. To make things flexible, the trailer for that particular run of the program could also be read in. Thus the loop to search for a target number and end correctly could be formulated as:

Reading a trailer
value first.

```
read(trailer);
read(target);
```

```
read(number);
WHILE (number <> trailer) and (number <> target) do
    read(number);
if number = target then writeln('Found ',  target:1)
                    else writeln(target:1, ' not there);
```

Typical data for such a loop would be

```
0 5
1 2 7 4 5 9 0
```

The trailer is 0 and the target 5, so the loop will read values until the 5 is reached, and then stop. Since the target was found, the message *Found 5* will be printed. Since there are values left in the data, it may be helpful to skip over them. The if-part of the loop could be extended to include a loop, thus:

```
if number = target
  then begin
    writeln('Found ',  target:1);
    repeat
      read(number);
    until number = trailer;
    end
  else writeln(target:1, 'not there.');
```

Example 4.4   Controlling an apparatus

| Problem | An engineering apparatus is controlled by readings from a device. The readings are numbers that must always be in descending order. As soon as the sequence is no longer descending, the machine must stop. How would this aspect of its operation be programmed?

| Example | An example of an input sequence would be

100   67   33   32   31   54

At this stage the machine must stop.

| Solution | We assume that the numbers will be read into a program, and that for the purposes of the investigation they can then be ignored. What is important is to get the algorithm for checking on the sequence correct.

| Algorithm | To check that a number is in sequence, we have to have both it and the previous number in hand. Each time round the loop, we replace the previous number with the one read in. As far as starting off goes, we cannot make an assumption as to the value of the first number, so the remembered number cannot be preset to a special value. Instead, the first two numbers are read in separately, and then the while-loop starts, checking

Checking for numbers in sequence.

that even these are in sequence.

| Program | The relevant portions of the program would be:

```
VAR
  N, previous : integer;

  read(previous);
  read(N);
  while N < previous do begin
    previous := N;
    read(N);
  end;
```

| Extension | Since the program is feasible, the maker of the apparatus has asked that it be written, but with the following additional conditions:

- the first number must be positive;

- the numbers must not go below 0.

If the numbers do go below zero, we have an abnormal stop. If they start to rise, we have a normal stop. For each number, we are asked to print out that many dots on the same line.

Exchanging a while-loop for a repeat-loop.

| Algorithm | The condition on the while-statement will need two parts now: to check the new number against 0 and to check it against *previous*. Ensuring that the variables in the condition on the while-loop have the correct values requires the same statements as its body, and so the loop is best tranformed into a repeat-loop. In addition, an if-statement is needed at the beginning to check that the very first number is positive. Printing the dots is best done in a separate procedure.

| Program |

```
PROGRAM Controller (input, output);
VAR
  previous   : 0 .. maxint;
  N          : integer;

PROCEDURE React ;
VAR dot : 1 .. maxint;
  BEGIN
    for dot := 1 to N do write('.');
    writeln;
  END; {React}

BEGIN
  writeln('***** Controlling the apparatus *****');
  writeln('Type in the numbers');
  read(N);
  if N <= 0
```

```
      then writeln('The machine cannot work on that.')
      else
      REPEAT
        React;
        previous := N;
        read(N);
      UNTIL (N < 0 ) or (N >= previous);
      writeln;
      if n > 0 then writeln('Machine shut down okay.')
              else writeln('Emergency stop used');
   END.
```

| Testing |

Sample input and output for the program would be:

***** Controlling the apparatus *****
Type in the numbers
15 ....
12 ....
9 ....
7 ....
3 ...
−1
Machine shut down okay.

The testing should include the case where the data starts off negative.

4.3   The case-statement

The if-statement is a two-way selection statement based on conditions. However, if there are several simple tests for given values, successive else-if statements can become unwieldy. Pascal provides for so-called **keyed selection** with the case-statement. The form of the case-statement is

Case-statement

```
CASE key-expression of
    key-values  :  statement;
    key-values  :  statement;

    . . .

    key-values  :  statement;
END; {CASE}
```

Notes

Rules for the case-statement.

1.   The key-expression must be of type integer, boolean, character or enumerated (as defined in Chapter 7). It may not be real.
2.   The key-values must be literals or constants of the same type as the

key-expression.

3. At the time the case-statement is executed, the value of the key-expression is calculated and is compared against all the possible key-values listed.

4. If a match is found, the corresponding statement is executed, after which control passes to the end of the case-statement.

5. If a match is not found, an error should occur. (Some Pascal systems do not give an error, but they should.)

7. The key-values do not have to be in any order.

8. There may be one or more key-values for a given statement.

9. Key-values can only occur once each.

As an example, consider the little jingle which gives the number of days in a month:

> Thirty days hath September, April, June and November.
> All the rest have thirty-one, excepting February alone,
> Which has but twenty-eight days clear,
> And twenty-nine in each leap year.

If we assume that the following declarations and read statement have been made:

```
VAR
    month : 1 .. 12;
    days  : 1 .. 31;

BEGIN
    write('What month (1..12)? ');
    readln (month);
```

then a case-statement can be used to look at the month and set *days* to the appropriate value as follows (ignoring leap years):

```
CASE month of
    9, 4, 6, 11          : days := 30;
    1, 3, 5, 7, 8, 10, 12 : days := 31;
    2                    : days := 28;
END; {CASE}
```

As always, the statement mentioned in the form can be a compound statement and include several statements. This is needed to establish the correct day for February, taking account of leap years. To do this, the year has to be known as well and checked for a multiple of four (excluding multiples of 100, 200 and 300). With the extra declaration and read

```
VAR   year : 0 .. 2500;
```

```
write('What year (0 .. 2500)? ');
readln (year);
```

the case-statement now becomes:

```
CASE month of
   9, 4, 6, 11         : days := 30;
   1, 3, 5, 7, 8, 10, 12 : days := 31;
   2 : if (year mod 4 = 0)
           and not ((year mod 100 = 0)
                       and not (year mod 400 = 0))
       then days := 29
       else days := 28;
END; {CASE}
```

Multiple key values

In the previous example, the key was a single variable, and it mapped directly on to the values. Sometimes there are many values for each statement, and there is a simple way of adjusting them so that there is only one per statement. For example, suppose that given an examination mark, it is required to set a symbol depending on the multiple of ten, with anything over 80 being A, over 70 being B, and so on down to anything under 40 being F. The case-statement to achieve such a mapping is:

```
VAR
   mark   : 0 .. 100;
   symbol : 'A' .. 'F';

CASE mark div 10 of
   10, 9, 8  : symbol := 'A';
   7         : symbol := 'B';
   6         : symbol := 'C';
   5         : symbol := 'D';
   4         : symbol := 'E';
   3, 2, 1, 0 : symbol := 'F';
END; {CASE}
```

This is the clearest and most efficient way of solving this problem, but it is not the only way. The same effect could be achieved using successive else-ifs and some calculations on characters as follows:

```
if mark >= 80 then  symbol := 'A' else
if mark <  40 then  symbol := 'F' else
                    symbol := chr (ord('B')– mark div 10 + 7);
```

It is certainly easier to see what is going on in a table as opposed to a calculation, so case-statements should be used in preference to if-statements where possible.

When not to use case-statements

The clarity of the case-statement makes it a natural choice for many types of selections. However, it cannot be used in situations where the selection is based on conditions. For example, the following is not valid Pascal.

```
CASE number of
  < 0   : Addtonegatives;
  = 0   : Donothing;
  > 0   : Addtopositives;
END; {CASE}
```

The keys must be actual values. It is also not possible to have ranges of values so the next attempt is also invalid:

```
CASE number of
  −maxint . . −1   : Addtonegatives;
  0                : Donothing;
  1 . . maxint     : Addtopositives;
END; {CASE}
```

A suitable approach here would employ successive else-ifs, as discussed in section 3.4.

Menu handlers

Interactive programs generally have several paths through them, and the user is invited to choose a path from a menu. A common way of expressing a menu is to give each option a letter or number, and invite the user to type in the required choice. This is explored in the next example.

Example 4.5   Menu handler for controlling a database

| Problem | A database is being set up with the facilities to

- add a new record

- remove an existing record

- find a record and display all its details

- extract records with certain key values

- sort these

- print them.

We have been detailed to write the procedure which interfaces with the user and passes control to a specific procedure which will perform the action required.

| Solution | We should start off by doing a screen layout. The following is a fairly good first attempt:

```
┌─────────────────────────────────────┐
│        Database Main Menu           │
│        ==================           │
│                                     │
│        A   Add                      │
│        R   Remove                   │
│        F   Find                     │
│        E   Extract                  │
│        S   Sort                     │
│        P   Print                    │
│        Q   Quit                     │
│                                     │
│        Please type your choice:     │
└─────────────────────────────────────┘
```

There are many different styles of menus. Some favour numbers for choices, others letters in sequence. However, an association between the commands and the actions helps the user, and is generally thought to present a good interface. (We were fortunate in this case that the actions all had distinct first letters.)

Options for menu commands.

Algorithm The natural choice for a control construct is the case-statement. However, we must guard the statement against incorrect commands. In fact, one must program defensively, and **expect** the user to type incorrect commands. A loop around the reading of the command is therefore required. We also allow the user to type in upper- or lower-case letters.

Program defensively!

Program

```
PROCEDURE CommandHandler;
  VAR command : char;
  BEGIN
    REPEAT
      PrintMenu;   {Not shown here}
      repeat
        writeln(chr(bell),'Please type in your choice: ');
        read(command);
        writeln;
      until command in ['A','a','R','r','F','f','E','e','S','s','P','p','Q','q'];
      CASE command OF
        'A','a' : Add;
        'R','r' : Remove;
        'F','f' : Find;
        'E','e' : Extract;
        'P','p' : Print;
        'Q','q' : ;
      END; {case}
    UNTIL command in ['Q','q'];
  END; {CommandHandler}
```

Alert the user by ringing the bell.

Once a Q or q is typed, the command module exits, returning control to the program that called it.

4.4   Text files

Up to now, we have used the terminal for all our communication with our programs. As our programs become more sophisticated and the amount of data they handle and results they produce increases, a single device for all input and output will become inadequate. We need to bring in other devices, such as the printer and disk files. Which device is appropriate at a given time will depend on what the program is doing then, and on the size and meaning of the information.

Input-output streams

A program goes through several **stages** during its running time, and with each we can associate various **input/output streams**, as shown in the diagram.

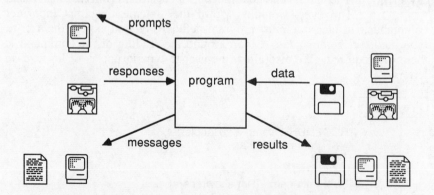

Diagram of input/output streams for a typical program

The common stages and streams are:

1. **Initialisation.** During this stage, there is dialogue with the user, consisting of **prompts** and **responses**. These are most typically directed to the screen and accepted from the keyboard of the terminal, respectively.

2. **Processing.** If there is a large amount of **data** to be processed, or if it consists of permanent information, then the most appropriate place for

it is a disk file. Similarly, **results** usually need to be read quietly after a program has run, which means sending them to a printer or to a file again. Also during this phase, errors may occur, or it may be desirable to output comforting status **messages** such as '2000 records processed so far...'. These would go onto the screen, so that the user could be informed immediately, or could go to a printer, to appear intermingled with the results.

3. **Finalisation.** It is a very good idea to end any program that processes or produces large amounts of information with a simple **message** indicating how much work was done. Once again, this could go to screen or printer.

The two key issues here are how to connect a particular device to the program and, in the case of the streams with the option of various devices, how to leave the decision to as late as possible – even to runtime. The ability to connect and reconnect devices for various streams relies on the Pascal concept of a **file.** In this section we shall consider files of text; Chapter 10 considers files of other types.

Operations on text files

In Pascal, all information that is read or written using the standard read and write statements is associated with a **text file**. This fact has been largely hidden from us because we have been using the default files, called *input* and *output*. These files are nearly always connected to the default devices, which are most often the keyboard and screen respectively. In order to use other devices such as the printer or the disk, we must declare other files and indicate in the appropriate read and write statements that we want to use these files, rather than the defaults. There are actually several steps in this process:

1. **Declare** a file in the program.
2. **Connect** a device to the file.
3. **Open** the file for reading or writing.
4. **Refer** to it in all input/output statements.

Steps in accessing a file.

The declaring, opening and referring can all be done in standard Pascal statements which have the following forms. To declare a text file called *F*, open it, and then use the device via the name of *F*.

Declaring a text file

```
VAR  F : text;
```

Opening a text file

```
reset (F);          {to open for reading}
rewrite (F);        {to open for writing}
```

Referring to text files

```
read (F, ...);
write(F, ...);
readln (F, ...);
writeln(F, ...);
eoln (F)
eof (F)
page(F);
```

It is important always to ensure that the file name has been added to each relevant *read*, *eof* and so on. Omitting them by mistake is a common source of odd errors in programs.

The only essential difference between setting up a file that is designated for reading and one that is designated for writing is in the procedure used to open it: *reset* or *rewrite*. However, there may be an additional requirement for output files. Some systems need to know when you have finished writing to a file so that they can close it: this is not always done automatically when a program ends. Therefore, you may have to call a close procedure, and if you want the file to be closed and saved, then typically the call would be something like

```
close (F);
```

Connecting up a text file

One of the problems with Pascal.

Unfortunately, the Pascal standard side-steps the issue of connecting devices to files (step 2 above). As a result, each Pascal system provides its own way of connecting files. For example, on a mainframe computer, there would be some Job Control Commands that would set up the required association, such as

```
FILEDEF OUTPUT DISK MARKS.OUT (RECFM=V)
```

whereas on a single-user microcomputer, it is more common to have a procedure which is called from within the Pascal program, such as

```
assign (output, 'MARKS.OUT');
```

This would associate the disk file MARKS.OUT with the Pascal file *output*. However, one of the more popular methods is just to extend the *rewrite* and *reset* procedures and give the actual file name after the Pascal file name. Thus we would have:

Different ways of connecting a file.

```
reset (input, 'STUDENTS');
rewrite (output, 'MARKS.OUT');
```

Finally, many modern systems, such as UNIX or DOS 4 enable files to be redirected. So we can write a program which deals with the Pascal files input and outout, and when we run it, we can redirect these to text files as in:

```
marker < Students > Marks.out
```

where *marker* is the name of the program being run.

Two considerations when connecting files are:

- checking whether a file exists before deciding whether to use it or not;
- connecting up to the standard devices such as printers and keyboards.

Most Pascal systems provide a method of ascertaining the status of a given file, and provide a set of standard names for the devices (e.g. PRN, KBD). Checking their status then requires further non-standard Pascal features, and at this stage we must refer you to your local manual.

Time to consult the implemetation manual for your compiler.

For the remainder of this book, we shall use the extension to the *rewrite* and *reset* procedures to connect files.

End-of-file

When we discussed loops in earlier chapters, we mentioned four ways of detecting the end of data:

- build in a count;
- preface with a count;
- end with a signal value;
- use a built-in signal value.

The last method has the decided advantage that the data can be of any length and does not need an additional terminating value. It can be achieved in Pascal by using the end-of-file function.

The data that is typed in from a keyboard, and which is shown simultaneously on the screen, forms a **file**. A file has an end, and on most systems it is possible to indicate this explicitly by typing some special character on the keyboard, such as ESC or CTRL-Z. (The particular character differs from computer to computer.) When this end-of-file character is typed, an end-of-file flag is set in the Pascal system, and it can be tested by calling the function *eof*.

Handling data of unspecified length.

Pascal defines *eof* as a boolean function which returns true or false depending on the value of the end-of-file flag. Thus if we have a simple loop such as

```
while not eof do
  read(ch);
writeln('All done');
```

data will be accepted from the keyboard, until the end-of-file character is pressed. This will cause the loop to end and the closing message to appear. The end-of-file character itself is not read because *eof* becomes true when the character is pressed, not when it is read.

One important property of data, when viewed as constituting a file, is that it may not be present at all. In other words, the file may be empty. To guard against this eventuality it is better to use while-loops rather than repeat-loops when processing files.

End-of-file can also be used with data consisting of numbers, though here we have to be a bit careful. Consider the following list of numbers:

```
81  53  12
97
34  2  704
```

The special end-of-file character must be pressed immediately after the 4, without any spaces or returns intervening. If this is not done, then after the 704, end-of-file will not be set, and a program may try to read another number – which isn't there.

Example 4.6   Document statistics

| Problem | A publisher requires prospective authors to indicate the number of words in a document, as well as the average number of words per sentence.

| Solution | We can write a program which reads the text, character by character, keeping a count of the number of words and the number of sentences. We can define a word as

- starting with a letter or an apostrophe,

- containing letters, apostrophes and hyphens,

- ending with anything that isn't one of those.

Similarly, we define a sentence as ending with a punctuation mark such as fullstop, question or exclamation. Examples would be:

It is hot today, isn't it?   words = 6

Good – that's OK.   words = 3

| **Algorithm** | There are two ways of tackling the algorithm. The first is to regard the sentence as consisting of words and gaps (as it does)

and having a loop to process these successively, i.e.

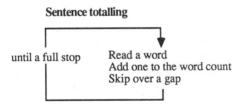

Sentence totalling

until a full stop   Read a word
                     Add one to the word count
                     Skip over a gap

Reading a word and skipping over a gap are actions that would require loops themselves. We can therefore call this the **nested loops** or **structured** solution.

The second approach is to regard the sentence as a single stream of characters, some of which trigger events such as incrementing a count. The structure of this algorithm is quite different, i.e.

Two solutions to the same problem.

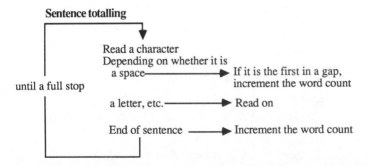

Sentence totalling

Read a character
Depending on whether it is
    a space ──────────▶ If it is the first in a gap,
                        increment the word count

until a full stop

    a letter, etc. ──────▶ Read on

    End of sentence ──────▶ Increment the word count

Looking at this algorithm, we can see that it depends on the state of a 'key' – the character just read. This would map into a program based on a case-statement, as described in the previous section. This is called the **state solution**.

Both algorithms have their difficult parts. In the nested loops version, the problem is that in order for one of the loops to stop, it will have to have already read the first character of the next item. For example, the end of a gap is determined by the presence of a non-space. If the word-reading loop is phrased as a read-count sequence, then a word with only one letter will be lost from the count. Instead, the loops should follow a read then count-read pattern, so that the read comes at the end of a loop, providing a trigger, but not actually processing the character.

In the state approach, the problem is to distinguish between the first space in a gap (which causes the word count to be incremented) and the other spaces, which must simply be ignored. This is handled by a boolean variable which is set and tested appropriately.

| Program | We shall proceed with the structured solution, using procedures to good effect to emphasise that we are dealing with |

words and gaps alternately. Notice that we can avoid having to list all possible punctuation marks, by only referring to the ones in words, and using *not* to get the others.

We would like to be free to start the text with a gap, and in fact to have no data at all. This is taken care of by setting *ch* to some gap character such as space, and going straight into the *skipagap* procedure. The while-loop then ensures that nothing happens if in fact no gap or no data exists.

We assume that the data is in a file called Document.data.

```
PROGRAM DocumentStatistics (input, output);

{Counts the words in the file called Document.data}

VAR
   data        : text;
   ch          : char;
   words,
   sentences   : 0 .. maxint;

PROCEDURE ProcessaWord;
   {called once a letter or apostrophe has been found}
   BEGIN
      WHILE not eof(data) and (ch in  ['A'..'Z', 'a'..'z', '-', '''']) do
         read(data, ch);
   END; {ProcessaWord}

PROCEDURE skipagap;
   {called once a non-word, non-sentence ender has been
      found}
   BEGIN
      while not eof(data) and not (ch in ['A'..'Z', 'a'..'z', '''']) do
         read(data, ch);
   END; {skipagap}

BEGIN
   writeln('****** Document statistics ******');  writeln;
   reset(data, 'Document.data');
   words := 0;
   sentences := 0;
   ch := ' ';

   while not eof (data) do begin
      repeat
         skipagap;
         Processaword;
         words := words + 1;
      until eof(data) or (ch in ['.', '!','?']);
      sentences := sentences + 1;
   end;

   writeln('The number of words is ', words:1);
```

```
        writeln('The number of sentences is ', sentences:1);
        writeln('The average words per sentence is ',
            round(words / sentences):1);
END.
```

| Testing | The test data should include all possibilities. Just looking at the program, what would it do if we had text which did not end with a punctuation mark, such as

> J A Jones

When we get into *ProcessaWord* to read Jones, we will read the 's', go round the loop and try to read again. Since this is the end of the file, the loop stops and we exit *ProcessaWord* into the main loop, and hence straight into *skipagap*. Since *eof* is now set, *skipagap* does nothing and we come out of that loop and end gracefully. The ending is not quite so graceful if there are no words at all because then the division at the end will fail. This situation should be checked for.

End-of-line

Text is composed of characters, as we have seen, but Pascal goes a step further in recognising that characters can also be composed into lines. Files that have this structure are given a special type, *text*. In such files, the end of each line of data has an additional special **end-of-line** marker. Just before the marker is read an end-of-line flag is set in the system. This flag can be tested using a function called *eoln*. Thus we can find out where lines end in the data, and take appropriate action.

Pascal defines *eoln* as a boolean function which is true if the character which is just about to be read is the end-of-line marker, and false otherwise. Thus if we wanted to count how many lines there were in a piece of text, we would use statements such as

Eoln is true when we reach the end of a line of data.

```
        lines := 0;
        WHILE not eof do begin
          read(ch);
          if eoln then lines := lines + 1;
        END;
```

When reading numbers, the fact that data comes on different lines can usually be ignored; this is made possible by the usual interpretation of the end-of-line marker as a space.

Example 4.7 Assigning product numbers

| Problem | A technical laboratory has a file of some 200 parts used in its products. We wish to assign these serial numbers, starting

from 5000 (the code for that laboratory).

A good
example of
multiple
streams.

| Solution | Regard the products as lines of text and copy them to a destination stream, adding on the product numbers. To add flexibility, the starting number can be read off the terminal in response to a query.

| Example | Given a disk file called PRODUCTS containing products such as

> Widgets, black
> Widgets, brown
> Ghizmos, khaki
> Thingies, purple

the numbers can be written to a disk file called NUMPRODS with numbers starting at 5000, i.e.

> **5000   Widgets, black**
> **5001   Widgets, brown**
> **5002   Ghizmos, khaki**
> **5003   Thingies, purple**

| Algorithm | This is a classic example of a copying program, where the twin concerns are recognising the end of a line, and checking for the end of a file. The simplest algorithm is as follows.

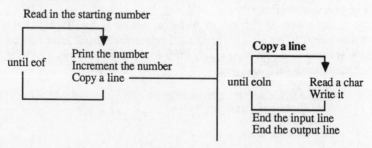

Number products

Read in the starting number

until eof — Print the number
Increment the number
Copy a line

Copy a line

until eoln — Read a char
Write it

End the input line
End the output line

Another consideration in this example is that there are now two places from which input is coming (the terminal for the starting number and the file for the lines), and two to which output must go (the screen for the prompt and the file, which may be the printer, for the numbered lines). This is handled quite simply by making sure that each read and write statement is directed to the correct place, with the default being the terminal.

It seems convenient to hive off the 'copy a line' part into a procedure, and this will be reflected in the program. Notice that handling the end of an input line can be done with *readln* – in fact it must be done, or else the next character read will be the end-of-line marker.

Finally, we assume that the input is to come from a file called PROD and the output to go to a file called NUMPRODS.

| Program |

```
PROGRAM NumberProducts (input, output, data, results);
  VAR
    data, results  : text;
    product        : 0 .. maxint;

  PROCEDURE initialise;
    BEGIN
      writeln('****** Numbering products ******');
      reset(data, 'PROD');
      rewrite(results, 'NUMPROD');
      write('What is the first product number? ');
      readln(product);
    END; {initialise}

  PROCEDURE copyaproduct;
    VAR ch  : char;
    BEGIN
      while not eoln(data) do begin
        read(data,ch);
        write(results,ch);
      end;
      readln(data);  writeln(results);
    END; {copyaproduct}

  BEGIN
    initialise;
    while not eof(data) do begin
      write(results, product:4,' ');
      product := product + 1;
      copyaproduct;
    end;
    writeln(product – firstproduct:1, 'products written');
    {close (results), if necessary}
  END.
```

| Testing | Given the data above, a test run would produce the following at the terminal:

****** Numbering products ******
First product number? 5000
4 products written

To test out the file part of the program thoroughly, you should run it with different devices for data and results and see what happens. How this can be achieved will depend on your own particular implementation.

The buffer variable

Every file has associated with it a buffer variable, which is denoted by the file name and the symbol ↑ (up-arrow). Thus the buffer variable for the default input file is called *input↑*. In an input file, the buffer variable is that item that is about to be read, and it can be accessed. This facility enables us to look ahead at the data before committing ourselves.

A typical use of the buffer variable would be to switch between reading numbers and characters, depending on what comes up. An example of such code would be:

```
if input↑ in ['0'..'9','+','–']  then read(n)
                                 else read(ch);
```

Some very popular Pascal systems, such as Turbo Pascal, do not support the buffer variable, so it is not used much in this book. However, there is further reference to it in section 10.4.

Re-using disk files

A disk file can be read to the end, and then read from the beginning again by the same program. All that needs to be done is to call *reset*, which will put the file back at the start. Similarly, a disk file that has been written by a program, can be read back by it. What is required here is that the file be closed (if the system demands this) and then reset, which will open it for reading.

Several devices can be connected to the same file, one after another. For example, suppose product numbers have to be assigned to parts from several laboratories, each held on a separate disk file. An additional loop can be placed around the existing *NumberProducts* program and on each iteration a new file can be connected and reset.

The question is how to communicate the file name to the program. Once again, we need to step outside the bounds of Standard Pascal and use something like:

```
reset (input, filename);
```

It is likely that the type of *filename* will be a non-standard built-in type called *string*. The sequence of statements to connect up *input* to a file with a name supplied when the program is running would be

Useful
sequence for
connecting
files.

```
VAR filename : string;

write ('For the input, connect to? ');
readln(filename);
reset (input, filename);
```

4.5 Graphics

Pascal was designed in the early 1970s before visual display units (VDUs) were commonplace. At the time, the vast majority of programmers – certainly the majority of students – would have had to type their programs on card punch machines, submit the deck of cards through a card reader, and wait for the printout to come from a line printer. Some would have been fortunate enough to be able to use teletype machines for editing and running programs on-line, but the nature of a teletype session was still line-oriented. That is, information was transmitted in a linear fashion, and there was no concept of moving freely around on the paper.

Early VDUs were essentially just faster teletypes in that they still regarded the interaction between the computer and the user as a linear conversation. It is this linearity that limits Standard Pascal today. The input and output procedures of readln and writeln make no provision for moving around a screen. Moreover, the input and output files are defined as of type text, that is, consisting of characters. Modern day VDUs can handle screens at a much finer grain than that, being able to address each of the individual pixels (or dots) that make up a character.

Pascal does not really support graphics.

In order to use the graphical facilities of the screen from Pascal, one has to link into a graphics package and call procedures to move and draw as required. Each Pascal system will have some way of doing this, but they will not be the same across systems. Nevertheless, there is a certain commonality that one can detect in terms of what can be done, and so by describing one system, insight can be gained into graphics in general.

The following subsections look at graphics from three levels, and describe some simple graphics programs.

Simple graphics

It is all very well to have programs that print tables of values, as in examples 3.3, 3.9 and 3.10, but the results would have additional impact if they were also displayed graphically. One of the simplest graphical techniques is to translate a table of figures into a bar chart or histogram. For each number, we print alongside it a corresponding number of stars. So for example, we might have

```
11        ***********
10        **********
6         ******
2         **
```

All that is needed to do this is to convert the number to an integer (if it is not already one), scale it so the stars give a good representation of the significant parts of the number, and then use this as the upper bound of a loop. The next example illustrates the technique in practice.

Example 4.8   Histograms

Problem	We would like to show the output from example 3.9 (Current fluctuation) using a histogram.

Solution	The values output by the program are in the range 0 to 2, and vary in the first decimal place. The first few are:

t	I
0.00	0.0000
0.10	0.3625
0.20	0.6593
0.30	0.9023
0.40	1.1013

If we take the first two figures, then we shall have values in the range 0 to 20, which will be suitable for the histogram.

Algorithm	Basically, we use the identical program, but add a call to a histogram procedure after the numbers are written, and before

the writeln.

Program	We give the program in its full structure, but with the bodies of the *Initialise* and *PredictorCorrector* procedures left out.

```
PROGRAM RLcurrentwithHistogram(input, output);
  VAR
    E, R, L, current, t, h   : real;
    reports,j,imax           : 1..maxint;

  PROCEDURE PredictorCorrector;
    {as before}
    END; {PredictorCorrector}

  PROCEDURE initialise;
    { as before}
    END; {Initialise}

  PROCEDURE HistogramofCurrent;
    BEGIN
      for i := 1 to round(current*10) do
        write('*');
    END;  HistogramofCurrent;

BEGIN
  initialise;
  writeln(t:10:2,'    ',current:10:4);
  FOR j := 1 to reports do begin
    PredictorCorrector;
    write(t:10:2,'    ',current:10:4,'      ' );
    HistogramofCurrent;
```

```
        writeln;
      END;
    END.
```

<table>
<tr><td>Testing</td><td>For typical values, the program produces:</td></tr>
</table>

***** Electrical current in an RL circuit *****
***** Using predictor-corrector algorithm *****

Solves: dI / dt = E / L - RI / L

Emf source in volts, E: 20
Inductance in henries, L: 5
Resistance in ohms, R: 10
Step length h: 0.01
Number of iterations before reporting:10
Stopping time in seconds, TS: 1
The current, I, is given in amps.

t	I		
0.00	0.0000		Aren't pictures
0.10	0.3625	* * * *	helpful?
0.20	0.6593	* * * * * * *	
0.30	0.9023	* * * * * * * * *	
0.40	1.1013	* * * * * * * * * * *	
0.50	1.2642	* * * * * * * * * * * * *	
0.60	1.3976	* * * * * * * * * * * * * *	
0.70	1.5068	* * * * * * * * * * * * * * *	
0.80	1.5962	* * * * * * * * * * * * * * * *	
0.90	1.6694	* * * * * * * * * * * * * * * * *	
1.00	1.7293	* * * * * * * * * * * * * * * * * *	

Clearly, it might not always be possible to predict the range of values in advance, and it would be useful if the program could do the scaling automatically. This is taken up in the problems at the end of the chapter.

Character level graphics

The first facility which graphics provides is the ability to move the **cursor** to a particular place on the screen. At the character level, a screen is typically an 80 by 24 matrix, with the columns being the x-axis numbered 0 to 79 and the rows being the y-axis numbered 0 to 24, say, with the **origin** in the top left corner. The screen therefore looks like this:

Use of gotoxy.

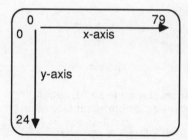

The simplest procedure is then one that moves the cursor to an *x,y* position. In the majority of Pascal systems, this is provided by the procedure *gotoxy*. In Turbo Pascal, this procedure is in a library called the *crt*. In addition, if one wants to control the screen, it is often necessary to clear it first, and this is provided by a procedure called *clrscr*. To print a string in the middle of the screen, therefore, would require

```
USES crt;

gotoxy (25,12);
writeln('Happy Birthday');
```

Example 4.9   Graphs

| Problem | We want to print a sin graph going across the page.

| Solution | In an early problem (3.11), a program was posed to print a sin graph going **down** the page, that is with the *x*-axis going down, and the *y*-axis across. Thus the known variable, *x*, could increase linearly and an asterisk be printed at the appropriate place on each successive line. The simplest program to do this is:

```
PROGRAM Graph1 (output);
  CONST pi = 3.141592;
  VAR
    d : 0..95;
    y : real;
BEGIN
  writeln('****** Sin Graph ******');
  writeln;
  d := 0;
  while d <= 90 do begin
    y := sin(d * pi / 180) * 30;
    if round(y) = 0
      then writeln('*')
      else writeln('*':round(y));
    d := d + 5;
  end;
END.
```

The output for *Graph1* would be:

```
****** Sin Graph ******

  *
    *
      *
        *
          *
            *
              *
                *
                  *
                    *
                      *
                        *
                          *
                            *
                              *
                                *
                                  *
                                    *
                                      *
                                        *
                                          *
                                            *
```

This program assumes that there is only one *y* value for each *x*, which is quite a restriction.

| Algorithm | Armed with *gotoxy*, we can turn the graph the correct way round, and not worry about problems of linearity. We still loop over the *x*-axis, but use the expression for *y* to take us into the screen's space, and there print the asterisk. In order to get the graph's origin in the centre of the screen, we must add about half the *x*- and *y*-axis lengths to each point. To make this more understandable, we declare more constants and variables, and also show the function for a full period from −180 to +180 degrees.

| Program |

```pascal
PROGRAM GraphAcross1 (output);
  USES crt;
  CONST
    start    = −180;
    finish   = 180;
    ycentre  = 10;
    yoffset  = 12;
    interval = 5;
  VAR
    d, xoffset : integer;
    x, y : real;
  BEGIN
    clrscr;
    writeln('***** Sin graph across *****');
    writeln;
    d := start;
    xoffset := abs (finish − start + 1) div 2;
    while d <= finish do begin
```

```
      y := sin(d * pi / 180) * ycentre + yoffset;
      x := (d  + xoffset ) div interval;
      gotoxy (round(x), round(y));
      write('*');
      d := d + interval;
   end;
END.
```

| Testing | Run the program and see what happens. The output should be a sin curve plotted across the screen with asterisks as follows:

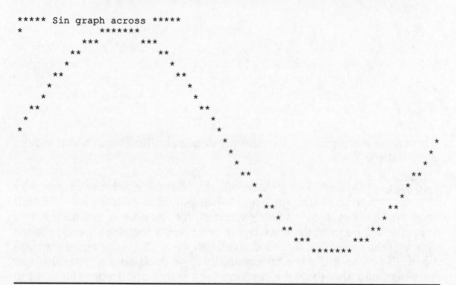

```
***** Sin graph across *****
*             *******
         ***           ***
       **                 **
      *                     *
    **                       **
   *                           *
   *                            *
  **                             **
  *                               *
  *                               *
```

Along with the ability to move, character level graphics also provides far more characters than are shown on the average keyboard. There are 256 values in Pascal's char type, and these are frequently mapped onto such interesting symbols as ♠♣♦♥ and bits of lines with which boxes can be drawn. The dot-matrix printers that are frequently used with personal computers are usually able to reproduce these symbols.

Pixel level graphics

At the pixel level the screen is divided into individual dots, with often as many as 640 across by 350 down. Working at the pixel level is very tedious, and so the computing system can provide a set of library routines which enable higher level operations to be done, such as drawing a box or a line, or just writing out characters. The advantage of writing characters at the pixel level is that a wide variety of fonts and styles can be made available. For example, consider the following selection from the computer on which this book was prepared:

𝕷𝖔𝖓𝖉𝖔𝖓 𝖇𝖗𝖎𝖉𝖌𝖊 𝖎𝖘 𝖋𝖆𝖑𝖑𝖎𝖓𝖌 𝖉𝖔𝖜𝖓.

𝕾𝖆𝖓 𝔽𝖗𝖆𝖓𝖈𝖎𝕾𝖈𝖔 𝖎𝕾 𝖆 𝖈𝖗𝖆𝖟𝖞 𝖕𝖑𝖆𝖈𝖊.

𝕿𝖍𝖊 𝕲𝖗𝖊𝖊𝖐𝖘 𝖐𝖓𝖊𝖜 𝖆 𝖙𝖍𝖎𝖓𝖌 𝖔𝖗 𝖙𝖜𝖔.

They write neatly down Chancery Lane.

When in Venice, catch a gondola.

Colour, too, can be used to good effect by calling routines which change the background colour of the screen, as well as the drawing colour.

With this increased resolution, we can do better than to plot a curve with asterisks. True graphics packages provide facilities to draw a line composed of pixels from one point to another. Typically, we would use procedures such as *Moveto* to get to a point on the screen (similar to *gotoxy*) and *Lineto* to draw a line from where we are to specific coordinates. In Turbo Pascal, these routines are in a library called *graphics*. Instead of *clrscr*, we have to call *initgraph* with parameters which tell the routines about the resolution of the screen. Given a high resolution screen, the graph program becomes:

```
PROGRAM GraphAcross2 (output);
  USES graphics;
  CONST
    start    = -180;
    finish   = 180;
    ycentre  = 150;  {given 350 on y-axis)
    yoffset  = 170;
    interval = 0.6;   {given 640 on the x-axis}
  VAR
    d, xoffset : real;
    x, y : real;
    driver, mode : integer;

  BEGIN
    driver := ega;
    mode := egahi;
    initgraph (driver,  mode, ' ');
    writeln('***** Sin graph across *****');
    writeln;
    d := start;
    xoffset := abs (finish - start + 1) / 2;
    Moveto (0, yoffset); {centre left of screen}
    while d <= finish do begin
      y := sin(d * pi / 180) * ycentre + yoffset;
      x := (d  + xoffset ) div interval;
      Lineto (round(x), round(y));
      d := d + interval;
```

```
        end;
    END.
```

And the output will be very fine indeed! Unfortunately, as mentioned earlier, it is not always possible to transfer a picture from a high quality screen to a printer.

4.6   Numerical methods using while-loops

The two methods discussed in this chapter are excellent example of conditional looping. The problem is to find the root of an equation by guessing it! However, we do not take random guesses, but iterate over a range of values until we are close enough. The first method finds the approximate position of a root, and the next is a popular and good method for finding roots exactly.

Method 3   Finding roots with the search method

Rationale   A large number of engineering applications include the need to solve an algebraic equation for x. We call this finding the root of the equation. The equations may be polynomials such as $x^2 - 2x + 1$ or include trigonmetric and other functions.

Finding the real roots of a quadratic equation (polynomial of order 2) is usually covered in school mathematics, and a good program for doing this is given later in example 8.4. Here we want to concentrate on general polynomial and transcendental equations. The kinds of applications for root finding would include surface temperatures resulting from heat transfer, terminal velocity of particles, frequency of vibration and so on.

Methods   There are several methods for finding such roots. They all rely on making a guess at the root and then iterating in some way towards a better guess until a value for x is found for which $|f(x)| < \varepsilon$ for some small value ε.

The simplest method is to search for the place in which the curve of the function cuts the x-axis. For example, in the graph following, if we start off searching from $x = 0$ and move along in steps of h then we shall find that $f(x_i)$ is negative and $f(x_{i+1})$ is positive. Therefore there must be a root in the interval x_i to x_{i+1}. To find the root more precisely, we reduce the size of h and proceed to search from x_i again. This process could be repeated until the root is found to the required accuracy.

Although simple and effective, the search method is not very efficient. We shall therefore leave its further development as a problem (see the end of the chapter) and proceed on to a more realistic method.

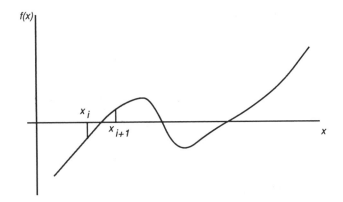

Method 4   The Newton-Raphson method

Rationale   Finding the roots of an equation is an essential task in engineering problems, and we would like to have a method which is reliable and quick. It should be applicable to a wide range of functions and produce real as well as complex roots.

Methods   The method we shall discuss here is the Newton-Raphson method, one of the most popular as it is simple and produces a root relatively quickly. In Chapter 5 we look at another method, the so-called **secant method**. Other methods that one may find in a text on numerical methods would be the search method, bisection method, *regula falsi* method and the method of successive substitution.

Sir Isaac Newton (1642–1727)

Theory   The Newton-Raphson method for finding a root of an equation $f(x) = 0$ relies on having a fairly good initial estimate of the root, and on knowing the derivative $f'(x) = df/dx$. If the derivative is not known, another method must be used (e.g. the secant method discussed in example 5.4).

If x_0 is an estimate of the root, then a better estimate x_1 is:

$$x_1 = x_0 - \frac{f(x_0)}{f'(x_0)}$$

This formula is obtained by modelling the curve by its tangent at the point x_0 as shown in the diagram overleaf. x_1 can then be used to calculate the next and better approximation x_2 and so on, but until when? That is going to depend upon what tolerance can be accepted for the error in the solution. The stopping criterion is given by

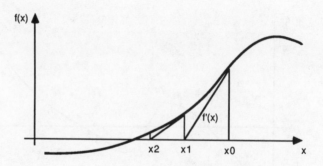

repeat

...

until | current estimate − previous estimate | < tolerance,

and a typical value for tolerance could be 10^{-6}. However, this is not the whole story for the stopping criterion. If the initial estimate of the root is too far out, the algorithm may never converge – e.g., in the figure, suppose the initial estimate had been $2x_0$ rather than x_0. To prevent the possibility of the program being caught in a loop from which it cannot exit, we place a limit on the number of times the loop is executed.

| Algorithm | The algorithm for the Newton-Raphson method is:

Newton-Raphson method

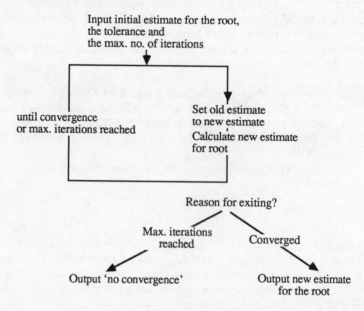

The method can also be used to find complex roots. This is discussed in Chapter 8, when a type for complex numbers is introduced.

Example 4.10   Specific volume of a gas

| Problem | We want to find the specific volume v of a particular gas whose state equation at a specific temperature and pressure is given by |

$$f(v) = 70v^3 - 3v^2 + 4v - 16$$

| Solution | Use the Newton-Raphson method to find the root. To do this we need to: |

- have an estimate of the root

- know the derivative of the equation.

$v = 1$ is a reasonable starting value, and the derivative is :

$$f'(v) = 210v^2 - 6v + 4$$

Using the algorithm developed as follows, the program follows easily.

| Program |

```
PROGRAM SpecificVolume(input,output);
  VAR
    imax        : integer;
    i           : 0..100;
    tolerance,
    x, x0       : real;

  PROCEDURE initialise;
  BEGIN
    writeln('******Newton-Raphson root-finding program******');
    writeln('for the specific volume of a gas');
    writeln('            3    2');
    writeln('Solves 70v - 3v + 4v − 16 = 0');
    writeln;
    write('Initial estimate for root:');
    readln(x);
    write('Required error limit:');
    readln(tolerance);
    write('Maximum number of iterations permitted:');
    readln(imax);
    i := 0;
    writeln(' i    x');
    writeln(i:4,xnew:10:6);
  END; {initialise}

  PROCEDURE NewtonRaphson;
    {Uses global variables      : i, imax, x, x0, tolerance
    Returns global variables   : i, x, x0}
    BEGIN
      REPEAT
        i := i + 1;
```

```
            x0 := x;
            x := x0 - (70 * x0 * x0 * x0 - 3 * x0 * x0 + 4 * x0 - 16) /
                (210 * x0 * x0 - 6 * x0 + 4);
            writeln(i:4, x:10:6);
        UNTIL ((abs(x - x0) < tolerance) or (i = imax));
      END;  {NewtonRaphson}

    BEGIN
      initialise;
      NewtonRaphson;
      if (i = imax)
      then writeln('Failed to converge: x = ',
                        x:10:6, '  x0 = ',x0:10:6,' i = ', i:3)
      else writeln('Root is:', x:10:6, '   ', i:3, ' iterations required');
    END.
```

Testing

*******Newton-Raphson root-finding program******
for the specific volume of a gas
$$70v^3 - 3v^2 + 4v - 16 = 0$$
Solves $70v^3 - 3v^2 + 4v - 16 = 0$

Initial estimate for root: 1
Required error limit: 1E-6
Maximum number of iterations permitted: 100

i	x
0	1.000000
1	0.735577
2	0.619165
3	0.595125
4	0.594157
5	0.594155
6	0.594155

Root is: 0.594155   6 iterations required

To see the method in real action, we tried an initial guess of 100: this
eventually converged, but took 17 steps. The root can be verified as correct
by substituting in the equation.

Summary

☐ The type *char* includes all characters that can be represented by your computer, which may be more than are available on the keyboard or printer. Some characters are printable, some have control functions such as ringing the bell.

☐ Operations on characters include the six relations, the in-operator and testing for set membership. There are four functions applicable to characters namely, *succ, pred, ord* and *chr.*

☐ Conditional loops can be constructed using either while-statements or repeat-statements.

☐ For conditional loops, the conditions must be initialised before the loop begins, and these conditions must be changed within the loop.

☐ The case-statement provides for selecting from a group of statements based on a key value. The key value actually supplied at runtime must appear in the list of possibilities.

☐ Case-statements can only be used with integer, char boolean or enumerated keys, not with real or string keys.

☐ Interactive programs usually have several streams of i/o for prompts, responses, messages, data and results. Most of these benefit from being handled by redirectable text files.

☐ Pascal provides facilities for declaring, opening and referring to text files, but does not specify how they are to be associated with devices either at compile time or at runtime: each Pascal system provides its own facility.

☐ The end of a file is detected when a control character is typed on the keyboard (such as CTRL-Z) or when the end of a disk file is reached. End of line is detected when RETURN is pressed on the keyboard, or when the last character in a line on a file is read.

☐ End of file and end of line can be checked with *eof* and *eoln* respectively.

☐ The buffer variable of *input* or any other text file *f* can be examined by using *input^* or *f^.* @ and ↑ are alternatives for ^.

☐ Character level and pixel level graphics use facilities provided by the implementation: they are not part of standard Pascal.

☐ The search method locates the approximate position of a root.

☐ The Newton-Raphson method enables roots of equations to be found efficiently, using an initial guess and the derivative.

Self-check quiz

1.   How does one get the computer to ring its bell?
2.   Would it be correct to say:

```
for s := 'AAA' to 'ZZZ' do write(s);
```

Why?

3.   What is the expression for obtaining the numerical value of a character that you suspect is a digit?
4.   Write a while-loop that reads and writes characters while they are not digits. Use the in-operator in the condition.
5.   How is end-of-file signalled when typing from the keyboard on your computer?
6.   How are files assigned to devices on the Pascal system you are using?
7.   If a file has been connected to a disk, can it later be connected to the printer without restarting the program?
8.   Identify all the mistakes in the following case-statement.

```
case letter of
  'p' : write('pico');
  'g' : write('giga');
  'k', 'kilo' : write('kilo');
  'g' : write('gram');
end case;
```

9.   The following loop reads and totals a temperature value every second:

```
total := 0;
for sec := 1 to 60 do begin
    write(sec);  readln(temp);
    total := total + temp;
end;
```

Rewrite the loop as a while-loop and as a repeat-loop.

10.   The totalling now has to be done every tenth of a second. Could the for-loop be adapted? If so, do it. If not, write it as a conditional loop.

Problems

4.1   A very old file of people's names was created using all capital letters. Convert it to the usual capital and lower-case letters. Take account of initials, but do not go as far as handling surname prefixes properly, e.g.

R A JONES   R A Jones
J. FOX-ROBINSON   J. Fox-Robinson
P DU PLESSIS   P Du Plessis

4.2   We already have a program to calculate the average length of words in a piece of text. Following on from this, reprocess the same file, counting how many words are above the average length.

4.3   A certain engineering apparatus is controlled by the input of successive numbers. If there is a run of the same number, the apparatus can optimise its performance. Hence we would like to arrange the data so as to indicate that a run is coming.

Write a program which reads a sequence of numbers and prints out each run of numbers in the form $(n*m)$ where m is the number to be repeated n times. These instructions are printed in brackets on a new line, to indicate that they are going to the apparatus. Note that a run could just consist of a single number. The numbers are terminated by a zero, which halts the apparatus. Sample input and output would be:

Sample input and output
20 20 20 20 20 20 20 20 20 20 50
(10*20)
50 50 50 50 60
(5*50)
60 60 60 60 20
(5*60)
30
(1*20)
30 30 30 90
(4*30)
0
(1*90)
(0)

4.4   A piece of text is stored on a file. It is divided into paragraphs separated by blank lines. Write a program which reads in the text and prints it out again, ignoring all text between Pascal comment brackets { }. Print suitable warning messages if

- a { is found inside a comment;
- a } is found without a matching { ;
- a paragraph ends without a matching }.

At the end of each paragraph print the percentage of text (excluding spaces) that occurred in comments. *Hint*: This program is a good one for testing character handling, but it will be easier to write with the additional use of boolean variables, described in the first section of the next chapter.

Sample input	**Sample output**
This is the same length	**This is the same length**
as the comment {This	**as the comment rest assured.**
assured comment is the	***** No ending bracket**
same length as the rest}	
rest assured. {And so	**Comment is 50% of the text**

4.5   A piece of text is stored on a file. It is divided into paragraphs separated by blank lines. Write a program which reads in the text and prints it out again, having made any changes necessary to have the text conform to the following standards:

- three spaces at the start of a paragraph;
- capital letter at the start of each sentence;
- two spaces between sentences or main clauses, i.e. after a fullstop, question mark, exclamation mark, semicolon or colon;
- only one space between words otherwise.

Sample input	**Sample output**
It is always hard to type	**It is always hard to type**
to a standard.Some people	**to a standard. Some people**
use different ones: single	**use different ones: single**
or double or no	**or double or no spaces**
spaces before a sentence.	**before a sentence. I think**
i think double looks best.	**double looks best.**

Hint: This program is a good one for testing character handling, but it will be easier to write with the additional use of boolean variables, described in the first section of the next chapter.

4.6   Write a program to produce a contents page for a book using data supplied in a fixed format. The data should be read off a file and the output sent to a printer. Consider the following input:

> (First steps (The computer, 5) (Problem Solving (Definition, 10) (Outline, 15) (Algorithms,20)) (Programs and Procedures, 25)) (Types and Looping (Types (Integer,30) (Character,36) (Boolean, 43)) (Looping (Counting loops,49) (Conditional Loops, 52)))

The parentheses indicate the chapters, sections and subsections and the numbers following them are the page numbers. Page numbers are only given when there is no further subdivision. The output for the data above would be:

CONTENTS

```
1.   First Step
     1.1 The Computer        5
     1.2 Problem Solving
          1.2.1        Definition       10
          1.2.2        Outline          15
          1.2.3        Algorithms       20
     1.3 Programs and Procedures  25
2.   Types and Looping
     2.1 Types
          2.2.1        Integer          30
          2.2.2        Character        36
          2.2.3        Boolean          43
     2.2 Looping
          2.2.1        Counting Loops   49
          2.2.2        Conditional Loops 52
```

4.7   The sine function can be approximated by the series

$$\sin (x) = x - \frac{x^3}{3!} + \frac{x^5}{5!} - \frac{x^7}{7!} \cdots$$

Write a program which will calculate the value of sin at an angle to be read in, using as many terms as necessary to achieve a) an accuracy of 10E-6. and then b) the same accuracy as the built in sin function. *Hint*: Don't calculate the powers and factorials anew for each term – keep running totals which are updated.

4.8   Consider how to generalise the root-finding program in example 4.10. The user might wish to try different initial estimates, error-limits or maximum number of iterations before reaching a satisfactory result. Redo the user-interface to the program so that it can accommodate multiple runs, and uses a menu to allow the user to change any one of the data values, whilst leaving the others fixed.

4.9   The Newton-Raphson method requires a guess at the root of the equation. One way of finding such a guess is to employ the search method. Use this method to find the rough positions of the other two roots in example 4.10, and the Newton-Raphson method to evaluate them to a better accuracy. *Hint:* They may not exist.

4.10   Adapt example 4.2 so that it reads the course codes from a file containing student registration details of the form

> **student number**   **courses**
> 56821   COMS100 PHYS101   BIOL104   CHEM103

where the student numbers are five digits long. Report the student number along with any incorrect course codes.

4.11   Extend the program in problem 3.5 to illustrate the intensity of illumination of using a histogram.

4.12   We would like to extend the program in example 3.9, which shows the current in an RL circuit with alternating voltage, so that the inductance is shown as a histogram. From the output, we see that the values range from approximately –0.0005 to 0.4000. Is it going to be possible to obtain a reasonable picture of the values?

4.13   A scientist needs to determine when she will run out of space to house her rabbits. She starts with two rabbits and it is known that a pair of adult rabbits (i.e. those more than three months old) produce on average two rabbits every three months. The scientist has space to house 500 rabbits. Write a program which will determine how many months it will be before she runs out of space. Adapt the program to print out a table of the rabbit populations (adult, non-adult and total) every three months for 5 years.

4.14   An examination paper has four questions in Section A and four in Section B. Each question is valued at 20 marks. Students must answer five questions in total, with at least two from Section A and two from Section B. If more questions than required are answered, then the first ones are counted and the latter ones disregarded. Unanswered questions are indicated by a zero mark.

Write a program to read in eight marks for each of several students and print out their final marks according to the rules. If rules are broken, print appropriate messages. Sample data and results are:

Sample Input		Sample Output	
Section A	Section B	Result	Comment
10 15 0 0	20 8 17 0	70	
10 9 7 20	0 0 0 10	36	Too many from A.
5 6 10 0	19 5 3 14	45	More than 5. Too many from B.

4.15   Use the search method followed by the Newton-Raphson method to find all the roots of

$$x = 2 \sin(x)$$

5

Parameters and functions

We have now learnt enough about programming and Pascal to build fairly complex programs. We have seen how this complexity can be controlled by organising a program so that we can deal with parts of it at a time. Such organisation is so important that we introduced the main mechanism for doing this – procedures – right at the start of the book. We now consider how to generalise procedures with parameters and how to declare functions. The chapter includes a discussion on the best ways to structure a program with procedures, and ends with a substantial case study.

5.1   Booleans

Conditions govern the decisions made in programs as to alternative paths to follow. A condition yields a value **true** or **false**. Another name for a condition is a **boolean expression** and the result of such an expression can be stored in a **boolean variable.** For example, given the declarations

```
VAR
    minor, pensioner : boolean;
    age     : 0 .. 140;
```

Booleans are named after George Boole (1815–1864).

we can store various facts about the age of someone as

```
minor := age < 18;
pensioner := age >= 65;
```

and then use these later to make decisions such as:

```
if minor then writeln('No driver"s license for you!');
if pensioner then writeln('You need not pay on the bus.');
```

It could be argued that the boolean variables are unnecessary because the statements

```
if age < 18 then writeln('No driver"s license for you!');
if age >= 65 then writeln('You need not pay on the bus.');
```

will achieve the same effect. However, this would not be the case if the value of *age* had been changed before the if-statement is executed. Thus boolean variables, like any variables, are really useful when the value of a condition must be remembered after other things have happened. This is illustrated in the following example.

Example 5.1   Counterfeit cheques

Problem   Counterfeit cheques are in circulation and the banks have discovered that they all have the same distinctive properties. In the 10 digit cheque number, if there are

- three or more zeros in succession

- and/or four or more non-zeros in succession

then the cheque could be counterfeit. We would like the computer to assist in warning of a possible counterfeit.

Solution   When the cheques are handled by the banks' computers, the first thing that is read is the number. For the purposes of this example, we could write a program to read in cheque numbers and to analyse them for the above properties. The analysis could detect the occurrence of either of the runs described above and if either is found then the cheque can be marked as suspect.

Algorithm   The algorithm for analysing a number involves reading it in, digit by digit, and counting the number of zeros and non-zeros. There is a similarity with example 4.2, which concerned validating course codes. However, in this case, we are concerned with runs and once a run is 'broken', the relevant count will be reset. It will therefore be necessary to remember that a critical count was reached at some stage: this is best done with a boolean variable. The algorithm looks like this

Checking cheques

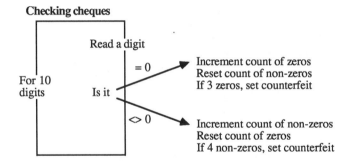

| Program | The program follows the algorithm closely, making use of procedures for clarity. However, this is the last time that we shall have to use global variables only for communicating to and from procedures. In the next section we shall see how to use parameters for this purpose as well. Note that the digits of the cheque have to be entered with spaces following, so that they can be read as integers using the read statement.

```
PROGRAM CheckaCheque (input, output);
   {For the occurrence of >= 3 zeros or >= 4 non-zeros in a row}

CONST
  NoofDigits = 10;
VAR
  counterfeit        : boolean;
  CountofZeros,
  CountofNonZeros  : 0 ..10;
  digit              : 0 .. 9;
  i, n               : 1 ..  10000;  {maximum in a batch}

PROCEDURE RecordZero;
   {Uses and updates globals        : CountofZeros,
                                       CountofNonzeros
                                       Counterfeit}
  BEGIN
    CountofZeros := CountofZeros + 1;
    CountofNonzeros := 0;
    if CountofZeros = 3 then counterfeit := true;
  END; {RecordZero}

PROCEDURE RecordNonzero;
   {Uses and updates globals        : CountofZeros,
                                       CountofNonzeros
                                       Counterfeit}
  BEGIN
    CountofNonzeros := CountofNonzeros + 1;
    CountofZeros := 0;
    if CountofNonzeros = 4 then counterfeit := true;
  END; {RecordNonzero}
```

```
                              BEGIN
                                writeln('****** Checking for counterfeits ******');
                                writeln('Enter each cheque number with digits separated ',
                                    'by a space');
Several                         writeln('Use your eof signal to stop (e.g. cntrl-z)');
cheques can be                  WHILE not eof do begin
read in one run.                  counterfeit := false;
                                  CountofZeros := 0;
                                  CountofNonzeros := 0;
                                  FOR i := 1 to NoofDigits do begin
                                    read (digit);
                                    if digit = 0 then RecordZero
                                                else RecordNonzero;
                                  END;
                                  if counterfeit then write('        COUNTERFEIT');
                                  writeln;
                                END;
                              END.
```

| Testing | Cheque numbers should be chosen so as to test the special cases. For example, a sample input and ouput might be:

****** Checking for counterfeits ******
Enter each cheque number with digits separated by a space
Use your eof signal to stop (e.g. cntrl-z)
0 0 0 3 3 0 0 4 4 0   COUNTERFEIT
0 0 3 3 3 0 0 3 3 3
0 0 3 3 3 0 3 0 0 0   COUNTERFEIT
4 4 4 4 0 0 5 5 0 0   COUNTERFEIT
6 6 6 6 6 6 0 0 0 0   COUNTERFEIT

Boolean values

Having seen how booleans are used, we can now discuss their properties more formally.

There are only two boolean values – false and true and the boolean type uses identifiers for its two values. This is in contrast to integers, which have a numeric notation, and to characters and strings, which also have a special notation, as we shall see later. The fact that boolean literals are identifiers means that care must be taken not to redefine them. If we had a declaration such as

```
        VAR true : integer;
```

implying that we were going to count or compute something in the variable called *true*, then this would hide the boolean meaning of the identifier *true*, and we would not be able to use it.

Boolean operators and functions

There are three boolean operators namely *and*, *or* and *not* which can be explained by means of tables:

```
not    |         and | false true     or    | false true
============     ================     ===============
false  | true    false | false false   false | false true
true   | false   true  | false true    true  | true  true
```

For the expression *x and y* to be true, both *x* and *y* must be true; for the expression *x or y* to be true, either *x* or *y* or both can be true.

Referring back to the earlier example with the minor and pensioner conditions, suppose information as to whether the person is working or not is held in the variable *employed*. Then further facts can be deduced as follows:

```
youngworker := minor and employed;
voter := not minor;
taxpayer := voter or employed;
```

Boolean operators can be combined to express more complex conditions. For example, if both minors and pensioners can go free on the buses provided they are not working, then we have:

```
freebus := pensioner or (minor and not employed);
```

Boolean operators are very useful in conjunction with the relational operators in establishing detailed conditions. For example, to test whether a number falls between two limits, *min* and *max*, we can say:

```
if (number >= min) and (number <= max) then . . .
```

Note the precedences!

In Pascal, the precedence between the relational operators and the boolean ones is such that the boolean operators will always be executed first (i.e. they have higher precedence). This is why the parentheses are needed in the above example. If they are omitted, the compiler would first try to group *min and number,* which would fail, as the *and* operator is not defined for integers.

Another example is an expression for deciding whether school should be cancelled because it is too cold or too hot, i.e.

```
gohome := (temperature > 40) or (temperature < 0);
```

It is necessary to mention the variable being tested for each test, i.e. it is incorrect to say

```
temperature > 40 or < 0
```

It is worth noting that expressions with *and* operators can be converted into equivalent expressions using *not* and *or* operators, such as

                          not a and not b   =>   not (a or b)
                          not a or not b   =>   not (a and b)

In programming, it is best to choose one style or the other and stick to it, so as
not to get confused. Note finally that when using *not*, the brackets are
important, in that *not a or b* is very different to *not(a or b)*.

A boolean can be used as the loop variable in a for-statement, though of
course the loop will never be more than two iterations long.

There are two useful functions which take an integer and return a boolean
value, i.e.

          odd(n)   returns true if *n* is odd, false if it is even
          ord(n)   returns 0 if *n* is false and 1 if it is true

An example of the use of the *odd* function would be in deciding whether one
is allowed to water the garden, which in times of drought may only be
permitted for even numbered houses on even days (Monday is 1), and odd
numbered houses on odd days or on Sunday (the seventh day). Given the
declarations

```
VAR
    housenumber : 1..500;
    day    : 1 .. 7;   {Monday is 1}
```

and appropriate values in the variables, we could say

```
AllowedtoWater :=
    (odd(housenumber) and odd(day))  or
    (not odd(housenumber) and not odd(day)) or (day = 7);
```

If instructions could be left that watering was to be done whenever possible,
then an if-statement would be appropriate, as in

```
if (odd(housenumber) and odd(day)) or
    (not odd(housenumber) and not odd(day)) or (day = 7)
then WatertheGarden;
```

In addition to *odd*, *ord*, *succ* and *pred* can be applied to boolean values, but
their use is fairly limited. Two other functions return boolean values. These
are *eoln* and *eof*, which were already discussed in Chapter 4.

Boolean values cannot be read. On most systems, they can be written, but
it is possible that the values will come out in capital letters. The space taken
by a boolean on output is 5 characters but can be altered by using a field
width.

An example of booleans in for-statements is the printing of truth tables.

```
PROGRAM Truthtables (output);
    VAR b, c : boolean;
    BEGIN
      writeln('****** Truth tables ******');
```

```
writeln('not  |          and  | false    true     ',
        'or   | false    true');
writeln('========        ===============   ',
        '==============');
FOR b := false to true do begin
  write(b, not b:7,b:10);
  FOR c := false to true do write(b and c:7);
  write(b:10);
  FOR c := false to true do write(b or c:7);
  writeln;
END;
END.
```

Other examples can be found in the problems at the end of the chapter.

5.2 Parameters

Why do we use procedures? Our experience to date would probably suggest:

- to avoid duplication;
- as a conceptual tool for breaking up a problem into sub-problems;
- as a documentation aid.

Procedures can be made more powerful by allowing the effect to differ slightly each time the procedure is called. Recall the example of printing a rectangle, from Chapter 2. The size of the rectangle was fixed by the write statements it embodied so that when we called

```
rectangle;
```

we always got the same sized box. It might well be useful to be able to say

```
rectangle (10, 8);
rectangle (25, 25);
```

instead, or indeed,

```
rectangle (length, breadth);
```

where *length* and *breadth* are variables with specific values.

This is called **generalising** or **parameterising** a procedure and the variables that are going to be different are known as **parameters**. The parts of the procedure that are to be generalised are listed in the declaration, straight after the procedure name, and are known as **formal parameters**. Correspondingly, when we call the procedure we list the specific instances for those parts and these are known as **actual parameters**. The appropriate forms are:

Introducing formal and actual parameters.

Procedure declaration

> PROCEDURE *name* (*formal parameter declarations*);
> *declaration*
> BEGIN
>   *statements*
> END; {*name*}

Procedure call

> *name* (*actual parameters*);

The list of formal parameters acts as a declaration of variables that are to be used in the procedure. As for any other variables, therefore, the appropriate types must be specified. Actual parameters can be variables, expressions, procedures or functions. Parameters fall into three categories, depending on the way in which the correspondence between the formals and actuals is set up, that is:

- **value** parameters for passing values in only,
- **VAR** parameters for passing access to variables,
- **procedural** parameters for passing procedures themselves.

Value parameters

With value parameters, the value of the actual parameter is passed into the procedure, and may be changed under its formal name there, but any changes do not affect the actual parameter, even if it is variable rather than an expression. For example, consider the following program:

```
PROGRAM Passing (input, output);
  VAR
    a : integer;
    b : char;

  PROCEDURE swallow (head : integer; tail : char);
    BEGIN
      writeln ('Swallow 1: ',head:4, tail:4);
      head := head * 2;
      tail := succ(tail);
      writeln ('Swallow 2. ', head:4, tail:4);
    END; {swallow}

BEGIN
  a := 25;
```

```
      b := 'X';
      writeln ('Main 1: ', a:4, b:4);
      swallow(a, b);
      writeln ('Main 2: ', a:4, b:4);
   END.
```

What output would it produce? We 'hand execute' the program, keeping track of the values of the variables and parameters at each stage, and recording the output as follows:

Statement	Passing a	b	Swallow head	tail	Output
before call	25	X	~	~	**Main 1: 25 X**
procedure begin	25	X	25	X	**Swallow 1: 25 X**
procedure end	25	X	50	Y	**Swallow 2: 50 Y**
after call	25	X	~	~	**Main 2: 25 X**

So *a* and *b* remain untouched throughout the call. *head* and *tail* are altered, but this does not affect the actual parameters. Furthermore, once the procedure has finished its operation the formal parameters become undefined. At the next call of *swallow*, they will not 'remember' any of their previous values.

The situation is different with VAR parameters, as described in the next section, and with procedurals, as described in Chapter 8.

Example 5.2   Skipping input

| Problem | A text file is being read and, at certain times, we wish to skip over characters until a certain one is found. |

| Solution | Define a procedure to do the skipping, and provide it with a parameter that is the character being searched for. |

| Examples | We might have calls such as |

```
      skiptoa ('.');
      skiptoa (space);
```

| Algorithm | The algorithm is a simple loop, similar to those in Chapter 4. The important point for the procedure is to define the parameter that is to form the interface. In this case, there is only one parameter – the target character that we wish to skip to.

Program

```
PROCEDURE skiptoa (target : char);
  VAR ch : char;
  BEGIN
    repeat
      read(ch);
    until ch = target;
  END;  {skiptoa}
```

Notice that a local variable was declared for *ch*, so that the procedure is completely self-contained. *Skiptoa* could now be copied into any program and used, since its interface with the program only consists of a parameter. We shall in fact make use of it later in the chapter.

To summarise, the following rules apply about value parameters:

Rules for value
paramemters.

1.   The actual parameters supplied must agree with the formal parameters in number, order and type. Thus the following are all incorrect calls of *swallow*.

```
swallow (10);       needs two parameters
swallow ('+', 7);   wrong order
swallow (4, 8);     tail must be a char
```

2.   The actual parameters can be any constants, variables or expressions. For example, we could have

```
swallow (sqr(trunc(pi)) + 1, chr(ord(b) − ord('A')));
```

3.   The names chosen for actual parameters are quite independent of those for the formals. This is illustrated in the many small examples in the rest of this chapter.

Var parameters

A procedure may have the task of calculating a result which needs to be passed back to the calling program. Pascal provides for this by means of parameters which are specially designated in the list of formals as VAR. These formal parameters act as channels to the actual parameters and any changes made to a formal parameter affect the actual parameter. The form of a VAR parameter declaration is simply:

VAR parameter declaration

VAR *formal parameter identifiers* : *type identifier* ;

Suppose we have a number of occasions when we need to place two numeric values in order. We could write a procedure that has two var parameters, and alters them so that their values are in numeric order. If we have *x* as 9 and *y* as 5, then the call

    order (x, y);

will result in *x* being 5 and *y* being 9. If *a* is 10 and *b* is 20, then

    order (a,b);

will have no effect. The procedure is:

```
PROCEDURE order (VAR n, m : integer);
  VAR temp : integer;
  BEGIN
    if n > m then begin
      temp := n;  n := m;  m := temp;
    end;
  END; {order}
```

Example 5.3   Counterfeit cheques with parameters

| Problem | We would like to consider whether the *Checkacheque* program in example 5.1 cannot be better written using parameters.

| Solution | First look for global variable usage. Both the procedures make use of globals, so we should declare them with parameters instead. Next we should look for repetition. In fact, the two procedures *RecordZero* and *RecordNonzero* are nearly identical, and we can rationalise by making them into one, with parameters.

| Program | Consider the two procedures:

```
PROCEDURE RecordZero;
    {Uses and updates globals      : CountofZeros,
                                     CountofNonzeros
                                     Counterfeit}
      BEGIN
        CountofZeros := CountofZeros + 1;
        CountofNonzeros := 0;
        if CountofZeros = 3 then counterfeit := true;
      END; {RecordZero}

PROCEDURE RecordNonzero;
    {Uses and updates globals      : CountofZeros,
                                     CountofNonzeros
                                     Counterfeit}
      BEGIN
        CountofNonzeros := CountofNonzeros + 1;
```

```
                    CountofZeros := 0;
                    if CountofNonzeros = 4 then counterfeit := true;
                    END; {RecordNonzero}
```

We can write a single procedure which does the same operation as either, and would be called by one of:

```
            if digit = 0
            then Register (CountofZeros, CountofNonzeros, 3, counterfeit);
            else Register (CountofNonzeros, Countofzeros, 4, counterfeit);
```

The procedure can be written generally in terms of runs as follows:

```
            PROCEDURE Register (VAR CurrentRun, OtherRun : integer;
                                max : integer;
                                VAR counterfeit : boolean);
              BEGIN
                CurrentRun := Currentrun + 1;
                OtherRun := 0;
                if CurrentRun = max then counterfeit := true;
              END; {RegisterNonzero}
```

Inserting this in the program and rerunning it is left as an exercise.

This example emphasises that the choice of formal parameter names is important, but that one should not feel obliged to think of new names for the sake of it: *counterfeit* is a perfectly adequate name as a formal and an actual.

Behind the scenes

In order to reinforce the notion of VAR parameters being channels to their actual counterparts, let us look at how they operate inside the computer. In essence, the formal VAR parameter is a variable which is supplied with the **reference** of the actual parameter at the time of the call. The effect of the actual parameters being changed by any changes to the formal parameters is a facility that should not be used lightly. It is also possible that it may not be exactly what is intended in a particular situation, as illustrated in the following example.

Suppose we wish to use the *order* procedure in another context, that is, we have my age and your age in two variables and we wish to put them in order. If we call

```
            order (myage, yourage);
```

then the 'before and after' pictures that follow apply to the variables concerned.

What has happened here? The actual parameters have been altered, which is not what we wanted in this case. We probably only wanted to *know* who was older.

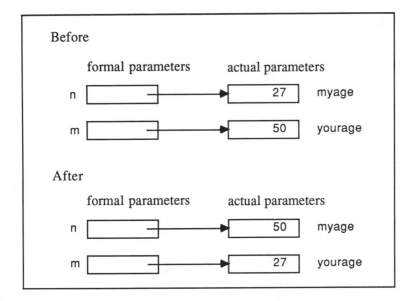

What we need is a procedure with these two parameters as value parameters and another, VAR, parameter for the result. This gives:

```
PROCEDURE firstisolder (n, m : integer;  VAR b : boolean);
BEGIN
  b := n > m;
END; {firstisolder}
```

and we could call this with

```
firstisolder (myage, yourage, me);
if me then writeln('I am older');
```

To summarise, the rules about var parameters are:

1. Actual VAR parameters must be variables. They may not be constants, because values of the actual parameters may be changed. It would therefore be incorrect to say:

    ```
    skipandcount ('.', 8);          8 is not a variable
    ```

    Rules for VAR parameters.

2. A variable should only be used once as a VAR parameter in any one call. The reason for this is that a variable used, say twice, as an actual parameter would end up having two formal names, with confusing results. For example, we should not write

    ```
    order (a,a);
    ```

More examples of VAR parameters

In the previous example we developed a procedure to skip to a given character. Now suppose we wish to know how many characters were skipped in the process. To return this figure, we shall need a VAR parameter.

Skip and count
procedure.

```
PROCEDURE skipandcount (upto : char;  VAR i : integer);
    VAR ch : char;
BEGIN
  i := 0;
  read(ch);
  while ch <> upto do begin
    i := i + 1;
    read(ch);
  end;
END; {skipandcount}

{called by}
skipandcount ('.', count);
writeln('skipped ', count, ' characters till a full stop.')
```

Another useful procedure is one that can read in an integer followed by any character, not necessarily a space. (On many systems the ordinary read statement will only work correctly if a space or end-of-line follows the number.) The procedure follows the definition of integers given in the bubble diagrams in Appendix C.

Procedure to
read an integer
as characters.

```
PROCEDURE readinteger (VAR n : integer);
    {Assumes at least one digit after a sign,
    but  the sign is not compulsory}
    VAR
      negative : boolean;
      ch       : char;
BEGIN
  n := 0;
  read(ch);
  if ch in ['+','–'] then begin
    negative := ch = '–';
    read(ch);
  end else negative := true;
  while ch in ['0'..'9'] do begin
    n := n * 10 + ord(ch) – ord('0');
    read(ch);
  end;
  if negative then n := –n;
END; {readinteger}
```

5.3   Functions

We have already seen the use of built-in functions such as *sin*, *sqrt*, *abs* and *eof*. In Pascal, we can also define our own functions, with the properties that they:

- return a single value as the function value,
- are called as part of an expression.

Functions can have parameters, along the same lines as procedures.

A function is declared in much the same way as a procedure, with the added bit of information being its type which may be integer, real, boolean or character. (Subranges of these and enumerated types are also permitted, as described in Chapter 8). The form below shows how a function is declared. There is no form for a call: calls have to be part of an expression, appearing in another statement such as an assignment or writeln.

No form for a call – calls are part of expressions.

Function declaration

```
FUNCTION name (formal parameter declarations) : type;
declarations
BEGIN
    statements
END; {name}
```

The following rules apply for functions:

1. The function must be assigned a value at least once somewhere inside its body before it terminates. The value must be of the correct type.
2. The function name may not be used as if it were a variable inside its own body.

Rules for functions.

Example 5.4 Modulo counters

| Problem | We wish to provide various counters which count within certain ranges only.

| Example | For example, the counter for the minutes on a digital clock goes from 0 to 59 and round again, while the hour counter goes from 1 to 12.

| Solution | Provide a function called next which has three parameters – the counter and its upper and lower bounds. The function will check the counter against the upper bound and reset it if necessary.

| Program |

```
FUNCTION next (c, upper, lower : integer) : integer;
BEGIN
```

```
                    if c = upper then next := lower else next := succ(c);
                    END; {next}
```

Testing   A suitable test would be to print out the time from a given start
                   to a given finish – carefully choosing these so that each of the
hours, minutes and seconds will tick over, without producing too much
output. To keep it manageable, we can list several times on each line, and in
fact, use the modulo counter to keep track of this too! The program would
be:

```
PROGRAM TestTicker (input, output);
{Testing the next function using a clock and a counter}

VAR
   H, startH, endH    : 1..12;
   M, startM, endM,
   S, startS, endS    : 0..59;
   counter,
   timesperline       : 1..10; {or so}

FUNCTION next (c, lower, upper : integer) : integer;
   BEGIN
      if c = upper then next := lower else next := succ(c);
   END; {next}

BEGIN
   writeln('***** Testing the next function *****');
   write('Starting hours, minutes and seconds :');
   readln(startH, startM, startS);
   write('Ending hours, minutes and seconds : ');
   readln(endH, endM, endS);
   write('How many times per line? ');  readln(timesperline);
   H := startH;
   M := startM;
   S := startS;
   counter := 1;
   REPEAT
      write(H:2,':',M:2,':',S:2,'   ');
      counter := next(counter,1,timesperline);
      if counter = 1 then writeln;
      S := next (S, 0, 59);
      if S {ticked over i.e.} = 0 then M := next (M, 0, 59);
      if M {ticked over i.e.} = 0 then H := next (H, 1, 12);
   UNTIL  (H = endH) and (M = endM) and (S = endS);
END.
```

A typical run would look like this:

```
***** Testing the next function *****
Starting hours, minutes and seconds : 12 59 50
Ending hours, minutes and seconds: 1 0 5
How many times per line? 5
12:59:50   12:59:51      12:59:52      12:59:53      12:59:54
```

12:59:55	12:59:56	12:59:57	12:59:58	12:59:59
1: 0: 0	1: 0: 1	1: 0: 2	1: 0: 3	1: 0: 4
1: 0: 5				

There is obviously a better way of outputting the clock time: it should be in a single place, and should 'tick over' in the same way that a digital watch does. To do this, we need to be able to position the cursor on the screen, using the *gotoxy* procedure discussed in section 4.5. This is left as an exercise for the reader.

Example 5.5 Checksums

Problem   Zanyland University gives each student a student number which consists of four digits and ends with a checksum character which is computed by taking the sum of the preceding digits modulo 4. These checksums need to be verified.

Solution   Define a boolean function which will take a number, analyse it, and return true or false, depending on whether the checksum digit is correct or not.

Examples   Some sample numbers might be:

1234 2	$1 + 2 + 3 + 4 = 10$;	$10 \bmod 4 = 2$;	correct
5682 1	$5 + 6 + 8 + 3 = 21$;	$21 \bmod 4 = 1$;	correct
7007 1	$7 + 0 + 0 + 7 = 14$;	$14 \bmod 4 = 2$;	incorrect

Algorithm   The number will have to be decomposed, digit by digit. This can be done simply by repeatedly taking modulo 10. At the same time, the digits can be added and then the sum checked against the check digit. The interface to the function consists of the number and the checksum digit.

Program

```
FUNCTION checksum (number, digit: integer; ) : boolean;
  VAR
    i    : 1 ..4;
    sum  : 0 .. 9999;
  BEGIN
    sum := 0;
    for i := 1 to 4 do begin
      sum := sum + number mod 10;
      number := number div 10;
    end;
    checksum := (sum mod 4) = digit;
  END; {checksum}
```

Testing   To test the function, we would need to embed it in a program and call it as in

```
readln (n, d);
if not checksum (n,d) then writeln('Checksum error in', n:1,d:2);
```

Notice that in this function, one of the value parameters, *number*, is used as if it were a variable. This is quite permissible, and any changes made to *number* will not be reflected back in the calling program.

Example 5.6   Trigonometric and hyperbolic functions

| Problem | Pascal only provides sine, cosine and arctan functions. We would like to extend this repertoire to include: tan, sinh, cosh, tanh and all the inverses.

| Solution | First of all, we have to find expressions for these functions, in terms of functions that are already known. These are:

$$\tan(x) \qquad \frac{\sin(x)}{\cos(x)}$$

$$\cot(x) \qquad \frac{\cos(x)}{\sin(x)}$$

$$\sec(x) \qquad \frac{1}{\cos(x)}$$

$$\csc(x) \qquad \frac{1}{\sin(x)}$$

$$\arcsin(x) \qquad \arctan\left(\frac{x}{\sqrt{1-x^2}}\right)$$

$$\arccos(x) \qquad \arctan\left(\frac{\sqrt{1-x^2}}{x}\right)$$

$$\sinh(x) \qquad \frac{e^x - e^{-x}}{2}$$

$$\cosh(x) \qquad \frac{e^x + e^{-x}}{2}$$

$$\tanh(x) \qquad \frac{e^x - e^{-x}}{e^x + e^{-x}}$$

and so on, for the inverses of the hyperbolics.

What to do when a function is ill-defined.

| Algorithm | Armed with these formulae, we can construct functions which will return the correct values. This will work for most of the functions, but what about those where the denominator may be zero, such as tan? These could be protected against division by zero, but this raises a

dilemma: should such a function return some value, so that the computation from which it was called may proceed, or should it allow the division to fail, and crash the program?

Where these functions are ill-defined at the limit, it is more than likely that the call is erroneous, and so crashing is probably the correct course. However, arcsin(1) and arccos(0) are well-defined and division by zero occurs because of the formula used for calculating them. In these cases, the function should protect against division by zero. Notice, however, that we cannot check exactly for x being 0 or 1, since real numbers are not stored exactly. Rather, we check that x is within some tolerance of 0 or 1.

| Program | We give here two of the functions – the rest are left as exercises. In evaluating arcsin using the formula, the critical value is x being 1. Instead of the function being undefined, it is in fact correctly defined as $\pi/2$. We therefore treat this as a special case.

```
FUNCTION arcsin (x : real) : real;
  CONST piover2 = 1.5707956;
  BEGIN
    if abs(x – 1) < 1E-6
    then arcsin := piover2
    else arcsin := arctan(x / sqrt(1 – sqr(x)));
  END; {arcsin}

FUNCTION tanh (x:real) : real;
  BEGIN
    tanh := (exp(x) – exp(–x)) / (exp(x) + exp(–x));
  END; {tanh}
```

More useful functions

Functions can be boolean or character, as well as numeric. Without going through the problem solving process, we present a few useful functions here. The first decides whether a given year is leap or not, based on the usual formula.

Leap year function.

```
FUNCTION leap (y : integer) : boolean;
  {Decides whether a year is a leap year i.e.
  divisible by 4, but not a century, unless it's a quad-century}

  BEGIN
    leap := (y mod 4 = 0)
         and not ((y mod 100 = 0) and not (y mod 400 = 0));
  END; {leap}

{called as in}
if (day = 29) and (month = 2) and not leap(year)
  then writeln('incorrect');
```

The next function is very useful. It looks at a character, and if it is a capital letter, it converts it into a small one. The conversion is based only on the offset of the capital letters from the small letters, as given by the predefined function ord, and is therefore completely independent of the underlying character set.

Converting to lower case.

```
FUNCTION lower (letter : char) : char;
    {A function to convert upper-case letters to lower case }
    {Will work for any character set}
      BEGIN
        if letter in ['A'..'Z'] {i.e. it is an upper-case letter}
        then lower := chr(ord(letter) − ord('A') + ord('a'))
        else lower := letter;
      END; {lower}

    {called as in converting a surname from capitals to the usual form}
    read(ch);  write(ch); {the first letter}
    read(ch);
    while ch <> space do begin
      write(lower(ch)); read(ch);
    end;
```

Note, in passing, that the above bit of program will handle names with hyphens and apostrophes, since calling *lower* with one of these will simply return it back again.

Finally, we have a function which calculates how many digits there are in an integer, using the characteristic of its logarithm.

Calculating the digits in an integer.

```
FUNCTION digits (n : integer) : integer;
    VAR d : integer;
    BEGIN
      if n < 0 then begin
        d := 1;
        n := abs(n);
      end else
        d := 0; {plus sign not printed}
      d := d + trunc (ln(n) / ln(10) + 1);
      digits := d;
    END; {digits}
```

This function could be used in cases where formatting is required. For example, to find out if a number will fit on a line 60 characters wide on which *count* characters have already been written, we could use

```
if  count + digits(number) > 60  ...
```

Notice that the function name cannot be used as a variable and therefore the local variable *d* had to be defined for the summing, and assigned to *digits* at the end.

5.4   Modular decomposition

We discussed in Chapter 1 the importance of decomposing a solution into modules which had a strong sense of identity, and limited interfaces with the rest of the program. In this way, programs consist of manageable portions, are easier to read and write, and the chances of making an error are considerably diminished. Now that we have the formal structures for defining procedures and functions with the power of parameters, we shall look more closely at how exactly to achieve a good modular decomposition. The techniques that are described here are well illustrated in the example that follows, as well as in the many examples in future chapters. We are concerned here with practical techniques, not with semantics: there is more about the semantics of procedural decomposition in Chapter 9.

Notice that we use the term *modular* decomposition although Pascal itself does not have a construct for modules as such. Modules, in other languages, are collections of procedures data which together serve a common purpose. In Pascal, we can only collect procedures by nesting them, but the decomposition process is the same.

The size of a procedure

The first practical question to ask is: what size of procedure or function should we be aiming at? A rule of thumb is anything between one line and one page. A procedure that is longer than a page ought really to be subdivided. The programs in this book are mostly less than a page, yet we still seem to use two or three procedures per program. In practice, therefore, there is no strict guideline, and each program must be adapted to the circumstances.

It is, however, true that functions are in general shorter than procedures. The tasks they need to accomplish are related to returning a single value, and this can usually be done in a few statements.

Defining the interface

A key issue when decomposing an algorithm into procedures and functions is the definition of the interfaces. It is these that dictate the flow of data between the parts of a program. The overriding concern is **self-containedness**, i.e. ensuring that a procedure defines all its own private data and communicates with the rest of the program only through parameters.

Strictly speaking, this means that a procedure should not access even functions, or files which are declared global to it. Consider the *secant* procedure which is to be defined in the next section. It has seven parameters and two local variables, but in addition makes use of a function *f*, and writes to the output file; conceivably, it could have been writing to a named file, say *out*.

```
               PROCEDURE secant (var x, x1, x2  : real;
                                 tolerance      : real;
                                 var iterations : integer;
                                 imax           : integer;
                                 monitor        : boolean);
            {Uses the function f(x:real):real}

            VAR
              f1,f2 :real;

            BEGIN
              iterations := 0;
              f1 := f(x1);
              REPEAT
                iterations := iterations + 1;
                x2 := x1;
                x1 := x;
                f2 := f1;
                f1 := f(x1);
                x := (x1 * f2 – x2 * f1) / (f2 – f1);
                IF monitor THEN
                writeln('New estimate = ', x:10:6);
              UNTIL ((abs(x – x1) < tolerance) or (iterations = imax));
            END; {secant}
```

Accessing the outer function can be avoided by means of procedural parameters (as described in section 9.3), but writing is a problem. If all non-parameter communication with the rest of the program is classified as a **side effect**, then writing (especially monitor printing, as this is) would be termed a **benign side effect**. In the pragmatic world of scientific programming, we generally permit such effects.

The rule about parameters applies to constants as well. A procedure can rely on implicit constants, but this weakens its usefulness as a building block in other programs. Take for example the checksum function. It mentions three constants: 1, 4 and 10. One may argue that 10 is genuinely intrinsic to the computation, since numbers are written in base 10, and that 1 is the start of a counting range. But the presence of 4 ties us to the specific case of a four digit number. It would be more general to have this as a parameter, giving:

```
               FUNCTION checksum (number, digit, size: integer; ) : boolean;
               VAR
                 i  : 1..4;
                 sum   : 0..9999;
               BEGIN
                 sum := 0;
                 for i := 1 to size do begin
                   sum := sum + number mod 10;
                   number := number div 10;
                 end;
                 checksum := (sum mod size) = digit;
               END; {checksum}
```

Not all procedures, of course, are intended to be re-used in other programs.

Some, particularly those that are declared nested inside another, serve a very specific purpose, and it is sometimes convenient for them to make use of non-local variables. These choices are illustrated in example 5.7 and the numerical methods in the next section..

Choosing a procedure or a function

The choice of whether to use a function or procedure, when both are possible, can be made according to

- how many values need to be returned
- how the routine is to be called.

If more than one value is to be returned, then necessity dictates that we use a procedure with VAR parameters. This can result in a messy program if the calling needs of the routine were in fact for a function. A case such as this occurs in example 8.4.

If we are only talking about a single value result, then a function is a nicer way of expressing things. However, if we need to know the result of the comparison again later in the program, then we won't want to call the function again, and so would like to have the result stored somewhere. The procedure with the VAR parameter serves this purpose, but there is another way of doing it. The essential point is to record the result of the routine, and this can be done with the function.

Recall the procedure,

```
PROCEDURE firstisolder (n,m : integer;  VAR b : boolean);
BEGIN
  b := n > m;
END {firstisolder}
```

We could replace this with a function

```
FUNCTION isolder (n, m : integer) : boolean;
BEGIN
  isolder := n > m;
END; {isolder}
```

and call it with

```
answer := isolder (myage, yourage);
```

Both are correct, and the choice will depend largely on circumstances.

Choosing parameter names

Finally we look at the somewhat confusing matter of parameter names. In many of the programs that follow, we will find that a global variable and a formal parameter are given the same name. For example, surrounding the above secant procedure, we could have the variables and call:

```
VAR
    x, x1, x2 : real;
    i, imax : integer;
    tolerance : real;

        PROCEDURE secant (var x, x1, x2   : real;
                          tolerance       : real;
                          var iterations  : integer;
                          imax            : integer;
                          monitor         : boolean);
        {Uses the function f(x:real):real}
        END; {secant}

    secant (x, x1, x2, tolerance, i, imax, true);
```

The first four parameters have exactly the same actual and formal names. There is nothing wrong with this, and in many ways it smooths the understanding of an algorithm. It is quite contrary to think of different names just for the sake of it. On the other hand, notice that the global variable *i* becomes *iterations* inside the procedure – a more definite name for the purpose. The last parameter, *monitor*, is passed a constant, true – which is perfectly acceptable in the circumstances.

Example 5.7   Calculating floor areas

Problem   Estate agents frequently provide information about houses that includes the dimensions of each room. It is very useful when comparing houses to be able to have a figure for the total floor area, based on these.

Solution   Enter the room dimensions into a data file, and have a program which reads them and calculates the area. We shall assume that the dimensions are given initially in feet and inches but that we wish to have them in metric as well.

Example   Assume we are dealing with input and output such as this:

14 Highfield Lane

Lounge	23'8"x11'2"	264.28sq ft	7.21m x 3.40m	24.55sq m
Bedroom1	12'3"x11'3"	137.81sq ft	3.73m x 3.43m	12.80sq m

Algorithm   We use stepwise refinement and start at the outer level, itemising the tasks that need to be done, in the correct order, and making assumptions about procedures and parameters as seems fitting.

```
BEGIN
    Setupfiles;
```

```
        Copyheadings;
        CalculateRoomsandTotal;
    END.
```

The idea is that there are no global variables at all (except the files), and that all the work is done inside the procedure *CalculateRoomsandTotal*. At the next level down, a likely sequence of events is given by this portion of the procedure:

```
        BEGIN
          aBlankLine := false;
          WHILE not aBlankLine do begin

            Echoto(' ');
            readftins (ft1, ins1);
            Echoto('x');
            readftins(ft2, ins2);
            multiply (ft1, ins1, ft2, ins2, area);

            convert(ft1, ins1, m1);
            convert(ft2, ins2, m2);
            writeln(area, m1, m2, m1 * m2); {with units, of course}

            Addtototals;
            Checkforblankline;
          END;
        END;
```

Each procedure can then be elaborated in turn, using as much old material as we can. For example, *Echoto* would be a version of *skipto*, with writing in it. *Readftins* is quite interesting, and also makes use of a version of a previously developed procedure

```
        PROCEDURE readftins (VAR ft, ins : integer);
          VAR  a : integer;
          unit : char;

          PROCEDURE readinteger (VAR n : integer;
                  VAR follow : char);
            {Reads an integer, and returns the following character}

            .......as before ......

          END; {readinteger}

        BEGIN
          readinteger(a, unit);
          if unit = '''' then begin {feet}
            ft := a;
            if data^ in ['0'..'9']
            then readinteger (ins, unit);
            else ins := 0;
          end else
```

```
        ins := a;
      END; {readftins}
```

A powerful use
of parameters. This procedure nicely illustrates the use of a nested procedure called with different parameters. In fact, we could not have done without the parameters here.

Finally, consider the case of checking for a blank line, being the end of the data. (We do not wish to use end-of-file because we are anticipating several sets of data coming in.) The results of the check will be stored in a boolean variable, which is defined outside the procedure, giving:

```
      PROCEDURE Checkforblankline;
        BEGIN
          readln(data);  writeln(results);
          if eoln(data) then begin
            aBlankline := true;
            readln(data);  writeln(results);
          end;
        END; {Checkforblankline}
```

Alternatively, the outer procedure could send its boolean variable as a parameter which *Checkforablankline* could call the same name, and do exactly the same with it, i.e.

```
      PROCEDURE Checkforblankline (VAR aBlankline : boolean);
        BEGIN
          readln(data);  writeln(results);
          if eoln(data) then begin
            aBlankline := true;
            readln(data);  writeln(results);
          end;
        END; {Checkforblankline}
```

Which is better, is a moot point. *Checkforablankline* is a one-off procedure, defined entirely for ease of reading and it does not actually need a parameter. *Addtototals* is in a similar position. However, if the procedure were either at the outer level, or could conceivably be called more than once, then a parameter should be used. The full text for this program is given later, as it will benefit from features yet to be introduced.

5.5   Numerical methods with functions

In this section we consider a third method for finding roots to equations (two others were covered in section 4.6), and follow that with a method for numerical integration.

Method 5   Root finding with the secant method

Rationale   In Chapter 4, we discussed how to find the roots of an equation $f(x) = 0$ using the Newton-Raphson method. This depended on a guess of the root, and on knowing the derivative of the function. Now suppose that the derivative df/dx is unknown (a case in which this happens is discussed in the case study at the end of the chapter.) So we cannot use the Newton-Raphson method, and use instead the **secant** method.

Theory   If x_1, x_2 ($x_1 \neq x_2$) are estimates of the root, then a better estimate is

$$x_3 = \frac{x_1 f(x_2) - x_2 f(x_1)}{f(x_2) - f(x_1)}$$

The formula is obtained by modelling the curve $f(x)$ by the secant through the points x_1, x_2 and taking the geometric relationship between the two triangles thus formed.

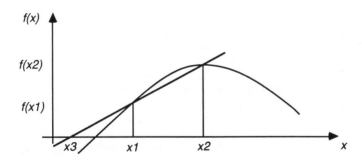

Algorithm   The algorithm, given overleaf, is very similar to the Newton-Raphson method. What we need to do now is to package the algorithm up in a self-contained procedure or function. We start by defining the interface required:

    Uses   : 2 initial estimates, tolerance, maximum iterations
    Returns   : 2 final estimates, iterations taken

From this, we can devise a list of parameters and a procedure header, and proceed to write the procedure. Since there is more than one result from the method, we need a procedure and not a function.

The Secant Method

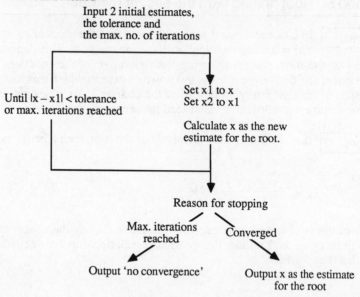

Input 2 initial estimates,
the tolerance and
the max. no. of iterations

Until |x – x1| < tolerance
or max. iterations reached

Set x1 to x
Set x2 to x1

Calculate x as the new
estimate for the root.

Reason for stopping

Max. iterations
reached

Converged

Output 'no convergence'

Output x as the estimate
for the root

Procedure   An important consideration when writing procedures to
implement iterative (i.e. looping) numerical methods is
whether they should print out temporary results or not. In some cases, a
program is working and only the result of the method is required, but in
many cases, it may be useful or necessary to have the intermediate results
printed out. In order to provide this flexibility, we add one more parameter,
called monitor, which is used to govern the output of the values as the loop
progresses. If monitor is true, then the values are printed, and if it is false
then they are not.

```
PROCEDURE secant (var x, x1, x2  : real;
                  tolerance       : real;
                  var iterations  : integer;
                  imax            : integer;
                  monitor         : boolean);
{Uses the function f (x : real) : real}

VAR
  f1,f2 :r eal;
BEGIN
  iterations := 0;
  f1 := f(x1);
  REPEAT
    iterations := iterations + 1;
    x2 := x1;
    x1 := x;
    f2 := f1;
    f1 := f(x1);
```

```
        x := (x1 * f2 – x2 * f1) / (f2 – f1);
        IF monitor THEN
          writeln('New estimate = ',x:10:6);
      UNTIL ((abs(x – x1) < tolerance) or (iterations = imax));
    END; {secant}
```

We notice that *secant* is not completely self-contained: it still relies on the function *f* being defined. We would not wish to define *f* inside *secant* since this would tie it down to that function. Later, in Chapter 9, we shall discuss ways of achieving generality without sacrificing self-containedness.

Example 5.8   Heat exchange unit

| Problem | In a heat exchange unit, energy is tranferred from condensing steam to water. The mass flow rate of the water, *w* in kg/s, is to be found from the energy balance equation. The desired rate of transfer of energy is 200kW. For a particular heat exchange unit, the conservation equation is

$$276\,w\left(1 - \exp\left(\frac{-942}{101 + 371w}\right)\right) - 200 = 0$$

| Solution | We need to solve the above equation for *w*. The secant method is ideal, since we do not have to differentiate the equation first.

| Program | The program consists of three parts: inputting the values, calculating *w* using the secant procedure we have already defined, and considering the results and outputting them.

```
PROGRAM HeatExchangeUnit(input,output);
  {Calculates the mass flow rate in kg/s in a heat
    exchange unit with a given energy balance equation}

VAR
  imax,
  i              : 1 .. maxint;
  tolerance,
  w,w1,w2    : real;

PROCEDURE initialise;
  BEGIN
    writeln('*******Flow Rate in a Heat Exchange Unit*******');
    writeln('Solves f(w)=0, with');
    writeln('f(w) = 200 – 276w(1 – exp(–942 / (101 + 371w)))');
    writeln;
    write('First estimate for flow rate:');
    readln(w);
    write('Second estimate for flow rate:');
    readln(w1);
    write('Required error limit:');
```

```
                    readln(tolerance);
                    write('Maximum number of iterations permitted:');
                    readln(imax);
               END; {initialise}

          FUNCTION f(w:real) : real;
            BEGIN
              f := 200 - 276 * w * (1 - exp(-942 / (101 + 371 * w)));
            END; {f}

          PROCEDURE secant (var x, x1, x2   : real;
                                 tolerance    : real;
                                 var iterations : integer;
                                 imax         : integer;
                                 monitor      : boolean);
            {Uses the function f(x:real):real}
            {defined earlier}
          END;  {secant}

          BEGIN
               initialise;
               secant (w, w1, w2, tolerance, i, imax, true);
               if (i = imax)
               then writeln('Failed to converge: w =', w:10:6,
                         ' w1 = ', w1:10:6,' i = ',i:3)
               else writeln('Flow rate is:', w:10:6, ' kg/s ',
                              i:3, ' iterations required');
          END.
```

Testing

*******Flow Rate in a Heat Exchange Unit*******
Solves f(w)=0, with
f(w) = 200 - 276w(1 - exp(-942/(101 + 371w)))

First estimate for flow rate: 0.5
Second estimate for flow rate: 1.0
Required error limit: 10e-6
Maximum number of iterations permitted: 10

New estimate =   0.817831
New estimate =   0.801046
New estimate =   0.799410
New estimate =   0.799420
New estimate =   0.799420
Flow rate is: 0.799420 kg/s   5 iterations required

The result can be checked by hand.

Method 6   Integration using Simpson's rule

Rationale   Having looked at differential equations and finding roots of ordinary equations, we now consider how to integrate a function between two limits, that is, to find

$$\int_a^b f(x)\ dx$$

| **Methods** | The basic technique is to divide the area under the curve into strips and to calculate the area of each of these, summing them to obtain the integral. There are various methods for doing this. Simple ones are the mid-point rule and the trapezoidal rule. These are examined in the problems at the end of the chapter. Here we shall look at a method which gives a better accuracy and is in daily use by engineers.

| **Theory** | Simpson's rule is a numerical method which computes the integral as the sum of an even number of strips underneath the curve. The area of each pair of strips is approximated by fitting a parabola through the three points at the top of each strip. This is shown in the diagram.

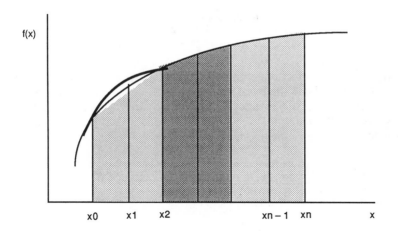

We start by dividing the interval of integration a,b into an even number, n, of equal subintervals. The length of each subinterval h is

$$h = \frac{b - a}{n}$$

Simpson's rule estimates the integral s as

$$s = \frac{h}{3}\left(f(a) + 4\sum_{\substack{i=1 \\ (i=1,3,5...)}}^{n-1} f(a + ih) + 2\sum_{\substack{i=2 \\ (i=2,4,6...)}}^{n-2} f(a + ih) + f(b)\right)$$

In other words, we compute the value of $f(x)$ at the start of the interval and at the end, then add in 4 times the value of $f(x)$ at the odd subintervals and twice the values at the even subintervals, then multiply the whole thing by $h/3$.

Algorithm The evaluation of the formula given by Simpson's rule involves summing two series. Since they are independent, we can do them together. Two subtotals will be needed into which we add the values of the odd numbered and the even numbered strips. The pseudo-code chart is:

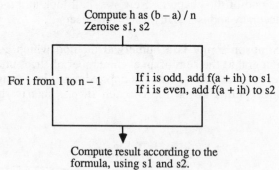

Simpson's Rule

Compute h as (b − a) / n
Zeroise s1, s2

For i from 1 to n − 1   If i is odd, add f(a + ih) to s1
                             If i is even, add f(a + ih) to s2

Compute result according to the
formula, using s1 and s2.

Function Simpson's rule returns a single value, so we can envisage it as a function. The interface needs the values of a and b, the number of subintervals, n, and the function to be integrated. As in the previous method, we shall assume that the function is called f and that it is declared elsewhere.

```
FUNCTION Simpson (a, b : real; n : integer) : real;
  {Integrates f(x) from a to b using n subintervals,
   where n is even}

VAR
  i : 0 .. maxint;
  h, s1, s2, x : real;
BEGIN
  h := (b − a) / n;
  s1 := 0;
  s2 := 0;
  x := a;
  for i := 1 to n − 1 do begin
    x := x + h;
    if odd(i)
    then s1 := s1 + f(x)
    else s2 := s2 + f(x);
  end;
  Simpson := h / 3 * (f(a) + 4 * s1 + 2 * s2 + f(b));
END; {Simpson}
```

In this function, there is an example of an *optimisation*. In scientific On optimising a programs, there are often many calculations to be done, and although program. computers are fast, the cumulative effect can sometimes make a program run unacceptably slowly. Good programmers, therefore, try to reduce the calculations, provided this does not make the program obscure. In the *Simpson* function, instead of calling the function $f(x)$ with $a + i * h$, which is what the formula said, we keep a variable, x, initialised to a and add h to it at each iteration. Thus we eliminate the multiplication, which is a slow operation.

Notice, too, the use of the *odd* function to decide whether to add the term to *s1* or *s2*.

Example 5.9   Charge and voltage across a capacitor

Problem	A capacitor in an electrical circuit is initially at zero charge.

At time $t = 1$s, a switch is closed and a time-dependent electric current $I(t)$ charges up the capacitor according to the formula

$$I(t) = 4(1 - e^{-0.5})\, e^{-0.5(t-1)}\, (1 - e^{-t})$$

We want to compute the charge Q and voltage V across the capacitor as functions of time up to 10s.

Solution	The charge stored by the capacitor is given by the integral

$$Q(t) = \int I(t) dt$$

and the voltage computed by simply dividing this by C:

$$V(t) = \frac{Q(t)}{C}$$

We can use Simpson's rule to compute the integral at each second, print out the values of Q and C, and finally for $t = 10$s.

Algorithm	The main program consists once again of three stages –

initialisation, computation and output. The computation involves a loop which runs through the seconds over the specified range, say 0 to 10s. For each such t, the integral is calculated using Simpson's rule, and this involves looping over the n steps. Notice n must be an even number, and we check this in the initialisation phase.

Program

```
PROGRAM CapacitanceCharge(input,output);
VAR
  a,b,t,n  : 0..maxint;
```

```
Q       : real;  {charge in amps}
C       : real;  {farads}

PROCEDURE initialise;
 BEGIN
  writeln('***** The voltage across a capacitor *****');
  writeln('Integrates the formula for I(t) using Simpson" s rule');
  writeln('finding the charge and voltage for t = 1..10');
  writeln('Use 20 intervals at each second');
  write('What is the capacitance in farads, C: '); readln(C);
  writeln;
  writeln('    t','Q':14,'V':14);
  a := 1;
  b := 10;
  n := 20
 END; {initialise}

FUNCTION f (t : real) : real;
 BEGIN
  f := 4 * (1 – exp(–0.5)) * exp(–0.5 * (t – 1)) * (1 – exp(–t));
 END;  {I}

FUNCTION Simpson (a, b : real; n : integer) : real;
 {Integrates f(x) from a to b using n subintervals}
 BEGIN
  {as before}
 END; {Simpson}

BEGIN
 Initialise;
 for t := a to b do begin
  Q := simpson(a, t, n);
  writeln(t:4, Q:14:6, Q / C:14:6);
 end;
END.
```

> **Testing**

```
***** The voltage across a capacitor *****
Integrates the formula for I(t) using Simpson' s rule
finding the charge and voltage for t = 1..10
Use 20 intervals at each second
What is the capacitance in farads, C: 0.05
```

t	Q	V
1	0.000000	0.000000
2	0.938675	18.773497
3	1.622979	32.459583
4	2.063680	41.273609
5	2.336695	46.733910
6	2.503549	50.070980
7	2.605009	52.100185
8	2.666572	53.331432
9	2.703867	54.077335
10	2.726411	54.528214

We should run the program for different values of a, b, and n and compare the results. Obviously, with more intervals, the answer will become more accurate.

5.6   Case study 1: Process control

The purpose of this case study is to take a real engineering problem and work through the methods, algorithms and programming required to solve it. In the process, we shall make use of several of the techniques – both programming and numerical – that have gone before. The reader thus has a chance to consolidate earlier knowledge and gain an appreciation of how and where it can be effectively applied.

Background

Many industrial processes can be viewed as a process with two inputs and an output, as shown in the diagram.

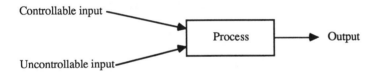

Some of the input can be controlled in that we can freely choose the values (within limits). This could apply to the flow rates of the input materials, the rate of heat input, the pressure, temperature, etc. However, some of the input cannot be controlled, e.g. the composition of the raw materials may change significantly from one batch to another. We probably want the output to remain constant. In a simple control problem we monitor the uncontrolled input, then calculate an adjustment to the controllable input so as to achieve the desired output.

Problem – liquid in a catalytic unit

We consider the case of a liquid being passed through a catalytic unit of length L. The liquid contains in solution an uncontrolled concentration of chemical A; a controlled concentration of chemical B is added on input. On output, we want the concentration of chemical A to have a fixed value. The chemicals A and B react together in the catalytic unit, and their concentrations are described by the equations shown:

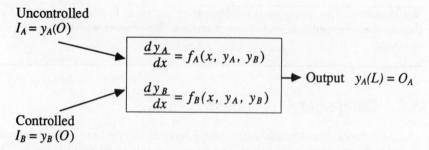

Uncontrolled
$I_A = y_A(O)$

$$\frac{dy_A}{dx} = f_A(x, y_A, y_B)$$

$$\frac{dy_B}{dx} = f_B(x, y_A, y_B)$$

Output $y_A(L) = O_A$

Controlled
$I_B = y_B(O)$

The variables, input and output values, can be summarised as follows:

Concentrations of A, B in catalytic unit: $y_A(x)$, $y_B(x)$
Input concentration of control B: $I_B \; (=y_B(0))$
Output concentrations: O_A, O_B, $(=y_A(L), y_B(L))$
Desired output concentration of A: A_{wanted}
Measured input concentration of A: $I_A(=y_A(0))$

Objective   To find I_B such that $O_A = A_{\text{wanted}}$

The following diagram shows how different values of the control input concentration I_B lead to different output concentrations O_A.

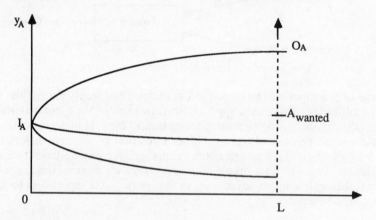

We wish to find the root of the equation

$$O_A(I_B) - A_{\text{wanted}} = 0$$

where we regard O_A as depending on I_B. Because it is difficult to work out the derivative dO_A/dI_B we cannot use the Newton-Raphson method, but we can use the secant method (example 4.5). Thus at the top level our algorithm is the same as the secant method root finding algorithm, with each function evaluation being the solution of a pair of differential equations.

Method 7   The shooting method

How are we to solve such a pair of equations? We saw in section 3.7 that one differential equation can be solved by the predictor-corrector method. We use a method known as the 'shooting method'. We solve (numerically) the ordinary differential equations for y_A, y_B with initial conditions

$$y_A(O) = I_A,$$
$$y_B(O) = \text{various estimates of } I_B.$$

and then adjust the estimate of I_B until we hit the target, i.e. until $O_A = A_{\text{wanted}}$. We will then have found the correct control I_B.

| Methods | We already have a secant method program, and one to solve an ordinary differential equation by the predictor-corrector method (example 3.7). We need to make the (straightforward) extension from one to two d.e.'s in the predictor-corrector algorithm. Consider several such equations, for example

$$\frac{dy}{dx} = p(x,y,z)$$
$$\frac{dz}{dx} = q(x,y,z)$$

with $y(0) = y_0$ and $z(0) = z_0$

This case is a straightforward generalisation of that for one equation. For the Euler method the formulae become

$$y_{i+1} = y_i + h\, p(x_i, y_i, z_i)$$
$$z_{i+1} = z_i + h\, q(x_i, y_i, z_i)$$

and for the predictor-corrector method the formulae are

$$y_p = y_i + h\, p(x_i, y_i, z_i)$$
$$z_p = z_i + h\, q(x_i, y_i, z_i)$$
$$y_{i+1} = y_i + \tfrac{1}{2}h\ (p(x_i, y_i, z_i) + p(x_{i+1}, y_p, z_p))$$
$$z_{i+1} = z_i + \tfrac{1}{2}h\ (q(x_i, y_i, z_i) + q(x_{i+1}, y_p, z_p))$$

| Algorithm | Then we need to combine the two programs together. We write the differential equation solver as a procedure, with O_A as a VAR parameter. A procedure call specifies a value for a boolean variable *finished*. Once the correct control I_B has been found the differential equation solver is called with *finished* = true, and the concentrations of A, B at various points within the catalytic unit are printed out.

Shooting method

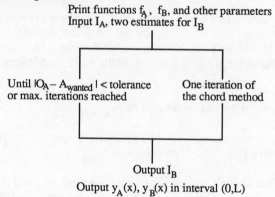

Print functions f_A, f_B, and other parameters
Input I_A, two estimates for I_B

Until $|O_A - A_{wanted}| <$ tolerance   One iteration of
or max. iterations reached   the chord method

Output I_B
Output $y_A(x)$, $y_B(x)$ in interval $(0,L)$

Program

```
PROGRAM ProcessControl(input,output);
  {For a catalytic unit of length L = 1, this program
   determines the level of controlled input IB such that
   a desired output level OA = Awanted is achieved.

   Uses the secant method for finding the root of the
   equation OA(IB) – Awanted = 0 and a shooting version
   of the predictor-corrector method for working out
   the pair of differential equations which give the
   value of the function OA.}

  CONST

     L          = 1.0;      {Length of the unit}
     Tolerance  = 1e-6;
     imax       = 20;  {Maximum permitted iterations}
     reports    = 10;
     n          = 50;       {Iterations per report}

  VAR
     i  : integer;
     Awanted, IA,
     IB, IB1, IB2, h,
     OA, OA1, OA2: real;

  PROCEDURE shoot (IA, IB : real; VAR OA : real;
                        monitor : boolean);
     {Predictor corrector method for two d.e.s}
     {Uses global constant      : L
      Uses global variables      : n, reports}

     VAR
       i, j                      : 1..maxint;
       x, yA, yAp, yBp, yB       : real;
```

```
FUNCTION fA (x, yA, yB : real) : real;
  BEGIN
    fA := - yB / exp(yA);
  END; {fA}

FUNCTION fB (x, yA, yB : real) : real;
  BEGIN
    fB := 1;
  END; {fB}

BEGIN
  h := L / (n * reports);
  x := 0;
  yA := IA;
  yB := IB;
  FOR i := 1 to reports do begin
    FOR j := 1 to n do begin
      yAp := yA + h * fA(x, yA, yB);
      yBp := yB + h * fB(x, yA, yB);
      yA := yA + 0.5 * h * (fA(x, yA, yB) + fA(x + h, yAp, yBp));
      yB := yB + 0.5 * h * (fB(x, yA, yB) + fB(x + h, yAp, yBp));
      x := x + h;
    END;
    IF monitor then
      writeln(g, 'x = ', x:10:6, '   yA = ',yA:10:6,'   yB = ', yB:10:6)
    else write('.');
  END;
  OA := yA;
END; {shoot}

PROCEDURE initialise;
  BEGIN
    writeln('********Process Control program********');
    writeln('Solves yA"(x) = fA(x, yA, yB), with fA = - yB/exp(yA)');
    writeln('       yB"(x) = fB(x, yA, yB), with fB = 1');
    writeln('     In interval (0,L) with L = ',L:5:2);
    writeln('Required error limit,  tolerance:',tolerance:10:8);
    writeln('Maximum number of iterations permitted,',
            'imax:', imax:3);
    writeln;
    writeln('Desired output value of A, Awanted:');
    readln(Awanted);
    write('Input value of A,  IA:'); readln(IA);
    write('First estimate of control B, IB:'); readln(IB);
    write('Second estimate of control B, IB1:'); readln(IB1);
    writeln;
    writeln('Iterating towards a solution...');
  END; {initialise}

FUNCTION f (w : real) : real;
  {Uses global variable : IA, Awanted}
  VAR
    outputA : real;
  BEGIN
    shoot(IA, w, outputA, false);
```

```
                f := outputA – Awanted;
            END; {f}

            PROCEDURE secant (var x, x1, x2 : real;
                                    tolerance : real;
                                    var iterations : integer;
                                    imax : integer;
                                    monitor : boolean);
            VAR
              f1, f2 :real;

            BEGIN
              iterations := 0;
              f1 := f(x1);
              REPEAT
                iterations := iterations + 1;
                x2 := x1;
                x1 := x;
                f2 := f1;
                f1 := f(x1);
                x :=  (x1 * f2 – x2 * f1) / (f2 – f1);
                IF monitor then
                    writeln ('New estimate of IB = ', x:10:6);
              UNTIL ((abs(x – x1) < tolerance) or (iterations = imax));
            END;  {secant}

        BEGIN
          initialise;
          secant(IB, IB1, IB2, tolerance, i, imax, true);
            {IB1 and IB2 are not looked at on return:
             the solution is in IB}
          writeln;
          IF (i = imax)
          then writeln('Secant algorithm did not converge in ',
                        ' given iteration limit')
          else begin
            writeln('Finished after ',i:2,' iterations: ',
                    'Control IB = ',IB:10:6);
            writeln;
            writeln('Values of yA, yB in the catalytic unit:');
            writeln('x = 0.0    ',' IA =',IA:10:6,'  IB =',IB:10:6);
            shoot(IA, IB, OA, true);
          end;
        END.
```

> **Testing**

```
*******Process Control program*******
```

Solves $yA'(x) = fA(x, yA, yB)$, with $fA = -yB/exp(yA)$
$yB'(x) = fB(x, yA, yB)$, with $fB = 1$
In interval (0,L) with L = 1.00
Required error limit, tolerance:0.00000100
Maximum number of iterations permitted,imax: 20

Desired output value of A, Awanted: 1

```
Input value of A, IA: 2
First estimate of control B, IB:  3
Second estimate of control B, IB1:  4

Iterating towards a solution...
New estimate of IB =  4.204990
New estimate of IB =  4.163832
New estimate of IB =  4.170732
New estimate of IB =  4.170776
New estimate of IB =  4.170776

Finished after  5 iterations: Control IB =  4.170776

Values of yA, yB in the catalytic unit:
x =  0.0           IA =  2.000000  IB =  4.170776
x =  0.100000  yA =  1.941182  yB =  4.270776
x =  0.200000  yA =  1.877157  yB =  4.370776
x =  0.300000  yA =  1.807112  yB =  4.470776
x =  0.400000  yA =  1.730016  yB =  4.570776
x =  0.500000  yA =  1.644548  yB =  4.670776
x =  0.600000  yA =  1.548964  yB =  4.770776
x =  0.700000  yA =  1.440904  yB =  4.870776
x =  0.800000  yA =  1.317061  yB =  4.970776
x =  0.900000  yA =  1.172593  yB =  5.070776
x =  1.000000  yA =  1.000000  yB =  5.170776
```

In order to test the program, we have to choose specific functions f_A, f_B. The functions must be such that we can solve the problem analytically, so that there is an exact solution with which to compare the numerical solution. Whether or not the solution is realistic – e.g. y_A or y_B may go negative – does not matter for the purpose of testing the program. The exact solution of the differential equations is

$$y_A = \ln \left(-I_B x - \frac{1}{2} x^2 + e^{IA}\right)$$
$$y_B = I_B + x$$

From which we find that the correct control is

$$I_B = e^{IA} - e^{A \text{wanted}} - 0.5$$
$$= 4.170774$$

in the above example. We see that the error in the numerical solution is in the 6th decimal place.

Summary

☐ Boolean values are true or false. They can be written but not read.

☐ Booleans are useful for recording the state of conditions for later use.

☐ Values can be sent into a procedure or function by means of parameters using either value parameters or VAR parameters.

☐ Values can be returned from a procedure by means of a function value (only one) or VAR parameters (many).

☐ Parameters listed in the procedure are termed formal parameters, while those listed in a call are termed actual parameters.

☐ Actual parameters may be any expression or variable for value parameters, but only variables for VAR parameters.

☐ Formal parameters act like local variable declarations for the procedure, and their identifiers are only visible within the scope.

☐ Matching of actual parameters with their formal parameters is according to their order in the list, and they must agree in number and type.

☐ Value parameters are used for passing values into a procedure and provide security against accidental changes. They are the default and should be used unless the particular facilities of call-by-reference are needed.

☐ VAR parameters are used for passing values into and out of a procedure. They should only be used in preference to value parameters when passing values out is necessary.

☐ Functions must execute an assignment to the function name before returning.

☐ A function name may not be used as a variable within the function.

☐ Good programming practice involves only declaring variables when needed, thereby keeping global variables to a minimum.

☐ Self-contained procedures communicate only through parameters.

☐ The secant method solves an equation when the derivative may not be known. It needs two guesses at the root.

☐ Simpson's rule enables the integration of a function to be done by summing the areas of an even number of subintervals.

☐ Procedures and functions written for one purpose can be reused in other programs.

Self-check quiz

1. What would the result be of the following expressions is x is true and y is false?

    not x and y
    not x or y
    not (x and y)
    not (x or y)

2. Can a function have both value and VAR parameters?
3. Is there a maximum to the number of parameters a procedure or function can have?
4. Do parameters have to be declared in any specific order?
5. Write the declaration for a procedure which needs two integer value parameters, a real VAR parameter and real value parameter.
6. Is it permissible for an actual parameter and a formal parameter to have the same name?
7. Is it permissible for two actual parameters to have the same name?
8. Is it permissible for a formal parameter to have the same name as a local variable in its procedure?
9. Study the following program.

```
PROGRAM Picture (output);
  VAR row, length : integer;
  PROCEDURE modify (v : integer;  VAR x : integer);
    BEGIN
      x := v * v − v;
    END; {modify}

  PROCEDURE line (long : integer);
    VAR index : integer;
    BEGIN
      for index := 1 to long do write(row:2);
      writeln;
    END; {line}

  BEGIN
    FOR row := 1 to 4 do begin
      modify (row, length);
      write (row:2, length:4);
      line (length);
    END;
  END.
```

    What will *Picture* print out when it is run?

10. Explain why v and x are listed separately in the formal parameter list for *modify*.

Problems

5.1 A board of directors consists of three members, each of which has a two-way switch marked yes/no. When votes are taken, a lamp comes on if the yes-votes are in the majority. The circuit that implements the turning on of the lamp is represented by the boolean function

$L = a$ *and* (b *or* c) *or* b *and* c

Write a program which prints out a table of the alternate yes/no values for a, b and c, and the value of L. Implement L using a boolean function.

5.2 In the olden days, exercise books used to have multiplication tables printed neatly on the back. These would be arranged 3 across and 4 down, with each row being of the form:

```
4 times table      5 times table      6 times table
1 x  4 =    4      1 x  5 =    5      1 x  6 =    6
2 x  4 =    8      2 x  5 =   10      2 x  6 =   12
3 x  4 =   12      3 x  5 =   15      3 x  6 =   18
4 x  4 =   16      4 x  5 =   20      4 x  6 =   24
5 x  4 =   20      5 x  5 =   25      5 x  6 =   30
6 x  4 =   24      6 x  5 =   30      6 x  6 =   36
7 x  4 =   28      7 x  5 =   35      7 x  6 =   42
8 x  4 =   32      8 x  5 =   40      8 x  6 =   48
9 x  4 =   36      9 x  5 =   45      9 x  6 =   54
10 x  4 =   40     10 x  5 =   50     10 x  6 =   60
11 x  4 =   44     11 x  5 =   55     11 x  6 =   66
12 x  4 =   48     12 x  5 =   60     12 x  6 =   72
```

Write a program which makes good use of procedures and parameters to print out a complete set of all the 12 multiplication tables.

5.3   Write a procedure to read in a given number of real numbers and return the maximum and minimum values found. Test the procedure with a small program.

5.4   Example 4.2 presents a program which checks whether a course code is valid according to a given format. Convert the checking part into a boolean function and verify that the program still works correctly.

5.5   Using the procedure *skipandcount* from section 5.2, write a program to solve problem 4.4, i.e. calculating the percentage of text within comments in a program. *Hint*: In order to allow for no close comment bracket, *skipandcount* will have to check for end-of-file and return a result as a boolean VAR parameter.

5.6   We want to write a proper student data checking program. Make use of example 4.2, problem 4.10, example 5.5 and problem 5.4 to check student numbers for checksums as well as checking course codes. Use *readinteger* to read the student numbers, and report any strange characters.

5.7   Other approximations for integrals are given by the

Midpoint Rule

$$\int_a^b \hat{f}(x)\, dx \;=\; \sum_{i=1}^{n} h\, f\left(\frac{x_i + x_{i-1}}{2} \right)$$

Trapezoidal Rule

$$\int_a^b f(x)\, dx \;=\; \frac{h}{2}\left(f(x_0) + 2 \sum_{i=1}^{n} f(x_i) + f(x_n) \right)$$

Implement these as functions and incorporate them in example 5.6. Calculate the charge across the capacitor using all three methods and compare their accuracy.

5.8   By reducing the size of the subinterval, h, Simpson's rule will give a more accurate result. Alter the program in example 5.6 so that it repeatedly reduces h until a result within a required tolerance is found. *Hint*: Will rounding error (as described in example 3.8) have an effect?

5.9   Double integrals can also be computed numerically. We simply apply the rule

(Simpson's or whatever) in a nested loop. The work W done by a force $F(x,y)$ in a two-dimensional dynamics problem is given by the integral

$$W = \int_0^1 \int_0^1 x^2 - 2xy + 3xy^2 + y^3 \, dy \, dx$$

Adapt the program in example 5.6 to handle double integrals, and compute W.

5.10   Write a procedure NewtonRaphson for finding the root of an equation. The procedure should have an interface similar to that for the secant procedure in section 5.5. *Hint*: The algorithm required is in section 4.6.

5.11   Use the secant method to find the strictly positive root of $x = 2 \sin(x)$.

5.12   Suppose we have a file of numerical readings, some of which are negative and some of which are positive. We wish to create two new files, one with all the positive numbers, and one with the negative numbers, and then go back and print both out from the program, with the positive numbers file first.

5.13   The Matriculation Board in Zanyland wishes to computerise the calculation of final examination results. Students take six or seven subjects and must pass five subjects with at least 40% in these. The final mark is computed as the average of the best six subject marks, and a symbol is given: A for over 80%, B for 70–79%, C for 60–69%, D for 50–59%, E for 40–49% and F for anything under 40%. The exams can be taken at higher or standard grade, and in order to pass overall, there must be at least three passes at higher grade and one of these must be a language or a science.

If a rule is broken, then the pass symbol is followed by one of the following symbols.

X   did not pass five
H   did not pass three at higher grade
L   did not pass a language or science at higher grade.

Subjects are identified by a single letter, with a sample list being:

A   Art
B   Biology
C   Chemistry
D   Divinity
E   English
F   French
G   Geography
H   History
L   Latin
M   Mathematics
P   Physics

In this list there are three languages and five sciences. Art, divinity and history do not qualify as either. A capital letter indicates higher grade and a small letter standard grade. Assume that the name is on a line by itself. Thus a typical set of input marks would be:

Jones A D
E 67   A 45   f 70   M 80   P 75   C 55   h 60

Specimen output might be:

Name	Subject marks						Excluded	%	Symbol
Jones A D	E 67	f 70	M 80	P 75	C 55	h 60	A 45	67.83	C

which indicates clearly which mark was not used.

Write a program which will process a file of marks as described here and output to another file a report of the results.

5.14   Construct a procedure that will print a box of variable dimensions, where the values for the width and depth are given as parameters. Incorporate this in a program which will read in widths and depths for four boxes in turn, and print them out, one underneath each other. Then improve the program in two ways:

- let the dimensions be read in in whole metres and suitably scaled so that they fit on a screen of 80 across and 20 down;

- add checks to reject any box that cannot be drawn nicely in an 80 by 20 space.

5.15   The temperature $T(x)$ in a moving rod, which loses energy to the environment at temperature T_∞ is given by the equation:

$$\frac{d^2T}{dx^2} - \frac{1}{10}\frac{dT}{dx} - 20\,(T - T_\infty) = 0$$

where x is the distance from a die out of which the material emerges at temperature T_0. The boundary conditions are as follows:

At $x = 0$: $T = T_0$
At $x = \infty$: $T = T_\infty$

Taking $T_0 = 600K$ and $T_\infty = 300K$ adapt the program for the shooting method to find $T(x)$. For the second boundary condition, start with a large value of x, say, 1m, to represent ∞, and then vary this value until the results are not significantly affected by the increase.

5.16   A popular method for solving an ordinary differential equation $dy/dx = f(x,y)$ is the classic 4th order Runge-Kutta method. The algorithm for getting y_{i+1} and x_{i+1} from y_i and x_i is:

$$\begin{aligned}
q_1 &= f(x_i, y_i) \\
q_2 &= f(x_i + h/2, y_i + h\,q_1/2) \\
q_3 &= f(x_i + h/2, y_i + h\,q_2/2) \\
q_4 &= f(x_i + h, y_i + h\,q_3)
\end{aligned}$$

$$\begin{aligned}
y_{i+1} &= y_i + h/6\,(q_1 + 2q_2 + 2q_3 + q_4) \\
x_{i+1} &= x_i + h
\end{aligned}$$

Using the same approach as described with the predictor-corrector method, write a procedure *RungeKutta* for solving a differential equation. Apply it to the problems that have already been solved by the predictor-corrector method (example 3.5, problem 3.17, problem 3.19). How do the two methods compare for accuracy?

6

Arrays and matrices

Vectors and matrices are mathematical constructs that are used all the time in engineering and science, and all computer languages have a way to represent them. In Pascal this is done by means of the type **array**, which is introduced in this chapter, together with subrange types, which form an integral companion to arrays. We can now look at four more numerical methods – the least squares fit, two methods for solving systems of linear equations and the solution to a linear boundary value problem involving higher order differential equations.

6.1 Types and subranges revisited

There are five predefined types in Pascal – integer, real, char, boolean and text. The first four are known as **scalar** types. The last type, text, is a **structured** type in that it is a collection of characters in a certain structure – a file. In the next few chapters we shall be looking at the seven ways Pascal provides for creating new types from existing values and types. The table below gives the full list of Pascal's predefined types and existing type mechanisms. The user-defined types are created by means of a type statement, which gives a name to a chosen new structure.

	Predefined types	**Mechanisms for user-defined types**
Scalar	integer real char boolean	subrange enumerated
Structured	text	record set array file pointer

Form of the type statement

A type statement associates a name with a type formation as follows:

Type declaration

```
TYPE
    identifier = type;
    identifier = type;
        . . .
    identifier = type;
```

Order of declaration sections is fixed.

Each of the six type mechanisms has its own form, as we shall see in the next few chapters. In any one declaration section, the keyword TYPE appears only once, but several types may be listed under it, as is done for the CONST and VAR sections. The order of the three sections is fixed as : CONST, TYPE, VAR, and they come before any procedure or function declarations.

Subrange types

The first type we shall look at enables constraints to be placed on the range of values available in three of the other scalar types – integer, char and enumerated. This is done by specifying precise lower and upper bound values. In earlier chapters, bounds were given for individual variables; now they will have official status and can be used over and over again by name. As before, any such bounds will used by the Pascal system to check that the use of variables conforms with their declaration. The form for defining a subrange type is

Subrange type

```
identifier = lower bound .. upper bound;
```

where the bounds must both be of the same type, known as the **base type**. Permissible base types are integer, char or enumerated. The bounds must be constant values or named constants: they may not be expressions. Examples of subrange types are:

The symbol .. must not have a space between the dots.

```
TYPE
    weights      = 0..200;      {kgs}
    temperatures = –50..60;     {degrees celsius}
    money        = 0..maxint;
    initials     = 'A'..'Z';
    digits       = '0'..'9';
    counters     = 1..10;
    marks        = 0..100;
```

Variables of these types can then be declared, as in

```
VAR
    myweight,
    yourweight   : weights;
    income, tax  : money;
    initial      : initials;
    i, j, counter : counters;
```

The importance of subrange types

Variables of subrange types can only take values in the specified range. If assignment of a value outside this range is attempted, the program will stop with a 'value out of range' error. For example,

```
initial := 'p';      and      counter := 0;
```

are erroneous.

It is possible to assign an expression of the base type to a subrange variable, and the Pascal system will then check at runtime that the values are compatible. For example, in

```
counter := counter + 1;
```

the Pascal system should always check that the range of *counter* is not exceeded.

'Value out of range' errors often indicate that the original algorithm is defective in some way. In other words, the declarations stated that the variables have certain properties, but the statements were not keeping the values within these. Without the proper use of subranges, many of these

Getting a 'value out of range' error is better than nothing!

errors go undetected or are very hard to find.

A subrange type inherits the operators and functions from its base type. However, care must be taken with the functions *succ* and *pred* so that the range is not exceeded.

Example 6.1 Chemical expiry dates

| Problem | A laboratory uses chemicals which, once mixed, last for ten days only. Given a date of mixing, calculate the expiry date.

| Solution | The basic calculation is to add the 10 days to the day of mixing, and to check whether this takes us into the next month. By making various simplifying assumptions, the solution breaks up into several parts. In the first place, we assume that all months have the same number of days, say 31, and we set this up as a named constant in the CONST section. Then we assume that the months will be known by number, not by name. (In Chapter 8 see how to deal with the names of months.) Given these assumptions, the calculation becomes

> Add 10 to the mixing day, taking modulo days in the month
> If the mixing day plus 10 is more than the days in the month
>   add 1 to the mixing month.

| Program | Because this seems such a simple solution, we go straight into the program, using suitable subranges for the day and month types, and a named constant for the expiry period.

```
PROGRAM ChemicalExpiry1 (input, output);
  CONST
    daysinmonth  = 31; {for now}
    period       = 10;  {days}
  TYPE
    days         = 1..daysinmonth;
    months       = 1..12;
  VAR
    mixday,
    expiryday    : days;
    mixmonth,
    expirymonth  : months;

  BEGIN
    writeln('****** Chemical expiry dates ******');
    write('Type in the day and month: ');
    readln(mixday, mixmonth);
    expiryday := (mixday + period) mod  daysinmonth;
      if mixday + period > daysinmonth then
        expirymonth := mixmonth + 1
      else
        expirymonth := mixmonth;
    writeln('Expires on ', expiryday:1, '/', expirymonth:1);
  END.
```

Testing	Running the program with a selection of values seems to work, until we try to issue a chemical on the 21st. The Pascal system stops the program and complains that a value is out of range on the line

expiryday := (mixday + period) mod daysinmonth;

The program does not work!

Studying this, we see that the computer *has* detected a mistake: $(21 + 10)$ mod 31 is 0, which is not a valid day. The correct answer is 31. Suppose we quickly change the statement to

expiryday := (mixday + period) mod daysinmonth − 1;

and rerun the program. The 21st is still incorrect and now the 22nd gives the wrong answer as well: 0 instead of 1.

From all this, we realise that this statement is really not correct, and that using *mod* is not going to work because it will sometimes return a zero, which we don't want. The answer is to treat the two cases of being within a month and going over a month boundary separately. The revised program becomes:

Program 2

Fix number 1.

```
PROGRAM ChemicalExpiry2 (input, output);
  CONST
    daysinmonth  = 31;  {for now}
    period       = 10;  {days}
  TYPE
    days         = 1..daysinmonth;
    months       = 1..12;
  VAR
    mixday,
    expiryday    : days;
    mixmonth,
    expirymonth  : months;

  BEGIN
    writeln ('****** Chemical expiry dates ******');
    write ('Type in the day and month: ');
    readln (mixday, mixmonth);
    if mixday + period > daysinmonth then begin
        expiryday := mixday + period − daysinmonth;
        expirymonth := mixmonth + 1;
      end else begin
        expiryday := mixday + period;
        expirymonth := mixmonth;
      end;
    writeln('Expires on ', expiryday:1, '/', expirymonth:1);
  END.
```

Testing 2	Testing proceeds as before, and all seems well until we try

Christmas Day – 25 and 12. The system stops again and says a value is out of range on the line

Caught again!

```
expirymonth := mixmonth + 1;
```

This makes sense, because there is no such month as 13! The use of a subrange has caused another silly error to be detected. To fix this one, another circular addition is needed, as in

```
if mixmonth = 12
  then expirymonth := 1
  else expirymonth := mixmonth + 1;
```

Solution 2   Turning now to the days in the month, we recall that a case-statement was used in Chapter 4 to set this up. This can be incorporated in the beginning of the program. We shall also need to know the year, in order to handle leap years. However, we shall not report on a change of year, since with the small period of ten days, the year should be obvious.

Getting it right at last.   **Program 3**

```
PROGRAM BetterChemicalExpiry (input, output);
  {Calculates the date 10 days hence}
  CONST
    daysinmonth  = 31;
    period       = 10;  {days}
  TYPE
    days    = 1..daysinmonth;
    months  = 1..12;
    years   = 1900 .. 2500;

  VAR
    mixday,
    expiryday     : days;
    mixmonth,
    expirymonth   : months;
    daysinmonth   : days;
    mixyear       : years;

  FUNCTION daysof(month : months, year : years): days;
  BEGIN
    CASE month of
      9, 4, 6, 11  : daysof := 30;
      1, 3, 5, 7, 8, 10, 12      : daysof := 31;
      2   : if (year mod 4 = 0)
                  and not ((year mod 100 = 0)
                  and not (year mod 400 = 0))
              then daysof := 29
              else daysof := 28;
    END; {CASE}
  END; {daysof}
```

```
BEGIN
  writeln ('****** Chemical expiry dates ******');
  write ('Type in the day, month and year: ');
  readln (mixday, mixmonth, mixyear);
  if mixday + period > daysof(mixmonth, mixyear) then begin
    expiryday := mixday + period - daysof(mixmonth, mixyear);
    if mixmonth = 12
      then expirymonth := 1
      else expirymonth := mixmonth + 1
  end else begin
    expiryday := mixday + period;
    expirymonth := mixmonth;
  end;
  writeln('Expires on ', expiryday:1, '/', expirymonth:1);
END.
```

Testing 3   For the record, a sample run would produce:

****** Chemical expiry dates ******
Type in the day and month: 22 2
In what year? 1990
Expires on 4/3

Reading into a subrange

Subrange values can be read and written with the same facilities as their base types. The one difficulty is that caution must be exercised in reading a value that might potentially not be in range. Some computer systems will detect such an attempt and will not allow the value to be stored, stopping the program with the familiar 'value out of range' error. This kind of reaction can actually be a disadvantage in that if a value is incorrect, we might wish to give the user another chance, rather than have the program stop.

There is a general method for reading integer subranges which makes use of the following procedure

```
PROCEDURE readrange (VAR x : integer;  min, max : integer);
  BEGIN
    REPEAT
      read(x);
      if (x < min) or (x > max)
      then writeln('NO!  Range is ',min:1,'..',max:1,' : ');
    UNTIL (x >= min) and (x <= max);
  END; {readrange}
```

The caller supplies an integer variable with the two relevant ranges and *readrange* will repeatedly read numbers until it receives one within the given range. The caller follows this up with an assignment into the actual variable that is to be read. So, for example, with the declarations

```
TYPE
  weights = 0..200;
  temperatures  = -50..60;  {degrees celsius}
VAR
  myweight      : weights;
  temperature   : temperatures;
  num : integer;

readrange (num, 0, 200);    myweight := num;
readrange (num, -50, 60);   temperature := num;
```

Similar procedures could be written for the other base types.

Macintosh
users take note. It is worth noting that some Pascal systems will not let you read into a subrange variable, on the grounds that it is unclear what the system should do if the data is outside the range. In these circumstances, the above procedure will be particularly useful.

Hints on using subranges

1. The **bounds** required for a subrange are not always as clear cut as the above examples for days or months might suggest. Numbers of children, amount of tax, even the year should have upper limits, but these have to be decided on the basis of what is sensible. A comment to the effect that the bounds are 'for now' or 'approximately' will be useful as documentation.

2. Notice that subranges cannot apply to **real numbers**; instead, we continue to use comments to define the range of reals to be used for each variable.

3. Subranges are always checked when a variable is **assigned to** or when an expression is passed as a **value parameter** to a procedure or function. Some Pascal systems check subranges when variables are read, but some do not. This point is taken up in the example on records at the end of the chapter.

4. The **shorthand** for subrange types with the range specified directly on a variable declaration as in

Avoid this.   VAR age : 0..140;

is not good practice. Often the same range is needed again, for example as a parameter type, and without a type name to unify the properties, mismatches can occur.

5. To distinguish between **type names** and variable names, a nice convention (used in this book and elsewhere) is to make types plural. Thus we have the variable *day* of type *days*, and so on.

6. Making use of **named constants** as subrange bounds is very helpful if the ranges have to be changed.

6.2 Arrays

Consider the following problem. We have several hundred scores between 0 and 20, and wish to analyse the frequency of occurrence of each score.

We could set up 21 counters, one for each score. As the scores are read in, the counter corresponding to the score would be incremented. It would be very unwieldy to have to invent 21 different names for the counters, and then have to use a big case-statement every time one of them needed updating. Clearly, we want to have a structure like this

Scores

```
        Scores
 1  ┌──────────┐
 2  ├──────────┤
 3  ├──────────┤
 4  ├──────────┤
 5  ├──────────┤
 6  ├──────────┤
 7  ├──────────┤
 8  ├──────────┤
 9  ├──────────┤
10  ├──────────┤
11  ├──────────┤
12  ├──────────┤
13  ├──────────┤
14  ├──────────┤
15  ├──────────┤
16  ├──────────┤
17  ├──────────┤
18  ├──────────┤
19  ├──────────┤
20  └──────────┘
```

with one name, *scores*, and refer to each of its 'boxes' by number. So the 9th box would be $scores_9$, and the ith box would be $scores_i$. Pascal provides for this facility with the array.

Form of an array type

An array is formally defined as a bounded collection of elements of the same type, each of which can be selected by indexing. The relevant form is:

Array type

> *identifier* = ARRAY [*bound type*] of *element type*;

where the bound type is a subrange of integer, char, boolean or enumerated type and the element type is any type not containing a file type. Examples of declarations are:

```
TYPE
  scores      = 0..20;
```

```
classrange    = 0..100;
frequencies   = ARRAY [scores] of classrange;
capitals      = 'A'..'Z';
occurrences   = ARRAY [capitals] of boolean;
daycounts     = ARRAY [daysofweek] of natural;
```

To use an array, we must first declare a variable of that type, then each element can be accessed by mentioning the name of the array variable and an index expression enclosed in square brackets. The index is sometimes known as the subscript. For example, we have

```
VAR
   counter    : frequencies;
   occurred   : occurrences;
   daycount   : daycounts;

FOR score := 0 to 20 do counter[score] := 0;
occurred['Z'] := false;
daycount[day] := daycount [day] + 1;
```

Array operators and functions

In Pascal, there are no operators that apply to whole arrays. However, assignment is possible. For example, given

```
TYPE
   range    = 1..100;
   vectors  = array[range] of real;
VAR a, b    : vectors;
```

we can say

Arrays can be
copied.

```
b := a;
```

Operations on the elements of an array depend on their type. Additional operators apply to strings, as described in section 8.2.

There are no functions that operate on whole arrays nor can they be read from or written to text files with the read and write statements. Arrays can however be transferred to files of the same array type as described in Chapter 10.

Example 6.2   Frequency counts

| Problem | The frequencies of several hundred game scores between 0 and 20 have to be calculated as well as the frequency of occurrence of the first letter of the surname of each player. |

| Example | Suppose we have a file with the data |

```
19  Jones A
10  Bighead P G
19  Smith T
```

then the result required would be that all the score frequencies would be zero, except

$$\text{scorecount}_{19} = 2 \qquad \text{scorecount}_{10} = 1$$

and all the letter frequencies would be zero except those for B, J and S which would be 1.

| Solution | We need to set up two arrays and as each score is read, the appropriate element of the array is incremented. Similarly for the letters. The algorithm is so simple that we go straight on to the program.

| Program |

```
PROGRAM CountingFrequencies (input, output, inp);
CONST
   maxscore     = 20;
   classlimit   = 250;

TYPE
   scores       = 0..maxscore;
   class        = 0..classlimit;
   capitals     = 'A'..'Z';
   frequencies  = ARRAY [scores] of class;
   initials     = ARRAY [capitals] of class;

VAR
   scorecount   : frequencies;
   initialcount : initials;
   score   : scores;
   ch           : char;
   inp          : text;

BEGIN
   writeln('****** Frequency counting ******');
   writeln('Data must be in freq.data');
   reset(inp,'freq.data');

   {Initialise the arrays}
   FOR score := 0 to maxscore do scorecount[score] := 0;        Remember to
   FOR ch := 'A' to 'Z' do initialcount[ch] := 0;               initialise!

   {Count the scores and initials}
   WHILE not eof(inp) do begin
      read(inp, score);
      scorecount [score] := scorecount [score] + 1;
      repeat read(inp, ch) until ch <> ' ';
      initialcount[ch] := initialcount[ch] + 1;
   END;
```

```
                    {Print the frequencies}
                    writeln('Table of Score Frequencies');
                    for score := 0 to maxscore do
                      writeln(score,scorecount[score]:6);
                    writeln;
                    writeln('Table of Initial Frequencies');
                    for ch := 'A' to 'Z' do
                      writeln(ch,initialcount[ch]:6);
                  END.
```

This program has been written without procedures or functions. Clearly, it could have been formally broken up and parameter interfaces created. However, in this case, we deemed it simpler to present the program as one unit, so that the idea of arrays can be understood on its own. In later examples, we shall see how arrays can be passed as parameters and procedures written which operate on arrays.

A note on security

Pascal is quite firm about only allowing access to array elements that actually exist. Every time an array is accessed, the index supplied is checked against the bounds given in the type definition. If the index is out of bounds, an error message such as 'Invalid subscript' is given and the program halts.

These checks are done at compile time whenever possible. Thus the following may all result in compilation errors:

```
    scorecount[25]
    initialcount['a']
    initialcount['*']
```

Always wear your 'seat belt'. However, some Pascal systems allow this checking to be switched off, and may even have it switched off by default. The idea is to make the program run faster by omitting checks. This is false economy: during development, most programs contain errors, and any checks the system can make to enable those errors to be detected as soon as possible will probably reduce the number of times the program needs to be compiled and tested. Thus it is worthwhile turning the checks on for every program. As an example, for the Turbo Pascal system, the compiler directive {$R+} at the start of the program will achieve the desired effect.

Example 6.3   Scalar product of two vectors

Problem   One of the more common operations on vectors is finding the scalar product. We would like to develop a self-contained procedure to do this for vectors of various lengths.

Solution   The scalar product is defined as $\sum\limits_{i=1}^{n} a_i b_i$, and involves a straightforward looping algorithm. However, we consider how to accommodate vectors of different lengths in different runs of the program. That is, in run 1 we may want to find

$$(1, 2) . (0, 3)$$

and in run 2

$$(1, 2, 2, 3, 4, 5) . (7.5, 2, 3.1, 4, 5, 5).$$

The problem is that an array must be defined with a fixed number of components, so that the compiler may allocate a definite region of storage for the array. However, although the number of components is fixed, we do not have to use them all. We decide on some maximum and then specify the precise size within that maximum. This size is passed to the procedure and used by it as its upper bound.

Algorithm   The declarations related to defining an array with the flexibility required are:

```
CONST
  nmax = 100;
TYPE
  range = 1 .. nmax
  vector = array [range] of real;
VAR
  a, b : vector;
  n : range;
```

So the arrays *a and* b will run from 1 to n, where $n \leq nmax$. The data will consist of n, an integer of type *range*; then n real numbers for a_i, then another n real numbers for b_i, $(i = 1$ to $n)$. Many array programs involve large amounts of data, which are usually read from a file, and the procedure *Getdata* reads the data from a file 'scalar.data'.

Program

```
PROGRAM ScalarProduct (input, output);
  CONST
    nmax = 100; {Maximum vector size handled}
  TYPE
    range = 1..nmax;
    vector = ARRAY[range] of real;
  VAR
    a,b : vector;
    n : range;
```

```
FUNCTION product (n: range; a, b : vector) : real;
  VAR
    i : range;
    sum : real;
  BEGIN
    sum := 0.0;
    FOR i := 1 to n do
      sum := sum + a[i] * b[i];
    product := sum;
  END; {product}

PROCEDURE initialise;
  BEGIN
    writeln('********Vector Scalar Product********');
    writeln;
    writeln('Scalar product of 2 vectors  a, b of dimension n');
    writeln('with n <= 100 at present; the data n, a, b ');
    writeln('are read from a file: scalar.data');
    writeln;
  END; {initialise}

PROCEDURE getdata(VAR a,b : vector; VAR n: range);
  VAR f : text;
    i,j : range;
  BEGIN
    reset(f,'scalar.data');
    read(f,n);
    FOR i := 1 to n do read(f,a[i]);
    FOR i := 1 to n do read(f,b[i]);
  END; {getdata}

BEGIN
  initialise;
  getdata(a,b,n);
  writeln('The scalar product is: ',product(n,a,b):10:6);
END.
```

Testing	Given the data in the file:

```
5
3.0 4.5 6.0 7.5 9.0
2.0 2.0 2.0 2.0 10.0
```

Then the program will produce

**********Vector Scalar Product*********

Scalar product of 2 vectors a, b of dimension n
with n <= 20 at present; the data n, a, b
are read from a file: scalar.data
The scalar product is 132.000000

Example 6.4   The lifetime of light bulbs

Problem   A factory manufactures light bulbs, and from the production line, bulbs are chosen at random to see how long they last. For quality control purposes, there must be regular reports on the mean lifetime and standard deviation in hours.

Solution   If we have a set of measurements x_i we can analyse them to find the mean $\bar{x}$ which gives the average measurement, and the standard deviation s, which shows the amount by which measurements are likely to differ from the mean. In other words, the standard deviation indicates the spread of the measurements.

The mean of a set of measurements x_i ($i = 1, n$) is defined to be

$$\bar{x} = \frac{\sum_{i=1}^{n} x_i}{n}$$

and the formula for the standard deviation is:

$$s = \sqrt{\frac{\sum_{i=1}^{n} (x_i - \bar{x})^2}{n - 1}}$$

We can allow for expected errors and intrinsic randomness by saying that the result of a set of measurements will be within a certain standard deviation. In many cases we can say that the true result is in the range $\bar{x} \pm 2s$, i.e. the mean plus or minus twice the standard deviation.

Algorithm   We have already written a program to calculate the mean (example 3.3) because this can be done without using the array data structure. Because the formula for the standard deviation uses the mean, we have to calculate it after the mean has been decided. Thus we store the values in an array, and process them from there in a second stage.

As before, we declare a vector a_i, with $i = 1$ to *nmax*. In a run of the program we first ask the size of the data set n, then read n real numbers into a_i ($i = 1$ to n). Because the formula for s includes division by $n - 1$, we check whether $n = 1$, to prevent a runtime error. *Programming defensively.*

We also choose to set up the two formulae as functions, making them self-contained, and therefore able to be re-used in other programs. In the functions, the vector has its usual name of *a*; but in the main program we use a name more specific to the problem, i.e. *hourreadings*.

Program

```
PROGRAM LightBulbAnalysis (input,output);
CONST
```

```
                        nmax = 100; {Maximum vector size handled}
                      TYPE
                        range = 1..nmax;
                        vector = ARRAY[range] of real;
                      VAR
                        hourreadings : vector;
                        num: range;
                        ave : real;

                      PROCEDURE initialise;
                        VAR
                          i : range;
                        BEGIN
                          writeln('********Light Bulb Analysis********');
                          writeln;
                          writeln('Statistical analysis of the lifetime of light bulbs');
                          writeln('with  no. of readings <= 100 at present.');
                          writeln;
                          write('How many readings?  n =');
                          readln(n);
                          writeln('Enter the ', n:1, '  readings followed by return:');
                        END; {initialise}

                      PROCEDURE Getdata (var a : vector; n : range);
                        VAR i : range;
                        BEGIN
                          FOR i := 1 to n do
                            read(a[i]);
                          readln;
                        END; {Getdata}

                      FUNCTION mean (a : vector; n : range) : real;
                        VAR i : range;
                          sum : real;
                        BEGIN
                          sum := 0.0;
                          FOR i := 1 to n do
                            sum := sum + a[i];
                          mean := sum / n;
                        END; {Mean}

                      FUNCTION sigma (a:vector; n: range; m : real) : real;
                        VAR sum : real;
                          i : range;
                        BEGIN
                          sum := 0.0;
                          FOR i := 1 to n do
                            sum := sum + sqr(m − a[i]);
                          sigma := sqrt(sum / (n − 1));
                        END;  {sigma}

                      BEGIN
                        initialise;
                        Getdata(hourreadings, num);
                        IF num = 1 then
```

```
      writeln('Mean = ',hourreadings[1]:10:6,
           ' Standard deviation not defined for n = 1')
   else begin
     ave := mean(hourreadings, num);
     writeln('Mean = ', round(ave):1, ' hours ');
     writeln('Standard deviation = ',
           round(sigma(hourreadings, num, ave):1,' hours ');
   END; {IF}
   END.
```

Testing

********Light Bulb Analysis*********

**Statistical analysis of the lifetime of light bulbs
with no. of readings <= 100 at present.**

**How many readings? n = 5
Enter the 5 readings followed by return:**
1105   909   1043   989   961
**Mean = 1001 hours
Standard deviation = 75 hours**

6.3 Matrices

Arrays are very useful for storing tables of information, such as data in rows and columns, or matrices. Since Pascal permits array elements to be of any type, including arrays themselves, arrays of multiple dimensions can be built up. For a typical matrix such as

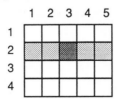

the declarations might be

```
CONST
   rowmax      = 4;
   columnmax   = 5;

TYPE
   rowrange     = 1..rowmax;
   columnrange  = 1..columnmax;
   rows         = array [columnrange] of real;
   matrices     = array [rowrange] of rows;
```

```
VAR
  matrix              : matrices;
  r,i,j               : rowrange;
  c                   : columnrange;
```

Then a single row of the matrix is represented by

```
matrix[r]
```

A row of a matrix
is a vector.

Each element of the row can also be selected, as in

```
matrix [r] [c]
```

or

```
matrix [r, c]
```

The two forms are equivalent, although the second one is more natural when a matrix is defined as a single type, without defining the row type first. This can be achieved by declarations such as

```
TYPE
  rectangles  = array [rowrange, columnrange] of real;
```

The difference between the two forms is that an array declared with subscripts listed in one declaration, like *rectangles*, cannot then be broken up into rows that can be manipulated independently. With the two-stage declaration, as for *matrices*, a row variable could be defined such as

```
VAR
  row : rows;
```

and rows from the matrix assigned directly to it. Thus to swap two rows of the matrix, we could say:

```
row := matrix[i];
matrix[i] := matrix[j];
matrix[j] := row;
```

As well as matrices, arrays with 2, 3 or more dimesions can be declared. However, it is possible that in many of these case, the rich data structuring facilities of Pascal will be more appropriate, as discussed in Chapter 8.

Example 6.5 Rainfall statistics

Problem The Zanyland Weather Department has kept statistics on monthly rainfall figures for the past 20 years. Now they would like to calculate

- the average rainfall for each month
- the standard deviation for each month.

| **Solution** | The table of rainfall figures that is provided by a clerk will look something like this: |

	Jan Feb Mar Apr May Jun Jul Aug Sep Oct Nov Dec
1971	
1972	
...	Each entry is a real number for the rainfall
1988	
1989	
1990	

The data can be read in nicely by drawing such a table on the screen and letting the user type in each value in turn. As the values are read in, they are stored in a matrix which is indexed by both the months and the years. Since the rainfall for a month seems to be the crucial figure, the matrix should be structured so that a whole column can be moved around at once. To do this, we make months the first subscript, and years the second, i.e.

```
CONST

TYPE
    months       = 1 ..12;
    years        = 1 ..20;
    rainfalls    = real;  {0.0..900.0, in millimetres}
    monthlyrains = array [years] of rainfalls;
    raintables   = array [months] of monthlyrains;

VAR
    raintable : raintables;
```

Once the figures are safely in the matrix, procedures can be designed to perform the required calculations. Each will make use of the matrix and be passed either a column of one month's rainfall figures or an index to such a column. For the actual processing, we shall be able to make use of the mean and standard deviation procedures defined in example 6.4.

| **Algorithm** | We already have the mean and standard deviation functions defined as |

```
FUNCTION mean (a : vector;  n : range)  : real;

FUNCTION sigma (a : vector;  n: range; m : real) : real;
```

We shall have to rename the types slightly to conform to the specific ones for this problem, and might as well rename the functions too. Thus we could have

FUNCTION monthlyaverage (rain : monthlyrains; n : years)
: rainfalls;

Alternatively, the declaration could be

FUNCTION monthlyaverage (m : months; n : years) : rainfalls;

where the parameter indicates an index into the rain table. If the index alone is sent as a parameter, then the function has to access the rainfall table as a global variable, which affects its self-containedness, and it has to perform double indexing to get to each element. If the whole column is sent, there is an initial overhead in copying the values into the function, but accessing the elements is by single indexing, and the self-containedness of the function is preserved. On balance, the first is a better choice.

If the value calculated by *monthlyaverage* is assigned to a variable *A* it can be passed to the next function which uses it to calculate the standard deviation. The declaration for this function is therefore:

FUNCTION monthlystddev (rain : monthlyrains;
mean : rainfalls) : rainfalls;

| Program | Much of the program is repetition of what has been in previous programs, especially the reading in and averaging. So here we just give the main program, together with any declarations not made so far.

```
VAR
  m   : months;

BEGIN
  ('****** Rainfall statistics ******');
  readinthedata;
  writeln('Month      Average      Std Deviation');
  FOR  m := 1 to 12 do begin
    a := monthlyaverage(raintable[m]);
    writeln(m:8, a:8:4, monthlystddev(raintable[m],a):6:4);
  END;
END.
```

6.4 Numerical methods using arrays

The three methods that follow are classics in the numerical methods repertoire and make good use of arrays and matrices in their algorithms.

Method 8   Least squares fit

| Rationale | Suppose that we measure a value of *y* for various different values of *x*, and that we know from theory, that the relationship

between y and x is a straight line: $y = a + bx$. A simple example of this would be the extension of a spring for various different loads. Because of experimental error, the measured points do not lie exactly on a straight line, as shown in the figure:

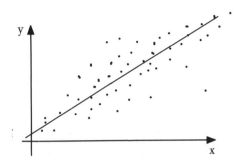

Of course, knowing that there is a straight line in the data, we could move a ruler around until we get a good fit to the eye, but we would like to do this in a precise way.

| Methods | Fitting lines – or in general, curves – to data is an important area of numerical methods. We shall look at the simplest form of linear curve fitting – known as linear regression. From this, the reader can move on to interpolating, that is, finding approximate fits, and will encounter methods such as Lagrange interpolation, Newton's divided difference interpolation, and interpolating with cubic splines.

| Theory | The notion of 'best fit' is open to interpretation, but the one usually used is the sense of minimising the sum of the squares of the errors. That is, we want to find a, b so as to minimise

$$s = \sum_{i=1}^{n}(y_i - (a + bx_i))^2$$

where the datapoints are (x_i, y_i) ($i = 1$ to n). Following this through we find that the solution reduces to two simultaneous equations in a and b, which are solved to give

$$a = (\sum x_i^2 \sum y_i - \sum x_i y_i \sum x_i)/D$$

$$b = (n \sum x_i y_i - \sum x_i \sum y_i)/D$$

where

$$D = n(\sum x_i^2) - (\sum x_i)^2$$

Although we shall not discuss it here, note that the above ideas can easily be extended to fitting data to curves other than straight lines.

| Algorithm | The above formulae use single and double summations repeatedly. We therefore define two functions for these, and incorporate them inside the function for the least squares fit. The function must return two real values, a and b, based on three input values – the vectors x and y and the length of them, n.

| Procedure |

```
PROCEDURE LeastSquares (var a, b : real; x, y : vector; n : range);
{Calculates a and b such that y = a + bx}

VAR D : real;

FUNCTION sumone (u : vector; n : range) : real;
VAR
  i : range;
  sofar : real;
BEGIN
  sofar := 0.0;
  FOR i := 1 to n do sofar := sofar + u[i];
  sumone := sofar;
END; {sumone}

FUNCTION sumtwo (u, v : vector; n : range) : real;
VAR
  i : range;
  sofar : real;
BEGIN
  sofar := 0.0;
  FOR i := 1 to n do sofar:=sofar + u[i] * v[i];
  sumtwo := sofar;
END; {sumtwo}

BEGIN
  D := (n * sumtwo(x, x, n) – sqr(sumone(x, n)));
  a := (sumtwo(x, x, n) * sumone(y, n) –
        sumtwo(x, y, n) * sumone(x, n))/D;
  b := (n * sumtwo(x, y, n) – sumone(x, n) * sumone(y, n))/D;
END; {LeastSquares}
```

Example 6.6   Hooke's Law

Robert Hooke
(1635–1703)

| Problem | Hooke's Law states that $F = k(x - L)$ where L is the natural length of a spring and k is the spring coefficient. The length x is measured for various different applied forces F, and we wish to calculate the best fit to the data for L and k.

Furthermore, we would like to plot the points (x, F) and the resulting line that is obtained.

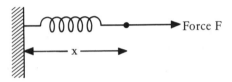

Solution   To obtain L and k, we read in the data points x_i and F_i for $i=1$ to n, and use the least squares function developed above.

The plotting can be done in two ways. Firstly, if a cursor-positioning procedure is available, such as *gotoxy*, then we can simply plot the (x, F) points as described in section 4.5. Secondly, we could set up a character matrix, and place an asterisk in each position corresponding to a point read in. Similarly, the line could be evaluated and the points inserted with, say, a dot. Then the whole of the matrix can be printed out, row by row. This part of the problem will not be taken further, being left as an exercise for the reader.

Algorithm   To use the function, y, a and b become F, $-kL$ and k.

Program

```
PROGRAM HookesLaw (input,output);
  CONST
    nmax    = 100; {Maximum data size handled}
  TYPE
    range   = 0..nmax;
    vector  = ARRAY[range] of real;
  VAR
    x,F   : vector;
    n : range;
    k, r   : real;

  PROCEDURE initialise;

  BEGIN
    writeln('********Least Squares Data Fitting*********');
    writeln('******** Hooke''s Law  ********');
    writeln;
     writeln('Given a set of data xi and Fi we find L and k');
     writeln('to give the best straight line fit  in F = k(x − L)');
    writeln;
    n := 0;
    writeln('Enter the data, with each  x  F  pair on a new line:');
    WHILE not eof and (n < nmax) do begin
      n := n + 1;
      readln(x[n],F[n]);
      END;
    {The loop will stop if the arrays fill up}
    writeln('That''s the data, thank you');
    writeln;
```

```
END; {initialise}

PROCEDURE LeastSquares (var a, b : real; x, y : vector; n : range);
{ as defined before}
END; {LeastSquares}

BEGIN
  initialise;
  LeastSquares (r, k, x, F, n);
  writeln('Solution is:  L = ', −r / k:1:6,' and k  = ', k:1:6);
END.
```

Testing   For a simple test, we choose a straight line, $F = 1 + x$, and then construct data for which the line would be the best fit. We try

$$(0, 1), \ (1, 1), \ (1, 3), \ (2, 3)$$

and as expected the program returns $L = -1$ and $k = 1$.

> ********Least Squares Data Fitting********
> ******** Hooke's Law ********
>
> Given a set of data xi and Fi we find L and k
> to give the best straight line fit in F = k(x − L)
>
> Enter the data, with each x F pair on a new line:
> 0 1
> 1 1
> 1 3
> 2 3
> That's the data, thank you
> Solution is: L = −1.000000 and k = 1.000000

Method 9   Solving linear equations with SOR

Rationale   Matrix calculations are very common in science and engineering applications. Usually we want to solve for x in

$$A x = b$$

where A is an $n \times n$ matrix, and b and x are vectors of dimension n. This problem is the same as that of solving a system of n linear equations, for example, if $n = 3$, we have:

$$A_{11} x_1 + A_{12} x_2 + A_{13} x_3 = b_1$$
$$A_{21} x_1 + A_{22} x_2 + A_{23} x_3 = b_2$$
$$A_{31} x_1 + A_{32} x_2 + A_{33} x_3 = b_3$$

Methods   There are two classes of methods for solving this problem: iterative methods, and direct methods, both of which will be discussed in this section.

We have already looked at iterative methods in the solution of one equation – Newton's method (section 4.5) and the secant method (section 5.6). These methods work by making an estimate of the solution and then successively providing a better estimate of the solution. We continue the process until the difference between two successive solution estimates is less than some tolerance.

This raises a question: what does 'less than some tolerance' mean when the solution is an n-dimensional vector? Of course there is not a unique answer, but for the purposes of this book we will use what is known as the L-infinity norm. For an n-dimensional vector x the norm is defined:

$$\|x\| = max|x_i|, \text{ where } i = 1 \text{ to } n$$

The L-infinity norm.

i.e. it is the value of the largest component in the vector. For example, if a convergence criterion $\|error\| <= 10^{-6}$ is satisfied then for every component of the vector $|xnew_i - xold_i| <= 10^{-6}$.

There are many different iterative matrix-solving algorithms. We give here a program for one of the more popular methods: SOR, which stands for Successive Over Relaxation.

| Theory | If we have an estimate $xold_i$ for the solution, then a better estimate is given by

$$x_i = (1 - \omega)\, xold_i + \omega\, \frac{\left(-(\sum_{j=1}^{i-1} a_{ij}x_j) - (\sum_{j=i+1}^{n} a_{ij}xold_j) + b_j \right)}{a_{ii}}$$

where ω is a parameter which depends on the matrix A. Unfortunately the relationship is not simple, and one can write down a value only in certain special cases. As a general guide, $1 < \omega < 2$, and usually in the middle of this range.

The right hand side involves x_i, but provided we calculate the components of x_i in order $x_1, x_2, \dots x_n$, we need only those components which have already been calculated. Then we set $xold_i = x_i$, and repeat the process.

As with all iterative methods, we have to decide when to stop. This will be when the norm of the difference between x and $xold$ is less than some tolerance. Here, we use the L-infinity norm and the tolerance required will depend very much on the physical properties that the equations represent. For example, if the results are expected to be real numbers, then a tolerance of 10^{-6} would be usual. But if the values are expected to be whole numbers, then a tolerance of 0.01 would be used. The program below adapts its output format to reflect this diversity of values.

| Algorithm | We express the algorithm for the method more briefly than usual, relying on the Pascal that follows to show the translation of the formulae.

Input (from screen): ω, tolerance, maximum number of iterations

Input (from file):   matrix A, vector b, solution estimate *xold*, vector size n

Repeat: Calculate x_i until either (a) maximum number of iterations reached, or (b) norm $(x - xold)$ < tolerance

Output: Case (a) 'Convergence not achieved'
Case (b) Solution x

Procedure We start off by defining the function for the L-infinity norm. This could be defined inside the SOR solver, but it seems a useful enough function to stand on its own.

```
FUNCTION normLinfinity(n:range; x,y: vector) : real;
  VAR
    highest: real;
    i : range;
  BEGIN
    highest := abs(x[1] – y[1]);
    FOR i := 2 to n do
      IF abs(x[i] – y[i]) > highest THEN highest := abs(x[i] – y[i]);
    normLinfinity := highest;
  END;


PROCEDURE SORsolver (VAR xold : vector;
                         a : matrix;
                         b : vector;
                         n : range;
                         maxiterations : integer;
                         omega, tolerance : real;
                         VAR convergence : boolean;
                         VAR iterations : integer);
  VAR
    i,j : range;
    sumax,sumaxold : real;
    x : vector;
  BEGIN
    convergence := false;
    iterations := 0;
    REPEAT
      FOR i := 1 to n do begin
        sumax := 0;
        sumaxold := 0;
        FOR j := 1 to i – 1 do sumax := sumax + a[i,j] * x[j];
        FOR j := i + 1 to n do sumaxold := sumaxold + a[i,j] * xold[j];
        x[i] := (1 – omega) * xold[i] –
                  omega * (sumax + sumaxold – b[i])/a[i,i];
      END;
      iterations := iterations + 1;
      IF (normLinfinity(n, x, xold) < tolerance)
      THEN convergence := true;
```

```
            FOR j := 1 to n do xold[j] := x[j];
         UNTIL convergence or (iterations = maxiterations);
      END; {SORsolver}
```

Example 6.7 Balancing manufacturing output

Problem   A factory manufactures six basic components and uses some of these in the manufacture of other items. The balance between the output and the production rate is given by the equations

$$4\,x_1 + x_3 + x_6 = 41$$
$$12\,x_2 + 4\,x_4 + 5\,x_5 = 109$$
$$x_1 + 10\,x_3 = 38$$
$$x_1 + 3\,x_4 + x_6 = 17$$
$$2\,x_2 + 5\,x_5 + 2\,x_6 = 67$$
$$2\,x_2 + 2\,x_3 + 8\,x_6 = 64$$

Solve this set of equations to establish the amount of each basic component that needs to be produced.

Solution   We shall use the SOR method. We set up the coefficients of the equations, including the zeros, in a 6×6 matrix. We also need an initial estimate for each x and a value for ω. Since the answers will be integers, the tolerance can be set low.

Program   The program has two interesting aspects. The first is that we echo the input data: this is important for the understanding of the results, and is very easily done. The second is that the output format is varied according to the tolerance required. This is done by finding the absolute value of the characteristic of the logarithm to the base ten, and adding one. This gives the number of decimal digits in the tolerance, and we use this in the field width for output.

```
      PROGRAM SORMatrixSolver(input, output);
      CONST
         nmax = 20; {Maximum array size handled}
      TYPE
         range = 0..nmax;
         matrix = ARRAY[range,range] of real;
         vector = ARRAY[range] of real;
      VAR
         a                 : matrix;
         b, x              : vector;
         omega, tolerance  : real;
         i, j, n           : range;
         kmax, k           : integer;
         finished          : boolean;

      PROCEDURE initialise;
```

```
                    BEGIN
                      writeln('******** Balancing manufacturing output*********');
                      writeln('using the SOR matrix solver');
                      writeln;
                      writeln('Solution of n by n matrix equation A x = b ;');
                      writeln('with n <= 20 at present.');
                      write('The data n, A, b, x (initial estimate)');
                      writeln('must be available in a file: sor.data');
                      writeln;
                      write('SOR parameter omega? :');
                      readln(omega);
                      write('maximum number of iterations? :');
                      readln(kmax);
                      write('Convergence criterion? Tolerance :');
                      readln(tolerance);
                      writeln;
                    END; {initialise}


  PROCEDURE getdata(VAR a : matrix;
                              VAR b, x : vector; VAR n: range);
    VAR
      f : text;
      i, j : range;
    BEGIN
      reset(f,'sor.data');
      read(f,n);
      FOR i := 1 to n do
        FOR j := 1 to n do read(f, a[i,j]);
      FOR i := 1 to n do read(f, b[i]);
      FOR i := 1 to n do read(f, x[i]);
    END; {getdata}


  PROCEDURE echodata(a : matrix;   b : vector; n : range);
    VAR i, j : range;
    BEGIN
      writeln('Equations are:');
      for i := 1 to n do begin
        for j := 1 to n do begin
          write(a[i,j]:3:0,' x',j:1);
          if j < n then write (' +');
        end;
        writeln(' = ',b[i]:3:0);
      end;
      writeln;
    END; {echodata}


  FUNCTION accuracy(x : real) : integer;
  {Works out how many digits of accuracy are being asked for}
  {using the characteristic of the log to the base 10}
    BEGIN
    accuracy := abs(trunc(ln(x) / ln(10))) + 1;
    END; {accuracy}


  FUNCTION normLinfinity(n:range; x,y: vector) : real;
  {As defined above}
```

```
END;

PROCEDURE SORsolver (VAR xold : vector;
                          a : matrix;
                          b : vector;
                          n : range;
                          maxiterations : integer;
                          omega, tolerance : real;
                          VAR convergence : boolean;
                          VAR iterations : integer);
  {as above}
  END; {SORsolver}

BEGIN
  initialise;
  getdata (a,b,x,n);
  echodata (a,b,n);
  SORsolver (x,a,b,n,kmax,omega,tolerance,finished,k);
  IF finished THEN begin
    writeln('Solution obtained after ',k:2,' iterations');
    FOR i := 1 to n do writeln('x[',i:2,'] = ',
                                  x[i]:1:accuracy(tolerance));
  END ELSE
    writeln('Algorithm did not converge in iterations specified');
END.
```

Testing

```
******** Balancing manufacturing output *********
using the SOR matrix solver

Solution of n by n matrix equation A x = b ;
with n <= 20 at present.
The data n, A, b, x0 (initial estimate)
must be available in a file: sor.data

SOR parameter omega? :1.1
maximum number of iterations? : 100
Convergence criterion? Tolerance : 10E-3
Equations are:
  4 x1 +  0 x2 +  1 x3 +  0 x4 +  0 x5 +  1 x6 =  41
  0 x1 + 12 x2 +  0 x3 +  4 x4 +  5 x5 +  0 x6 = 109
  1 x1 +  0 x2 + 10 x3 +  0 x4 +  0 x5 +  0 x6 =  38
  1 x1 +  0 x2 +  0 x3 +  3 x4 +  0 x5 +  1 x6 =  17
  0 x1 +  2 x2 +  0 x3 +  0 x4 +  5 x5 +  2 x6 =  67
  0 x1 +  2 x2 +  2 x3 +  0 x4 +  0 x5 +  8 x6 =  64

Solution obtained after 10 iterations
x[ 1] = 8.000
x[ 2] = 5.000
x[ 3] = 3.000
x[ 4] = 1.000
x[ 5] = 9.000
x[ 6] = 6.000
```

Discussion If we look at the equation for calculating the x_i, we see that it involves a_{ii} as a denominator. In order to avoid division by zero, a_{ii} must be non-zero for all $i = 1$ to n. If any $a_{ii} = 0$, we can often reorder the equations so as to make all the a_{ii} non-zero. If reordering is not possible then the matrix is singular and there is in any case no unique solution for x. There is some discussion of reordering methods in the next example.

More about the SOR method in the problems.

The SOR method has another restriction, which is discussed in problem 6.9 at the end of the chapter.

Method 10   Gaussian elimination

Rationale A direct method solves $Ax = b$ to give a solution for x that is exact apart from rounding errors. However, direct methods are computationally more intensive than iterative methods and are impractical for solving large systems of equations. (e.g. $n > 100$).

Carl Freidrich Gauss (1777–1855)

Formally, one can write down a solution of $Ax = b$ in terms of determinants. However, in practice this is never done because the computation is too long. The most commonly used method is some form of Gaussian elimination. It is interesting that this method has remained virtually unchanged for over 150 years.

Theory The solution strategy is to manipulate the equations so as to end up with a matrix A in upper triangular form, i.e.

$$
A = \begin{pmatrix}
a_{11} & a_{12} & \cdots & a_{1n} \\
0 & a_{22} & \cdots & a_{2n} \\
0 & & & \\
& & & \\
0 & & 0 & a_{nn}
\end{pmatrix}
$$

Then the solution of the system $Ax = b$ follows very easily by back-substitution. That is, we have immediately $x_n = b_n/a_{nn}$. Then the $n-1$th equation is

$$a_{n-1,n-1}\,x_{n-1} + a_{n-1,n}\,x_n = b_{n-1}$$

which is solved to give

$$x_{n-1} = (-a_{n-1,n}x_n + b_{n-1}) \,/\, (a_{n-1,n-1})$$

Thus we solve the x_i in order $x_n, x_{n-1} \ldots x_1$ using the formula

$$x_i = \frac{b_i - \sum\limits_{j=i+1}^{n} x_j\, a_{ij}}{a_{ij}}$$

The matrix A is changed to upper triangular form by a series of linear operations on the equations, in the same way as if the system were to be solved by hand. The first step is to arrange zeros everywhere in the column under a_{11}; then using only equations 2 to n we manipulate them to get zeros in the column under a_{22}, and so on.

The elements of A on the diagonal, i.e. a_{ii}, are called the pivot elements, and the algorithm involves division by the pivot elements. Thus the procedure will fail if any $a_{ii} = 0$, and, further, the accuracy is improved if a_{ii} is as large as possible. The equations under consideration at a given stage in the algorithm are reordered to achieve this. If this is not possible then a whole row of the matrix consists of zeros, and it is therefore singular and does not have a unique solution.

| Algorithm | We simply state the algorithm – derivations are given in many texts on numerical methods. Technically the version used is called Gaussian elimination with partial pivoting.

The algorithm is shown in the diagram below. Note that the right hand side vector b is incorporated into the matrix A, so that A is not a square matrix but is of size $nmax + 1$ by $nmax$. The vector b_i is $a_{i,n+1}$ for $i = 1$ to n.

Note also that the reordering of equations is achieved implicitly by means of a vector, row, whose elements are in the range 1 to $nmax$; so each component of row is an integer. Initially $row_j = j$ for $j = 1$ to n and elements of the matrix A are referred to as $a_{row_{j,i}}$. If it is necessary to swap two rows of A we simply interchange the values of two elements of row.

Gaussian elimination with pivoting

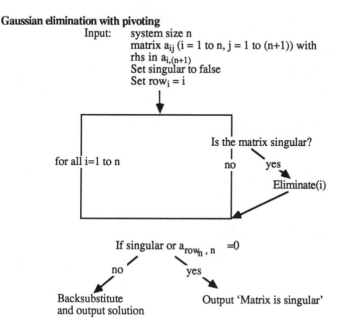

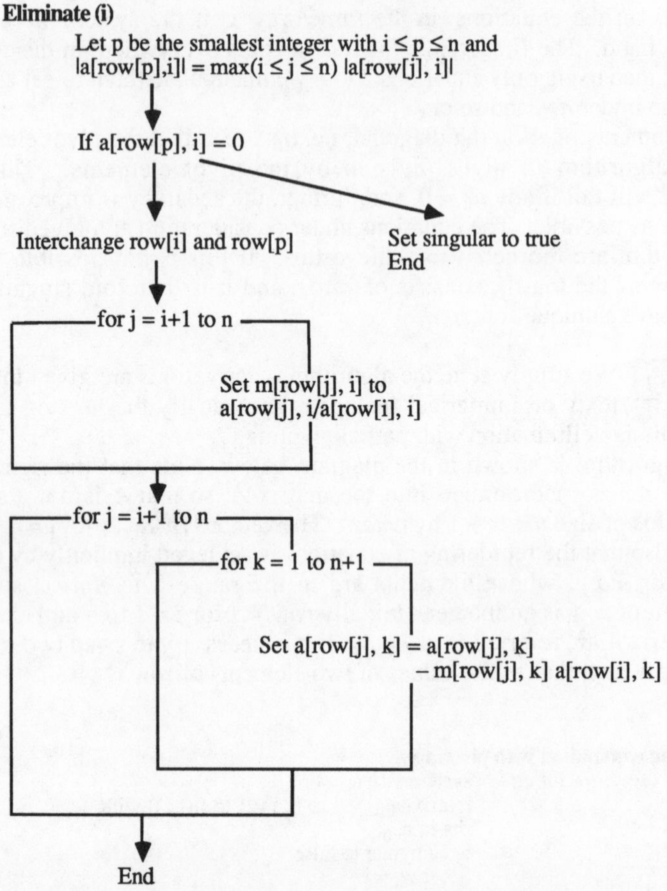

Eliminate (i)

Let p be the smallest integer with i ≤ p ≤ n and
|a[row[p],i]| = max(i ≤ j ≤ n) |a[row[j], i]|

If a[row[p], i] = 0

Interchange row[i] and row[p]   Set singular to true
                                     End

for j = i+1 to n

    Set m[row[j], i] to
    a[row[j], i/a[row[i], i]

for j = i+1 to n

    for k = 1 to n+1

        Set a[row[j], k] = a[row[j], k]
                − m[row[j], k] a[row[i], k]

End

| Procedure | The procedure for Gaussian elimination is called *UpperTriangular*, and is given in the program below. It includes the *eliminate* procedure, and *backsubstitute* is also defined. |

Example 6.8   Kirchhoff's Laws

| Problem | Given the electrical network shown below, we want to find the six currents labelled i_1 to i_6. |

Gustav Robert
Kirchhoff
(1824–1887)

| Solution | Kirchhoff's current law states that the sum of all the currents at a node in a closed circuit is 0. From this we can write down three equations for the three nodes indicated by a •. These are: |

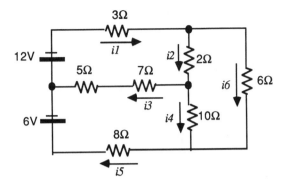

$$-i_1 + i_2 + i_6 = 0$$
$$i_1 - i_3 - i_5 \quad = 0$$
$$-i_2 + i_3 + i_4 = 0$$

Then Kirchhoff's voltage law states that the sum of all the voltages around a closed path is zero. From this we get equations from each of the three meshes.

$$3i_1 + 2i_2 + 12i_3 \quad = 12$$
$$-12i_3 + 10i_4 + 8i_5 = 6$$
$$2i_2 - 10i_4 + 6i_6 \quad = 0$$

From these equations, we can set up a 6×7 matrix of values which can be fed into the Gaussian elimination program which follows.

Program

```
PROGRAM Gauss (input, output);
  CONST
    nmax = 20; {Maximum array size handled}
    nmax1= 21; {nmax + 1}
  TYPE
    range        = 0..nmax;
    rangeplus1  = 0..nmax1;
    matrix       = ARRAY[range,rangeplus1] of real;
    realvector   = ARRAY[range] of real;
    rowlabel     = ARRAY[range] of range;
  VAR
    a        : matrix;
    row      : rowlabel;
    i,n      : range;
    singular : boolean;
    solution : realvector;

    PROCEDURE initialise;
    BEGIN
```

```
                              writeln('*********Gauss Elimination Method ',
                                  'Matrix Solver*********');
                              writeln;
                              writeln('Solution of n by n matrix equation      A x = b ,');
                              writeln('with n <= 20 at present.');
                              write('The data n, A, b');
                              writeln(' must be available in a file: gauss.data');
                              writeln;
                        END; {initialise}

                  PROCEDURE getdata(VAR a : matrix; VAR n: range);
                    VAR f : text;
                        i,j : range;
                    BEGIN
                        reset(f,'gauss.data');
                        read(f,n);
                        FOR i := 1 to n do
                            FOR j := 1 to n do read(f, a[i,j]);
                        FOR i := 1 to n do read(f, a[i,n+1]);
                    END; {getdata}

                  PROCEDURE echodata(a : matrix;  n : range);
                    VAR i, j : range;
                    BEGIN
                        writeln('Equations are:');
                        for i := 1 to n do begin
                          for j := 1 to n do begin
                            write(a[i, j]:3:0, 'x', j:1);
                            if j < n then write (' + ');
                          end;
                          writeln(' = ', a[i,n + 1]:3:0);
                        end;
                        writeln;
                    END; {echodata}

                  PROCEDURE UpperTriangular(
                                    VAR a: matrix;
                                    n : range;
                                    VAR row : rowlabel;
                                    VAR singular : boolean);
                    VAR i : range;

                    PROCEDURE eliminate(i,n: range;
                                        VAR a:matrix;
                                        VAR row : rowlabel;
                                        VAR singular : boolean);

                    VAR
                        j, rowcopy, p : range;
                        k : rangeplus1;
                        m : matrix;

                    FUNCTION pivot(row : rowlabel; a : matrix; n,i:range) : range;
                        VAR j, pivottry : range;
                        BEGIN
```

```
        pivottry := i;
        FOR j := (i + 1) to n do
          IF abs(a[row[j], i]) > abs(a[row[pivottry], i])
          THEN pivottry := j;
        pivot := pivottry;
    END; {pivot}

BEGIN {eliminate}
  p := pivot(row, a, n, i);
  IF a[row[p], i] = 0 THEN singular := true
  ELSE begin
    IF row[i] <> row[p] THEN begin {row interchange}
      rowcopy := row[i];
      row[i] := row[p];
      row[p] := rowcopy;
    end; {IF row..}
    FOR j := i + 1 to n do m[row[j], i] := a[row[j],i] / a[row[i], i];
    FOR j := i + 1 to n do
      FOR k := 1 to n + 1 do
        a[row[j], k] := a[row[j], k] − m[row[j], i] * a[row[i], k];
  END; {ELSE}
END; {eliminate}

BEGIN {UpperTriangular}
  singular := false;
  FOR i := 1 to n do row[i] := i;
  FOR i := 1 to n − 1 do
    IF singular = false
    THEN eliminate(i, n, a, row, singular);
  IF (a[row[n], n] = 0) THEN singular := true;
END; {UpperTriangular}

PROCEDURE backsubstitute(n : range;
                         row : rowlabel;
                         a : matrix;
                         VAR x : realvector);

VAR
  sum: real;
  i, j : range;
BEGIN
  x[n] := a[row[n], n + 1] / a[row[n], n];
  FOR i := n − 1 downto 1 do begin
    sum := 0;
    FOR j := i + 1 to n do
      sum:=sum + a[row[i], j] * x[j];
    x[i] := (a[row[i], n + 1] − sum) / a[row[i], i];
  END; {FOR i}
END; {backsubstitute}

BEGIN
  initialise;
  getdata(a, n);
  echodata (a, n);
  UpperTriangular(a, n, row, singular);
  IF (singular = true) THEN writeln('Matrix singular')
```

```
        ELSE begin
          backsubstitute(n, row, a, solution);
          writeln('Solutions are:');
          FOR i := 1 to n do
            writeln('x[',i:2,']= ', solution[i]:10:6);
        end; {ELSE}
      END.
```

<hr>

Testing

```
********Gauss Elimination Method Matrix Solver*********
```

Solution of n by n matrix equation A x = b ,
with n <= 20 at present.
The data n, A, b must be available in a file: gauss.data

Equations are:

−1x1 +	1x2 +	0x3 +	0x4 +	0x5 +	1x6 =	0
1x1 +	0x2 +	−1x3 +	0x4 +	−1x5 +	0x6 =	0
0x1 +	−1x2 +	1x3 +	1x4 +	0x5 +	0x6 =	0
3x1 +	2x2 +	12x3 +	0x4 +	0x5 +	0x6 =	12
0x1 +	0x2 +	−12x3 +	10x4 +	8x5 +	0x6 =	6
0x1 +	2x2 +	0x3 +	−10x4 +	0x5 +	6x6 =	0

Solutions are:
x[1] = 1.401806
x[2] = 0.951468
x[3] = 0.490971
x[4] = 0.460496
x[5] = 0.910836
x[6] = 0.450338

We can also run the program with the data from the SOR example, and verify
that the results are the same.

<hr>

6.5   Case study 2:   Linear boundary value problem

Problem   Consider the second-order differential equation

$$\frac{d^2y}{dx^2} = e(x)\,\frac{dy}{dx} + f(x)\,y + g(x) \tag{1}$$

We would like to solve it with y given at the end-points a,b :

$$y(a) = y_a, y(b) = y_b.$$

Rationale   The predictor-corrector method discussed in section 3.6 can be
used to solve an initial value problem in one or more
differential equations. **Initial value** means that conditions are specified at one

value of the independent variable x. Here we have a boundary value problem with conditions given at two values of x. Such problems arise in heat conduction, vibration of strings or membranes, deflection of beams under loading, fluid over a surface and diffusion through a porous medium.

| Methods | There are two methods available for this type of problem:

- Shooting method
- Finite difference method.

The shooting method was discussed in section 5.5. It can be used for linear problems as well as non-linear problems (those involving, for example, y^2 or $\sqrt{dy/dx}$, etc.). The finite difference method can only be used for linear problems. However, it is more stable than the shooting method, and is usually preferred for linear problems.

| Theory | We split the interval (a, b) into $n + 1$ subintervals:

$$a = x_0$$
$$b = x_{n+1}$$
$$x_i = a + h\,i$$

with $h = \dfrac{(b - a)}{(n + 1)}$ giving

$$a = x_0 \quad x_1 \quad x_2.\,.\,.\,.\,.\,. \qquad x_{n-1} \quad x_n \quad x_{n+1} = b$$
$$y_a = y_0 \quad y_1 \quad y_2 \qquad\qquad y_{n-1} \quad y_n \quad y_{n+1} = y_b$$

We use standard formulae to represent the derivatives at the point x_i:

$$\frac{dy}{dx} = \frac{y_{i+1} - y_{i-1}}{2h}$$
$$\frac{d^2y}{dx^2} = \frac{y_{i+1} - 2y_i + y_{i-1}}{h^2}$$

where $y_i = y(x_i)$. Then at the points x_i, for $i = 1$ to n, equation (1) becomes

$$\frac{y_{i+1} - 2y_i + y_{i-1}}{h^2} = e(x_i)\frac{y_{i+1} - y_{i-1}}{2h} + f(x_i)\,y_i + g(x_i) \qquad (2)$$

Since $y_0\ (= y_a)$ and $y_{n+1}\ (= y_b)$ are known, (2) is a set of n linear equations in the n unknowns $y_1, y_2, ..., y_n$, and can be solved by any of the methods discussed earlier in section 6.4. Specifically the matrix equation is $A\,Y = v$ where

$$A = \begin{pmatrix} p_1 & q_1 & 0 & . & . & 0 \\ r_2 & p_2 & q_2 & 0 & & \\ 0 & & & & & \\ & & & & & 0 \\ & & & r_{n-1} & p_{n-1} & q_{n-1} \\ 0 & & 0 & & r_n & p_n \end{pmatrix}$$

with $p_i = 2 + h^2 f(x_i)$, $q_i = -1 + \frac{h}{2} e(x_i)$, $r_i = -1 - \frac{h}{2} e(x_i)$ and

$$v = \begin{pmatrix} -h^2 g(x_1) + (1 + \frac{h}{2} e(x_1)) y_a \\ -h^2 g(x_2) \\ | \\ | \\ | \\ -h^2 g(x_{n-1}) \\ -h^2 g(x_n) + (1 - \frac{h}{2} e(x_n)) y_b \end{pmatrix}$$

Algorithm

Input	Number of subintervals in (a, b), y_a, y_b
Calculate	matrix A, vector v
Solve	$Ay = v$
Output	y (or message if matrix solver fails)

We use the SOR matrix solver as in section 6.4 (but see the problems below for a tridiagonal solver) so that an initial estimate of y is required: we use the straight line between the points (in the (x, y) plane) (a, y_a) and (b, y_b). We take the SOR parameter ω to be 1.8, and the tolerance 10^{-6}.

Program

```
PROGRAM LinearBVP (input,output);
   CONST
      nmax       = 50;   {Maximum array size handled}
      a          = 1.0;
      b          = 2.0;   {Interval end-points}
      omega      = 1.8;
      tolerance  = 1e-6;
      kmax       = 500;   {SOR parameters}

   TYPE
      range = 0..nmax;
      matrix = ARRAY[range,range] of real;
      vector = ARRAY[range] of real;
```

```
VAR
  k            : integer;
  m :            matrix;
  v,solution  : vector;
  h, ya, yb   : real;
  n,i         : range;
  finished    : boolean;

PROCEDURE CalculateMatrix(n : range;
                            VAR m : matrix;
                            VAR v, solution : vector);
  VAR i, j :range;

  FUNCTION e (x : real) : real;
    BEGIN
      e := –2/x;
    END; {e}

  FUNCTION f (x : real) : real;
    BEGIN
      f := 2 / sqr(x);
    END; {f}

  FUNCTION g (x : real) : real;
    BEGIN
      g := sin(ln(x)) / sqr(x);
    END; {g}

  BEGIN
    FOR i := 1 to n do
      FOR j := 1 to n do
        m[i, j] := 0.0;
    v[1] := (1 + h * e(a + h) / 2) * ya – g(a + h) * sqr(h);
    v[n] := (1 – h * e(b – h) / 2) * yb – g(b – h) * sqr(h);
    FOR i := 2 to n – 1 do
      v[i] := –sqr(h) * g(a + i * h);
    FOR i := 1 to n do
      m[i, i] := 2 + sqr(h) * f(a + i * h);
    FOR i := 1 to n – 1 do
      m[i, i + 1] := –1 + h * e(a + i * h)/2;
    FOR i := 2 to n do
      m[i, i – 1] := –1 – h * e(a + i * h)/2;
    FOR i := 1 to n do
      solution[i] := ya + (yb – ya) * i * h/(b – a);
  END; {CalculateMatrix}

PROCEDURE initialise;
  BEGIN
    writeln('*********Linear Boundary Value Problem*********');
    writeln;
    writeln('Solves y"(x) = e(x) y''(x) + f(x) y(x) + g(x)');
    writeln('with y given at the endpoints a, b');
    writeln('At present, a = ',a:10:6,'   b = ',b:10:6);
    writeln('e(x) = –2/x , f(x) = 2/(x * x) , g(x) = sin(ln(x))/(x * x)');
    writeln('The matrix equation is solved by the SOR method, ');
```

```
            writeln('with omega = ',omega:10:6,' tolerance = ',tolerance);
            writeln('maximum number of iterations = ', kmax:1);
            writeln;
            write('Value of y(a)? :'); readln(ya);
            write('Value of y(b)? :'); readln(yb);
            write('Number of subintervals in (a,b) (Max.',
                (nmax–1):1,')? :');
            readln(n);
            h := (b – a) / (n + 1);
          END; {initialise}


       FUNCTION normLinfinity(n : range; x, y : vector) : real;
       {as before}
       END;


       PROCEDURE SORsolver (VAR xold : vector;
                            a : matrix;
                            b : vector;
                            n : range;
                            maxiterations : integer;
                            omega, tolerance : real;
                            VAR convergence : boolean;
                            VAR iterations : integer);
          {as before}
          END {SORsolver}

       BEGIN {main program}
         initialise;
         CalculateMatrix(n, m, v, solution);
         SORsolver(solution, m, v, n, kmax,omega,tolerance,finished,k);

         IF finished = false THEN
           writeln('SOR algorithm ',
                   'did not converge in iterations allowed')
         ELSE BEGIN
           writeln('Solution is:');
           writeln('x = ',a:10:6, '  y = ',ya:10:6);
           FOR i := 1 to n do writeln('x = ', (a + i * h):10:6,
             '  y = ',solution[i]:10:6);
             writeln('x = ', b:10:6, '  y = ', yb:10:6);
           END; {ELSE}
       END.
```

Testing   The above program solves the problem

$$\frac{d^2y}{dx^2} = -\frac{2}{x}\,\frac{dy}{dx} + \frac{2}{x^2}\,y + \frac{\sin(lnx)}{x^2}$$

which has the exact solution

$$y = -\frac{3}{10}\sin(lnx) - \frac{1}{10}\cos(lnx) + Cx + \frac{D}{x^2}$$

Let us put $C = 1$, $D = 1$, then

$$y_a = y(1) = 1.9$$
$$y_b = y(2) = 1.981388$$

Using these boundary conditions in the program with 19 subintervals we find

$$y(1.5) = 1.734280$$

whereas the correct result is 1.734219, so the error is 6×10^{-5}. With 49 subintervals the error is 3×10^{-5}.

********Linear Boundary Value Problem*********

Solves y"(x) = e(x) y'(x) + f(x) y(x) + g(x)
At present, a = 1.000000   b = 2.000000
e(x) = −2/x , f(x) = 2/(x * x) , g(x) = sin(ln(x))/(x * x)
The matrix equation is solved by the SOR method,
with omega = 1.800000 tolerance = 1.000e-6
maximum number of iterations = 500

Value of y(a)? :1.9
Value of y(b)? : 1.981388
Number of subintervals in (a,b) (Max. 49)? :19

Solution is:
```
x =  1.000000  y =  1.900000
x =  1.050000  y =  1.842549
x =  1.100000  y =  1.798403
x =  1.150000  y =  1.765392
x =  1.200000  y =  1.741781
x =  1.250000  y =  1.726167
x =  1.300000  y =  1.717405
x =  1.350000  y =  1.714554
x =  1.400000  y =  1.716835
x =  1.450000  y =  1.723593
x =  1.500000  y =  1.734280
x =  1.550000  y =  1.748431
x =  1.600000  y =  1.765651
x =  1.650000  y =  1.785600
x =  1.700000  y =  1.807986
x =  1.750000  y =  1.832557
x =  1.800000  y =  1.859093
x =  1.850000  y =  1.887403
x =  1.900000  y =  1.917317
x =  1.950000  y =  1.948689
x =  2.000000  y =  1.981388
```

There is a sequence of extensions to this case study in the problems at the end of the chapter.

Summary

❑ Pascal's scalar types are integer, boolean, char, enumerated (8.1) and real, with subranges of the first four.

❑ Structured types in Pascal are formed using records (8.3), sets (section 8.4), arrays, files (10.3) and structures created with the pointer type (10.1).

❑ A type statement associates a name with a user-defined scalar or structured type.

❑ Subranges can be based on any scalar type but real, and enable a restriction to be placed on the values permitted from the base type.

❑ Subranges inherit all other properties of the base type, i.e. operators, functions, input and output facilities.

❑ Array subscripts should be declared as subrange types. Subscripts can be subranges of integer, boolean, char or enumerated types.

❑ An array can be assigned to another of the same type, or passed as a parameter. These are the only operations available on whole arrays.

❑ To ensure that the Pascal system checks that subscripts are valid at runtime, it may be necessary to turn on a compiler option such as {$R+}.

❑ The elements of an array can be another array, creating a multi-dimensional structure.

❑ It is better to declare each array dimension as a separate type which can be used as a parameter type for a procedure operating on only part of the array.

❑ Errors in data can usually be accepted in the range of the mean plus or minus twice the standard deviation.

❑ A straight line can be fitted to a set of points by means of the least squares fit.

❑ Systems of linear equations can be solved by several methods, two of which are the SOR (succesive over relaxation) and Gaussian elimination.

❑ These methods may require the matrices to have certain properties, e.g. non-zero diagonal elements.

Self-check quiz

1. Must type and variable names be different?
2. Is the following a valid subrange? kilograms = 0.4 .. 20.0;
3. What happens if a value outside a given subrange is assigned?
4. Must the lower bound of an array always be given?
5. Can subscripts be negative integers?
6. What happens if an array is accessed with a subscript of the wrong type, e.g. character instead of integer?
7. What happens if an array is accessed with a variable which has the right type but has a value outside those specified?
8. Can part of a matrix be passed as a parameter? If so, what part?
9. Can a function return a vector as a result?
10. Write a function which returns the mean of an array of numbers provided as a parameter. What restriction does your function have?

Problems

6.1 Histograms provide useful pictures of data by showing how many values occur in each of a given set of ranges. Assuming that we want a histogram of marks, write a procedure which will take an array of at most 500 marks, with a count of how many there actually are, and print out a histogram for the array. The output should look something like this:

```
  0- 9     ****
 10-19     *******
 20-29     ******
 30-39     **************
 40-49     ******************
 50-59     *****************
 60-69     *********************
 70-79     ********
 80-89     *****
 90-99     *
 100 +     ****
```

     Total items = 104

Test your program by reading in marks from a file.

     Now adapt the procedure to include also as a parameter a two dimensional array which has the ranges stored in it, and can therefore print histograms for any sort of data. Test it out by supplying data from the rainfall problem (example 6.5).

6.2 A simple coding system depends on an arrangement of 25 letters in a square depending on a keyword. The remaining letter is transmitted as itself. For example, if the keyword is PLANT and the letter to be sent unaltered is V, then the square would be

```
P L A N T
B C D E F
G H I J K
M O Q R S
U W X Y Z
```

The code works by considering pairs of letters and replacing each one by the one in the same row but in the column of the other. So M A becomes Q N. (The row of M is 4 and the column of A is 3 => Q, the row of A and column of M => N.) Thus

```
GO TO OUR CAVE NOW      =>      OGLSMWOEVNEWO
```

Write a program which reads in the five letter keyword and letter to remain unaltered and passes these to a procedure which reads a single line message and prints the coded form. Write another procedure to decode such a message.

6.3   The Senate at Zanyland University has decreed that at least 75% of students in each class must pass. This means that the pass mark for each class will differ. Write a program which will read in a file of marks and determine the highest pass such that the Senate's rule applies.

6.4   The mains voltage supplied by a sub-station is measured at hourly intervals over a 72 hour period, and a report made. Write a program to read in the 72 readings and determine:

- the mean voltage measured

- the hours at which the recorded voltage varies from the mean by more than 10%

- any adjacent hours when the change from one reading to the next was greater than 15% of the mean value.

Include in your program an option to print a vertical histogram of the voltage over the 72 hours. *Hint*: This should fit nicely on a screen.

6.5   A block of wood, resting on a horizontal surface, is attached to a wall through a spring, as follows:

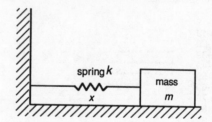

The displacement x of the block from its equilibrium position is governed by

$$\frac{d^2x}{dt^2} = -\frac{k}{m}x - \mu g \ \text{sign} \ \frac{dx}{dt}$$

where

sign $(x) = +1$ if $x > 0$, $= -1$ if $x < 0$, and $= 0$ if $x = 0$
t is time in seconds
k is the spring constant in Newtons/metre, say 300N/m
m is the mass of the block in kg, say 5kg
μ is the coefficient of friction, say 0.5, and
g is the gravitational acceleration, 9.8m/s².

Using the predictor-corrector method described in section 3.4 and example 3.5, extended for second order equations, compute x as a function of time up to 3s, with x starting at 0.2m and at rest.

6.6   Extend the program in problem 6.5 to illustrate the displacement of the block graphically, using the histogram method described in section 4.5.

6.7   The SOR method requires that the elements on the diagonal are non-zero. It is also only guaranteed to work if the matrix is diagonally dominant, in other words, if

$$|a_{ii}| > \sum_{i \neq j} a_{ij}$$

Write a procedure which looks at a matrix and establishes whether it is suitable for the SOR method, and if not, endeavours to reorder the rows such that it will be suitable. Insert the procedure in example 6.5 and run the program with the data from example 6.6.

6.8   Data has been collected which should fit the curve $A \exp(kx)$. Use linear regression to find A and k to give the best fit. The data is

x	y
1.00	5.10
1.25	5.79
1.50	6.53
1.75	7.45
2.00	8.46

6.9   Using both Gaussian elimination and the SOR method, solve the following matrix problems:

(a)
$$\begin{pmatrix} 4 & 2 & 0 & 1 \\ 1 & -6 & 1 & 2 \\ 2 & 1 & -5 & 0 \\ -3 & 0 & 0 & 4 \end{pmatrix} x = \begin{pmatrix} 9 \\ -9 \\ 4 \\ 1 \end{pmatrix}$$

(b)
$$\begin{pmatrix} 2 & 3 & 1 & 2 \\ -2 & 4 & -1 & 5 \\ 3 & 7 & 1.5 & 1 \\ 6 & 9 & 3 & 7 \end{pmatrix} x = \begin{pmatrix} 2 \\ 3 \\ 4 \\ 5 \end{pmatrix}$$

(c)
$$\begin{pmatrix} 4 & 2 & 1 & 0 \\ 1 & 6 & 2 & 1 \\ 3 & 0 & 0 & -4 \\ -2 & 1 & 5 & 0 \end{pmatrix} x = \begin{pmatrix} 14 \\ 19 \\ 2 \\ 8 \end{pmatrix}$$

Linear boundary value problem

6.10 Test the accuracy of the program. Instead of outputting the value of y, output the difference between the calculated value of y and the exact solution; and the L_∞ norm of this difference. Examine how the accuracy depends on the number of subintervals, and the value of tolerance.

6.11 Test the program with some other differential equations.

6.12 There is a much better way to solve $Ay = v$ than the SOR method. We can use a special method for a tridiagonal matrix – one, like A, which is non-zero only on the main diagonal and the two diagonals on either side of it. We write the matrix in terms of the diagonals, using the three vectors introduced earlier:

$$p_i = a_{ii} \qquad (i = 1 \text{ to } n),$$
$$q_i = a_{i, i+1} \qquad (i = 1 \text{ to } n - 1),$$
$$r_i = a_{i,i-1} \qquad (i = 2 \text{ to } n)$$

The solution of $Ay = v$ is calculated by the following algorithm.

1.   Introduce intermediate vectors u_i, w_i, z_i
2.   Let $u_i = p_i$

3.   For $i = 2$ to n
      (a)   let $w_{i-1} = q_{i-1} / u_{i-1}$
      (b)   let $u_i = p_i - r_i w_{i-1}$
4.   Let $z_1 = v_1/u_1$
5.   For $i = 2$ to n let $z_i = \dfrac{v_i - r_i z_{i-1}}{u_i}$
6. $y_n = z_n$
7.   For $i = (n-1)$ downto 1 $y_i = z_i - w_i y_{i+1}$

Revise the program so that it uses this algorithm. Test the accuracy of the program.

7

Projects

At this stage in the Pascal course, there is usually an opportunity to test your new-found knowledge by writing a fairly lengthy program. The following case studies serve as starting points for projects which present problems of the right size and complexity. The chapter starts by outlining what to look for in a project, and how to approach it so as to get the most out of it.

7.1 Getting the most out of a project

The primary aim of a major project in a programming course is to give one the opportunity to put into practice all one has learnt. The project topic should be carefully chosen so as to be manageable, and at the same time instructive and interesting. Many students like to feel that they are achieving something of lasting value when they take on a major project, and so it is often attractive to give a project a real life flavour. In the following sections are a selection of good case studies which lead to projects which fulfil these objectives.

What to avoid in a project

If devising one's own project, there are factors to consider, to avoid falling into the trap of doing a lot of work without exercising much skill.

Keep the data volume down

The purpose of a project is to program, not to type in data. Therefore, avoid problems that require a large amount of data to be entered before the program can sensibly do anything. Such problems include inventory and stock control systems, employee or student record systems, bank statement and payroll systems, and theatre or airline reservation systems. For all of these, one would have to both invent the data and type it in, which is time-consuming and does not add anything to one's programming experience. Moreover, Pascal is probably not the best language for solving these types of problems. A language specifically designed for data processing or transaction processing, such as COBOL, would be more suitable.

Keep the output simple

The second characteristic to watch out for is excessive output, and in particular, displayed or graphic output. Getting a pleasing format on a screen can take hours of one's time, but is not a challenging or learning activity. Therefore, it is best at this stage to go for problems that have fairly routine output, or at least for those that can have two levels of output, narrative and graphic.

Avoid interactive testing

Testing is an essential part of ensuring that one has grasped the principles of good programming. If the program does not perform correctly, then it is not worth much. In order to test effectively, one must be able to take the program through predefined paths repeatedly. If a certain place in the program can only be reached via a long dialogue, then there will be quite a temptation to omit testing it. Programs that need a lot of interactive testing are games (with the user as one of the players), computer aided instruction (CAI) and spreadsheets. These are popular systems on home computers, but they are not easy to write well, and the testing problem really rules them out at this stage.

Know the answers

Given the above bias against excessive input and output, it is clear that much of the program's efforts will be in calculating some results. Ensure that the expected result is well known. In other words, do not at this stage tackle a problem with a result that you could not produce yourself on paper. Statistical and mathematical problems fall into this category.

Where to start

Once you have decided on a project with a definable goal, the steps to follow are familiar, viz:

- define the problem
- consider solutions
- do examples and decide on the input and output

- devise the data structures and algorithms
- write the program(s)
- test the system.

In the case studies that follow, roughly half of the allotted time would be spent on the first four steps, and the process of writing and testing programs would only begin once everything is thoroughly thought out on paper.

Test data

During the design phase, set up one or more files of test data, and use them repeatedly. Do not rely on entering data interactively, as you will make mistakes and take up far too much time. In most cases, a project can be almost wholly completed with a basic input scheme, and then have a more fancy input procedure added at the end.

Generating sensible values for test data can also be a problem sometimes, and it may help to invoke a random number generator to do this automatically.

Narrative versus graphic output

The user-friendliness and effectiveness of a computer system can be greatly enhanced by a good use of graphics and colour on the screen. At the same time, it is also important that a printed record of the progress of a session be available. Unfortunately, screens and printers are seldom compatible and what works well on one does not easily transfer to the other, although this is changing as laser printers become more common.

One way of reconciling the capabilities of screens and printers is to go for narrative output. This gives the facts of what is happening as the program progresses, without any pictorial aids. Such narrative output can be the first record of the program's actions, and then later more exciting forms can be introduced.

A further advantage of narrative output is that it can be used during debugging. Printing to a file the state of important data structures at the start of each procedure can provide a valuable aid in deciding where to start looking for the cause of errors. If carefully designed, such output need not impact on any future graphics, and can remain in place as a back up.

7.2   Case study 3: Lunar landing simulator

| Problem | For the purpose of training astronauts we want a program that simulates landing a spacecraft on the moon under manual control. We need only consider the vertical motion.

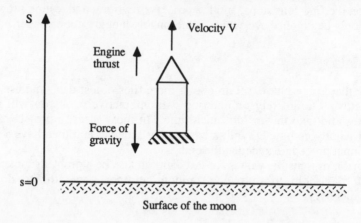

Surface of the moon

| Solution | The mass of the spacecraft consists of a fixed part – *mlander* – and a variable part *mfuel*, the mass of the fuel. Standard Newtonian mechanics leads to a system of differential equations

$$(mlander + mfuel) \frac{dv}{dt} = -\frac{g_m(mlander + mfuel)}{(1 + s/r_m)^2} + fuelrate * fuelfactor$$

$$\frac{ds}{dt} = v$$

$$\frac{d\ mfuel}{dt} = -fuelrate$$

where g_m is the gravitational acceleration on the surface of the moon; r_m is the radius of the moon; *fuelrate* can be adjusted by the astronaut, between 0 and an upper limit; and the *fuelfactor* converts fuelrate into units of force. As before, we will integrate the equations by the predictor-corrector method. (See section 3.4 or 6.5 for the equations.)

| Algorithm | The algorithm is fairly straightforward, apart from one matter. Throughout the integration we must test whether the height (*s*) or the fuel reserves become zero, and, if so, take appropriate action. In the former case, stop the integration, and in the latter case set the fuelrate to zero and keep it there.

Lunar lander

Set initial values of fuel, time, height (= s) and velocity

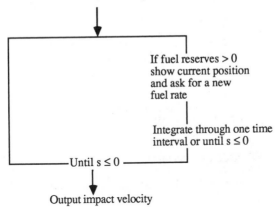

If fuel reserves > 0
show current position
and ask for a new
fuel rate

Integrate through one time
interval or until s ≤ 0

─Until s ≤ 0 ─

Output impact velocity

Program

```
PROGRAM LunarLander(input,output);
CONST
  imax          = 100; {Number of iterations in a call of
                       integrate}
  mlander       = 15000.0; {mass of the lunar lander - in kg}
  maxfuelrate   = 40.0; {kg per second}
  rmoon         = 1738000.0; {radius of the Moon - in metres}
  mg            = 1.62; {gravitational acceleration on the surface
                       of the Moon}
  forcefactor   = 4500.0; {Force (in Newtons) due to 1 Kg of fuel
                       per second}
  timeinterval  = 2.0; {in a call of integrate}
  initialfuel   = 1000.0; {kg}

VAR
  dt, fuel, fuelrate, v, s, t: real;
  warning : boolean;

PROCEDURE integrate (VAR fuelrate, fuel, v, s, t : real; dt : real);
{Uses global constants:      imax,
 plus those used in FUNCTION fv}
  VAR
    i : 0..imax;
    dfuel, vp, vc, sp: real;

    FUNCTION fv (fuel, s, t : real) : real;
    {Uses global constants:     mg, rmoon, forcefactor, mlander}
      BEGIN
        fv := -mg / sqr(1 + s / rmoon)
              + fuelrate * forcefactor / (mlander + fuel);
      END; {fv}

  BEGIN
    i := 0;
```

Fv is the
function that
calculates the
velocity.

```
REPEAT
  dfuel := -dt * fuelrate;
  i := i + 1;
  vp := v + dt * fv(fuel, s, t);
  sp := s + dt * v;
  vc := v + 0.5 * dt * (fv(fuel, s, t) + fv(fuel + dfuel, sp, t + dt));
  s := s + 0.5 * dt * (v + vp);
  v := vc;
  t := t + dt;
  fuel := fuel + dfuel;
  IF fuel <= 0.0 THEN fuelrate:=0.0; {Run out of fuel}
UNTIL ((s <= 0.0) or (i = imax));
END; {integrate}

PROCEDURE initialise;
BEGIN
  writeln('********Lunar  Landing  Simulator********');
  writeln;
  writeln('Computer control of engines has failed ',
          '- reverting to manual');
  writeln('control.  Flight monitoring data will be sent to the ');
  writeln(' screen every ',timeinterval:1:1,' seconds');

  writeln('Velocity - in metres per second,
          'negative sign for downwards');
  writeln('Height - in metres');
  writeln('Fuel - fuel reserves in kg.');
  writeln;
  writeln('Simply enter the fuel rate when requested: ',
          'it must be in the');
  writeln('range 0.0 to 40.0 (kgs per sec.); a fuel rate of ');
  writeln('about 5.5 balances the effect of lunar gravity');
  writeln;
  dt := timeinterval / imax; {timestep in integrate}
  fuel := initialfuel;
  warning := false;
  v := -200.0; {metres per second}
  t := 0.0;
  s := 2500.0; {metres}
END; {initialise}

PROCEDURE currentposition(v,s,fuel:real;VAR fuelrate:real);
  {Uses global constant: maxfuelrate}
  BEGIN
    write('velocity = ',v:8:2,' height = ',s:8:2,' fuel = ',fuel:8:2);
    write(' New fuel rate? : ');
    readln(fuelrate);
    WHILE ((fuelrate < 0.0) or
           (fuelrate > maxfuelrate)) do begin
      writeln('NO! fuelrate must be between 0.0 ',
              'and ',maxfuelrate:8:2);
      write('Enter a valid fuel rate : ');
      readln(fuelrate);
    END; {While}
END; {currentposition}
```

```
PROCEDURE ModuleHasLanded (v:real);
  {Uses global variable:        v}
  BEGIN
    writeln;
    writeln('Landed with velocity ',v:8:2,' at time ',t:8:2);
    writeln;
    IF v > -2.0 THEN
      writeln('Congratulations on a safe landing!')
    ELSE IF v > -5.0 THEN
      writeln('Some damage, but probably repairable')
    ELSE IF v > -20.0 THEN
      writeln('Severe damage - craft will never leave the Moon')
    ELSE writeln('You have created a new crater on the Moon');
  END; {finalise}

BEGIN {Lunar Lander Simulation}
  initialise;
  REPEAT
    IF ((fuel <= 0.0) AND (warning = false)) then begin
      writeln('****  WARNING - FUEL NOW FINISHED  ****');
      warning := true;
    END; {IF}
    IF fuel > 0.0 then begin
      currentposition(v,s,fuel,fuelrate);
    END; {IF}
    integrate(fuelrate,fuel,v,s,t,dt);
  UNTIL s <= 0.0;
  ModuleHasLanded(v);
END.
```

| Testing | A typical run might be:

*******Lunar Landing Simulator*******');

**Computer control of engines has failed - reverting to manual
control. Flight monitoring data will be sent to the
screen every 2.0 seconds**

**Velocity - in metres per second, negative sign for downwards
Height - in metres
Fuel reserves in kg.**

**Simply enter the fuel rate when requested: it must be in the
range 0.0 to 40.0 (kgs per sec.); a fuel rate of
about 5.5 balances the effect of lunar gravity**

```
velocity = -200.00  height = 2500.00  fuel = 1000.00  New fuel rate? : 6
velocity = -199.86  height = 2100.14  fuel =  988.00  New fuel rate? : 5
velocity = -200.27  height = 1700.02  fuel =  978.00  New fuel rate? : 6
velocity = -200.13  height = 1299.62  fuel =  966.00  New fuel rate? : 7
velocity = -199.41  height =  900.08  fuel =  952.00  New fuel rate? : 10
velocity = -197.01  height =  503.65  fuel =  932.00  New fuel rate? : 10
velocity = -194.59  height =  112.05  fuel =  912.00  New fuel rate? : 30
```

Landed with velocity –190.47 at time   12.60

You have created a new crater on the Moon

Run the program with the fuelrate at zero throughout, and find that the impact velocity is 219.31ms^{-1}. In this case the problem can be solved analytically

$$v\frac{dv}{ds} = \frac{-g_m}{(1 + s/r_m)^2}$$

so that

$$\frac{1}{2}v^2 = \frac{g_m r_m}{(1 + s/r_m)} + \text{constant}$$

The correct value for the impact velocity is calculated to be 219.29ms^{-1}.

We find that an initial fuelrate of 5.75 leads to no change in velocity, so that the engine thrust is balanced by the force of gravity; we can check this on a calculator.

The program can now be extended by considering further options. These are covered in problems 7.1 and 7.2 at the end of the chapter.

7.3   Case study 4: Communications simulator

Problem   When data is sent down a channel (e.g. telephone, radio link, etc.) some of it is corrupted due to noise in the channel. We want to write a program to simulate this effect, and to try out a strategy for detecting and correcting the errors.

Solution   A data stream consists of characters. Each character can be represented by an integer in the range 0..127 or 0..255, depending on the character set used. To send a character down a channel, it is first converted to an integer and then to a bit stream, i.e. it is represented as a binary number. For example, 's' is represented by 115 which in binary is 1110011.

The bits 0 or 1 are sent down the channel one after each other, and we represent noise in the channel by saying that there is a probability that a bit will be incorrectly transmitted, i.e. a 1 is received as a 0 or a 0 is received as a 1. In many channels, noise occurs in bursts, and we will use the Gilbert model of a discrete binary symmetric channel.

In the high noise state the probability of a bit error in the channel is $p(h)$, while in the low noise state the probability is $p(l)$, with $p(l) \ll p(h)$; typical values might be $p(h) = 0.1, p(l) = 1\text{e-}4$. Each time a bit is transmitted, there is a probability that the noise state of the channel will change. The probability of changing from high noise to low noise is $p(hl)$ (perhaps = 0.01), and the probability of changing from low noise to high noise is $p(lh)$, = 1e-4 say.

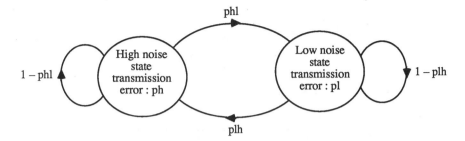

Theory There are many ways of detecting and correcting errors. Here, we will use a simple method based on a check digit. After a certain number of characters we calculate the check digit from the previous characters, and send it down the channel. We compare it with a check digit calculated in the receiver from the data actually received: if the two are different, the receiver asks the source to retransmit the previous group of characters.

Algorithm First some notation. The size of the character set is *charsize* and is 128 or 256 depending on the system. Note that *charsize* = 2^{base} with *base* = 7 or 8. The number of characters transmitted as a group, including the check digit, is *chmax*. The check digit is calculated as

$$\sum_{i=1}^{chmax-1} C_i \bmod charsize$$

The numeric representation of each character will have to be converted into an array of bits, and then back again to a number at the other end. The algorithms to do this rely on successively dividing by powers of two and taking the remainder. One of them is:

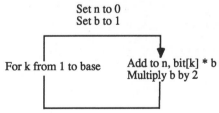

Convert a bit array to an integer
Set n to 0
Set b to 1

For k from 1 to base   Add to n, bit[k] * b
                        Multiply b by 2

At the top level, the algorithm in pseudo-code is

```
Print the initial output and initialise variables
While end-of file not reached
    Read (chmax−1) characters
    Convert characters to integers
    Make the check digit
    Convert integers, including check digit, to an array of bits
```

> Repeat
>> For each bit
>>> Calculate error state of channel
>>> Set received bit equal or not to sent bit
>> Convert array of bits to an array of integers (1..chmax)
>> Calculate new check digit and compare it with check digit received
> Until check digits are the same
> Convert integers to characters
> Write characters to file
> Increment counter if sent-character <> received character
Write counter

In addition, we must consider how to see what is going on in the simulator. We would wish to monitor any channel errors, as well as changes in noise level. This can be done by printing appropriate characters on the screen while the program is transmitting data from the input file to the output file.

Program

```
PROGRAM CommunicationSimulator(input,output);
  CONST
    chmax       =10;{base}
    base        =8; {size of character set: 2 to the base}
    basechmax   =80; {=base*chmax}

  TYPE
    noisestate       = (low,high);
    rangech          = 1..chmax;
    baserange        = 1..base;
    bit              = 0..1;
    rangebasechmax   = 1..basechmax;
    natural          = 0..maxint;
    arraych          = array[rangech] of char;
    arrayint         = array[rangech] of natural;
    arraybit         = array[rangebasechmax] of bit;

  VAR
    pl, ph, plh, phl    : real;
    sendint, receiveint : arrayint;
    sendbit, receivebit : arraybit;
    charsize,counter    : natural;
    state               : noisestate;
    seed                : real;
    channelerror        : boolean;
    fin, fout           : text;

  PROCEDURE initialise;
  VAR i : baserange;
  BEGIN
    writeln('******Communication System Simulator******');
    writeln;
    writeln('Simulates transmission of data using the');
    writeln('Gilbert model of a discrete binary symmetric');
    writeln('channel, with a check-digit to detect errors');
```

```
        writeln('and request re-transmission of a group of');
        writeln(chmax:2,' characters.');
        writeln;
        writeln('The model probabilities are:');
        write('Bit error in normal state: (1e-4) '); readln(pl);
        write('Bit error in noisy state: (0.1) '); readln(ph);
        write('Transition normal to noisy: (1e-4) '); readln(plh);
        write('Transition noisy to normal: (0.01) '); readln(phl);
        writeln;
        writeln('The input file "comsim.data" is now ',
          'sent down the channel');
        writeln('and the simulated output is written to "comsim.out" ');
        writeln('A dot indicates a group of ',chmax:1, ' characters');
        writeln('* indicates a channel error');
        writeln('< indicates a change to high noise,',
                ' > a change to low');
        writeln;
        rewrite(fout,'comsim.out');
        reset(fin,'comsim.data');
        charsize:=1;
        {Calculate the character size from the base}
        for i := 1 to base do charsize := charsize * 2;
        seed := 0.4567;
        state := high;
        counter := 0;
END;

PROCEDURE makedata(VAR sendint : arrayint;
                            VAR sendbit : arraybit);
    VAR
      sendch : arraych;
      i : rangech;

PROCEDURE ConverttoBits (n : natural;
                                var s : arraybit;
                                at : natural);
    VAR k : 1 .. base;
    BEGIN
      FOR k := 1 to base do begin
        s[k+at] := n mod 2;
        n := n div 2;
      END;
    END; {ConverttoBits}

    BEGIN
      sendint[chmax] := 0;
      FOR i := 1 to (chmax – 1) do begin
        IF eof(fin) THEN
          sendint[i] := 0
        ELSE
        IF eoln(fin) THEN begin
          read(fin, sendch[i]);
          sendint[i] := 1;
        end
        ELSE begin
```

```
              read(fin,sendch[i]);
              sendint[i] := ord(sendch[i]);
            end; {ELSE begin}
            sendint[chmax] := (sendint[chmax] + sendint[i])
                                mod charsize;
          end; {FOR i ...}
          FOR i := 1 to chmax do begin
            converttobits (sendint[i],sendbit,(i – 1) * base);
          end; {FOR i}
          write('.');
        END; {makedata}

FUNCTION random : real;
{Uses global variable: seed}
BEGIN
  seed := seed * 27.182813917;
  seed := seed – trunc(seed);
  random := seed;
END; {random}

PROCEDURE senddata(sendbit : arraybit;
                          VAR receivebit : arraybit);
    VAR
      j : rangebasechmax;

    FUNCTION error : bit;
      VAR s : noisestate;
      BEGIN
        s := state;
        IF (state = low) and (random < plh) THEN state := high;
        IF (state = high) and (random < phl) THEN state := low;
        IF s <> state then
          if state = low then write('>')
                    else write('<');
        error := 0;
        IF (state = low) and (random < pl) THEN error := 1;
        IF (state = high) and (random < ph) THEN error := 1;
      END; {error}

    BEGIN
      FOR j := 1 to basechmax do
        receivebit[j] := (sendbit[j] + error) mod 2;
    END; {senddata}

PROCEDURE receivedata(receivebit : arraybit;
                              VAR receiveint : arrayint;
                              VAR channelerror : boolean);
    VAR
      i : rangech;
      checkint : 0..maxint;

    PROCEDURE ConvertfromBits (var n : natural;
                                    a : arraybit;   at : natural);
      VAR k : baserange;
        b : 1 .. maxint;
```

```
     BEGIN
       n := 0;
       b := 1;
       FOR k := 1 to base do begin
         n := n + a[k + at] * b;
         b := b * 2;
       END;
     END; {ConvertfromBits}

   BEGIN
     FOR i := 1 to chmax do begin
       ConvertfromBits(receiveint[i], receivebit, (i − 1)*base);
     end; {FOR i ...}
     checkint := 0;
     FOR i := 1 to (chmax − 1) do
       checkint := (checkint + receiveint[i]) mod charsize;
     channelerror := checkint = receiveint[chmax];
     IF channelerror then write('*');
   END; {receivedata}

 PROCEDURE writedata(sendint, receiveint : arrayint;
                              VAR counter : natural);
   VAR
     i : rangech;
     receivech : arraych;

   BEGIN
     FOR i := 1 to (chmax − 1) do begin
       IF receiveint[i] = 1 THEN writeln(fout)
       ELSE IF receiveint[i] <> 0 THEN begin
         receivech[i] := chr(receiveint[i]);
         write(fout, receivech[i]);
       END; {ELSE IF}
       IF receiveint[i] <> sendint[i] THEN
         counter := counter + 1;
     end; {FOR i ...}
   END; {writedata}

 BEGIN
   initialise;
   writeln('Starting transmission ... ');
   WHILE not eof(fin) do begin
     makedata(sendint, sendbit);
     REPEAT
       senddata(sendbit, receivebit);
       receivedata(receivebit, receiveint, channelerror);
     UNTIL not channelerror;
     writedata(sendint, receiveint, counter);
   end; {WHILE}
   writeln;
   writeln('Number of errors: ', counter:1);
 END.
```

| Testing | To test the program, we used as data the program header and the initialise procedure from the program itself. Running with the recommended probabilities, we get the following report: |

> ******Communication System Simulator******
>
> Simulates transmission of data using the
> Gilbert model of a discrete binary symmetric
> channel, with a check-digit to detect errors
> and request re-transmission of a group of
> 10 characters.
>
> The model probabilities are:
> Bit error in normal state: (1e-4) 1e-4
> Bit error in noisy state: (0.1) 0.1
> Transition normal to noisy: (1e-4) 1e-4
> Transition noisy to normal: (0.01) 0.01
>
> The input file "comsim.data" is now sent down the channel
> and the simulated output is written to "comsim.out"
> A dot indicates a group of 10 characters
> * indicates a channel error
> < indicates a change to high noise, > a change to low
>
> Starting transmission ...
> .>*...
> ....
> Number of errors: 0

In other words, the simuator switched to low noise after the first group, and only had one channel error. All the data was received correctly.

Running again with slightly higher probabilities, a different picture emerges:

> ******Communication System Simulator******
>
> Simulates transmission of data using the
> Gilbert model of a discrete binary symmetric
> channel, with a check-digit to detect errors
> and request re-transmission of a group of
> 10 characters.
>
> The model probabilities are:
> Bit error in normal state: (1e-4) 9e-4
> Bit error in noisy state: (0.1) 0.05
> Transition normal to noisy: (01e-4) 9e-4
> Transition noisy to normal: (0.01) 0.005
>
> The input file "comsim.data" is now sent down the channel
> and the simulated output is written to "comsim.out"
> A dot indicates a group of 10 characters
> * indicates a channel error
> < indicates a change to high noise, > a change to low

Starting transmission ...
```
.**>*.........*_*<****><****>*_..._..*_<**_*><*****>*_._*_**<****><****>*...
._*_*<****><****>*_..*_*_<****><*****>*_..*_**<****><*****>.....*_*<***
**><****>*....*_*_*<****><*****>*_..*_*<****><*****>*_._*_*<****><****
>*....*_*_<****><*****>*_..*_*<****><*****>*_..*_*<****><****>*_.._*
<**_*>*<****>*_..*_*<****><*****>*_..**<****><****>*_.._*<*****><
****>*_..._*_<****><*****>*....*_**<****><****>*_...._*<*****><****>*...
*...*<****><*****>*_..._.._**<****><****>*....._*_<*****><****>*.
```
Number of errors: 8

Here there were many channel errors, and the checksum was able to detect all but 8 of them.

7.4   Case study 5:   Temperature in a plate

| Problem | A steady state temperature distribution satisfies Laplace's equation, that is |

Pierre Simon Laplace (1749–1827)

$$\frac{\partial^2 T}{\partial x} + \frac{\partial^2 T}{\partial y^2} = 0$$

Usually Laplace's equation is solved by finite difference methods that are beyond the scope of this book. We will look at the case where it is possible to express a solution of Laplace's equation as the sum of an infinite series. Then we will give a graphical representation of the results. The case we will solve is that of a semi-infinite strip, with the temperature on the boundary as shown in the diagram.

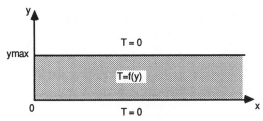

| Solution | The temperature as a function of x and y is |

$$T = \sum_{i=1}^{\infty} a_n \sin\left(\frac{n\pi y}{ymax}\right) \exp\left(\frac{-n\pi x}{ymax}\right) \qquad \textbf{(1)}$$

where the constants a_n are found by Fourier analysis and are

$$a_n = \frac{2}{ymax} \int\limits_0^{ymax} f(y) \, \sin\left(\frac{n\pi y}{ymax}\right) dy \qquad (2)$$

The specific problem that we will deal with in the program has $f(y)$ as shown

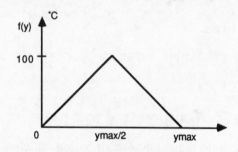

For this case the coefficients a_n work out to be

$$a_n = 0 \qquad\qquad\qquad \text{if } n \text{ even}$$
$$a_n = \frac{800}{(n^2\pi^2)} \qquad\qquad \text{if } n = 1, 5, 9,\dots \text{ (i.e. if } n \bmod 4 = 1\text{)}$$
$$a_n = -\frac{800}{(n^2\pi^2)} \qquad\quad \text{if } n = 3, 7, 11,\dots \text{ (i.e. if } n \bmod 4 = 3\text{)} \qquad (3)$$

On a computer we cannot work out $\sum\limits_1^\infty b_n$ but only $\sum\limits_1^N b_n$ and we must decide, for a given tolerance requirement, what value to use for N. We cannot just say take N such that $|b_N| <$ tolerance: for example if $b_n = \frac{1}{n}$, the true value of $\sum\limits_1^\infty b_n$ is infinite!

There are two techniques that can be used here to estimate N. Let

$$\text{error}(N) = \left| \sum\limits_1^\infty b_n - \sum\limits_1^N b_n \right|$$

Then if $b_n = \frac{k}{n^p}$, with k and p constant and $p > 1$

$$\text{error}(N) = \frac{k}{N^{p-1}} \, \text{p} - 1$$

For a geometric progression, $b_n = k \, r^n$ with k and r constant and $r < 1$,

$$\text{error}(N) = \frac{k \, r^N}{(1 - r)}$$

In the present problem we wish to find (1) with a_n given by (3). At $x = 0$, the series is of the type $\dfrac{800}{n^2\pi^2}$, so the error in summing to N is $\dfrac{800}{\pi^2 N}$. To obtain an accuracy of better than 1°C we should therefore take $N = 200$. For $x > 0$ we can regard the series as a geometric progression with

$$r = \exp(-\pi x \,/ ymax)$$

Then we can estimate N as

$$N = \frac{ymax}{\pi x \,\ln(tolerance\; \pi^2\,(1 - \exp(-\pi x \,/\, ymax))\,/\, 800)}$$

We do this because in general this value of N will be much lower than 200, and by using it we save computer time.

We calculate the temperature at every point on an x–y grid. So that the output will fit on a standard computer screen, we take the x–y grid size as 40×20. The next step is to discretise the temperature array, i.e. round the temperature at every grid point to an integer in some range. From the discrete array we can then produce a contour map of the temperature distribution.

| Algorithm | At the top level the algorithm is

```
Initial output etc.
Make Fourier coefficients aₙ
Calculate the temperature at every grid point
At every grid point, convert temperature to an integer in the range 0..9
Print contour map
```

The algorithm for making the discrete array is

```
Set tempmin to minᵢ,ⱼ temperatureᵢ,ⱼ
Set tempmax to maxᵢ,ⱼ temperatureᵢ,ⱼ
Set factor to number of contours / (tempmax – tempmin)
Set discrete temperature := round ((temperature – tempmin) * factor)
Write the mean temperature for each contour value
```

Two contour maps of the results are printed. The first one is simply a print-out of the array discrete temperature. In the second one we find contours by going along each row of discrete temperature until there is a change in value and then printing the latest value.

| Program |

```
PROGRAM Contour(output);
  CONST
    nmax      = 200;{Maximum number of terms in Fourier series}
    tolerance = 0.5; {nmax and tolerance are related}
    imax      = 40; {Number of grid points in x-direction}
    jmax      = 20; {Number of grid points in y-direction}
```

```
kmax      = 9; {Must be in range 0..9}
ymax      = 1.0; {Coordinate patch y: 0 to ymax}
xmax      = 1.0; {   "      "   x: 0 to xmax}
pi        = 3.141593;

TYPE
rangen      = 1..nmax;
rangei      = 0..imax;
rangej      = 0..jmax;
rangek      = 0..kmax;
realmatrix  = ARRAY[rangei,rangej] of real;
kmatrix     = ARRAY[rangei,rangej] of rangek;
nvector     = ARRAY[rangen] of real;

VAR
a             : nvector;
temperature   : realmatrix;
discrete      : kmatrix;
size          : real;

Procedure initialise;
  BEGIN
    writeln('*******Temperature contour plotting program*******');
    writeln;
    writeln('Semi-infinite strip with temperature 0 along the');
    writeln('semi-infinite edges and f(y), specified by a Fourier');
    writeln('series, along the remaining edge');
    writeln;
    writeln('Coordinate patch:  horizontally  x = 0 to ',xmax:6:2);
    writeln('                   vertically  y = 0 to ',ymax:6:2);
      writeln;
  END;

Procedure makea(VAR a : nvector; VAR size : real);
  {Uses global constants:    nmax and pi}
  VAR n : rangen;
  BEGIN
    FOR n := 1 to nmax do
      IF (n mod 2) = 0 THEN a[n] := 0.0
      ELSE IF (n mod 4) = 1 THEN a[n] := 800/sqr(n * pi)
        ELSE a[n] := –800/sqr(n * pi);
    size := 800/sqr(pi);
  END; {makea}

Procedure maketemperature(
                    tolerance, size : real;
                    a : nvector;
                    VAR temperature : realmatrix);
{Uses global constants: nmax, imax, jmax, xmax, ymax}
  VAR
    i : rangei;
    j : rangej;
    n : rangen;
    nlimit : 0..maxint;
    x, y, sum : real;
```

```
BEGIN
  FOR i := 0 to imax do begin
    x := i * xmax/imax;
    IF i = 0 THEN nlimit := nmax
    ELSE begin
      nlimit := round(-ymax / (pi * x) *
                   ln(tolerance/size * (1 - exp(-pi * x / ymax))));
      IF nlimit > nmax THEN nlimit := nmax;
    end; {ELSE}
    FOR j := 0 to jmax do begin
      y := j * ymax / jmax;
      sum := 0.0;
      FOR n := 1 to nlimit do
        sum := sum + a[n] * sin(n * pi * y / ymax)
                *exp(-n * pi * x / ymax);
      temperature[i,j] := sum;
    end; {FOR j ...}
  end; {FOR i ...}
END; {maketemperature}


Procedure makediscrete(temperature : realmatrix;
                       VAR discrete : kmatrix);
{Uses global constants: imax, jmax, kmax}
  VAR
    i : rangei;
    j : rangej;
    k : rangek;
    tempmin, tempmax, factor: real;
  BEGIN
    tempmin := temperature[0,0];
    tempmax := tempmin;
    FOR i := 0 to imax do
      FOR j := 0 to jmax do begin
        IF tempmin > temperature[i,j]
        THEN tempmin := temperature[i,j];
        IF tempmax < temperature[i,j]
        THEN tempmax := temperature[i,j];
      end; {FOR j ...}
    factor := kmax / (tempmax - tempmin);
    FOR i := 0 to imax do
      FOR j := 0 to jmax do
        discrete[i,j] := round((temperature[i,j] - tempmin) * factor);
    writeln('minimum temperature is: ', tempmin:10:4);
    writeln('maximum temperature is: ', tempmax:10:4);
    writeln;
    FOR k := 0 to kmax do
      writeln('Contour ', k:1, ' is at temperature: ',
                 tempmin + k / factor:10:4);
    writeln;
  END; {makediscrete}


Procedure printmaps(discrete : kmatrix);
{Uses global constants: imax, jmax}
  VAR
    i : rangei;
```

```
                              j : rangej;
                           BEGIN
                             FOR j := 0 to jmax do begin
                               FOR i := 0 to imax do
                                 write(discrete[i,j]:1);
                               writeln;
                             end; {FOR j ...}
                             writeln;
                             FOR j := 0 to jmax do begin
                               write(discrete[0,j]:1);
                               FOR i := 1 to imax do
                                 IF discrete[i,j]=discrete[i − 1,j]
                                 THEN write(' ')
                                 ELSE write(discrete[i,j]:1);
                               writeln;
                             end; {FOR j ...}
                           END; {Printmaps}

                        BEGIN {main program}
                          initialise;
                          makea(a,size);
                          maketemperature(tolerance,size,a,temperature);
                          makediscrete(temperature,discrete);
                          printmaps(discrete);
                        END.
```

Testing

******Temperature contour plotting program*******

**Semi-infinite strip with temperature 0 along the
semi-infinite edges and f(y), specified by a Fourier
series, along the remaining edge**

**Coordinate patch: horizontally x = 0 to   1.00
                            vertically y = 0 to   1.00**

**minimum temperature is: −0.0000
maximum temperature is: 99.7973**

**Contour 0 is at temperature: −0.0000
Contour 1 is at temperature: 11.0886
Contour 2 is at temperature: 22.1772
Contour 3 is at temperature: 33.2658
Contour 4 is at temperature: 44.3543
Contour 5 is at temperature: 55.4429
Contour 6 is at temperature: 66.5315
Contour 7 is at temperature: 77.6201
Contour 8 is at temperature: 88.7087
Contour 9 is at temperature: 99.7973**

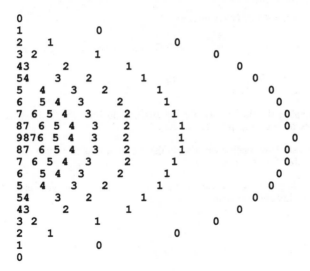

We see that we have the correct results on the edges. For $x > \sim\frac{1}{2}$ the series converges very rapidly, and in this region we can check on a calculator that correct results have been obtained for one or two grid-points.

Problems

Lunar lander simulator

7.1   Allow for horizontal motion. The spacecraft must land within 25m of a target point, because outside this region the moon's surface is not sufficiently flat. We need to specify extra initial data: horizontal velocity and horizontal displacement from the target point. As well as the fuelrate, the astronaut must also be able to control the angle from the vertical at which the engines thrust.

7.2   Make the simulator work in realtime. That is, the value of the fuelrate stays fixed until a new value is typed in at the keyboard.

Communications simulator

7.3   Remove the check digit facility, so that each character in the input file is sent down the channel once only. How does this affect the error count?

7.4   A more sophisticated Gilbert channel model has 3 noise states – low, medium and high – with transition probabilities plh, plm, pml, pmh, phl and phm. Modify the program to allow for this generalisation.

7.5   In the program, it has been assumed that the information that there has been a transmission error is communicated perfectly from receiver to sender. Of course, in reality that information must also be sent along the channel and is liable to corruption. Adjust the program to mirror the reality. *Hint*: Send a character along the channel from receiver to sender to indicate whether or not the previous group of characters has been accurately transmitted. What do you do if the character received at the sender is not one of the two possibilities?

Temperature in a plate

7.6   A different boundary condition is imposed on the edge $x = 0$:

$$f(y) = 400 \, y \, (y - ymax)°\text{C}$$

so that, with $ymax = 1, f\left(\frac{1}{2}\right) = 100°\text{C}$. The Fourier series coefficients are then

$$a_n = 3200 \, ymax^2/(n^3 \, \pi^3) \quad \text{for } n \text{ odd}$$
$$a_n = 0 \quad \text{for } n \text{ even}$$

What value should be used for the summation limit N? Adjust the program to produce a contour map for this case.

7.7   Investigate how much more slowly the program runs if we use the $x = 0$ value for N, i.e. 200, for all values of x.

7.8   If suitable graphics hardware and software is available to you, use it to produce a good quality contour map.

Data abstraction

8.1 Enumerated types
8.2 Strings
8.3 Records
8.4 Sets
8.5 Abstract data types

By this stage, most of the Pascal statements have been covered, and what remains is the rich selection of user-defined type constructs. The new concept of enumerated types is reinforced by an example on looping using state indicators, thus getting back to algorithms in a natural way. The structured type, records, fit in well here because they are simply collections of other types, and they provide good examples of the use of subranges and enumerated types. Pascal is unusual in providing a set data type, and some interesting applications of it are discussed. The chapter ends with a look at abstract data types which brings together the type definition features discussed so far.

8.1 Enumerated types

The objects that programs have to deal with go beyond the predefined types, which provide only for numbers, characters and boolean values. Good examples come from the data in a passport, with the following three items not falling into any predefined category:

sex	male or female
marital status	single, married, widowed, divorced, separated
colour of eyes	blue, grey, brown, hazel, green

In older languages, such values had to be forced into one of the predefined types, leading to **codes**, which were usually numeric. For example, male would be 1 and female 2. The disadvantage of this scheme is that it can easily lead to errors by using the wrong code, and there is no obvious check that a code is valid at all.

Pascal recognises that its predefined types do not cover everything and provides for new types to be constructed with the individual values listed as identifiers. This is known as **enumerating** the values, and hence these types are called **enumerated types**.

Form of an enumerated type

An enumerated type is declared in a type statement, with the type formation being a list of identifiers. Formally, this gives:

Enumerated type

> *identifier* = (*list of identifiers*);

Examples are:

```
TYPE
  sex        = (male, female);
  status     = (single, married, widowed, divorced, separated);
  eyecolours = (blue, grey, brown, hazel, green);
  machines   = (micro, mini, mainframe);
  states     = (found, notthere, looking);
  suits      = (clubs, diamonds, hearts, spades);
```

Enumerated values

All enumerated values must be different.

Each enumerated type can have as many values as one likes, but each must be a distinct identifier, and the identifiers must not clash with other identifiers within the same scope. Specifically, a given identifier cannot be a value in two different types, as in

```
TYPE
  lights     = (red, amber, green);
  eyecolours = (blue, grey, brown, hazel, green);
```

However, subranges of newly-declared enumerated types are possible, and can often be used to good effect, as in:

Subranges of enumerated values.

```
TYPE
  daysoftheweek = (Monday, Tuesday, Wednesday, Thursday,
                   Friday, Saturday, Sunday);
  weekdays      = Monday..Friday;
  weekend       = Saturday..Sunday;
```

> midweekbreak   = Tuesday..Saturday;

Unfortunately, these types are linear, and do not 'wrap around'. Subranges therefore must refer to values in order. For example, we cannot follow the above declarations with

> longweekend   = Friday..Monday;

The notation for an enumerated value is simply an identifier like *boolean*. As for any other identifier, the case of letter is unimportant. Thus the following all refer to the same value:

> Monday
> monday
> MONDAY

Enumerated functions and operators

There are three functions that apply to all enumerated types:

> ord(id)   gives the ordinal value of *id* in the list of the type
>
> succ(id)   gives the next value in the list, if it exists
>
> pred(id)   gives the previous value in the list, if it exists

The values in an enumerated type are said to be ordered, and there exist equivalent ordinal values starting from 0. Thus in the *eyecolours* type, *ord(blue)* is 0 and *ord(brown)* is 2. The ordering can be used to loop through the values, either using a for-statement, as in

> VAR day : daysoftheweek;
> for day := Tuesday to Saturday do

or with *succ* or *pred*, as in

> day := Tuesday;
> while day <= Saturday do begin
>   {whatever}
>   day := succ(day);
> end;

One problem with using *succ* and *pred* is that they are not defined for the last and first values in a list respectively. Thus *succ(Saturday)* is alright, but *succ(Sunday)* should cause a value out of range error.

The operators that are available for enumerated types are the same as those for characters, i.e. the conditional operators = <> <= >= < and >. The interpretation of the inequalities is once again based on the order of the values as specified in the declaration of the type.

Input and output is not available for enumerated types in standard Pascal. Thus the use of enumerated types is often confined to manipulations inside a program. However, it is sometimes essential to get values from the outside

world into a program and to store them in an enumerated type. In order to
do this, the ordinal values referred to above might have to be employed.
Alternatively, the words used as the values can be read in and decoded.

In the same way, outputting an enumerated value involves a translation
from the identifier values to items that can be printed, i.e. numbers or strings
or characters. Both of these processes can be neatly packaged in procedures,
so that for any given new enumerated type, *x*, *readx* and *writex* routines can be
written. For debugging purposes, the *ord* of a value can be printed.

Example 8.1 Calculating bills

The Relaxeeze Holiday Camp in Zanyland has a basic charge of D120 per
person per week, but has three billing strategies, depending on the season and
the day on which the guests arrive:

> Arrive on Saturday, Sunday or Monday: standard charge
> Arrive after Monday: half price
> In summer: add 50%

Given the day of arrival, the season and the number of people, we can write a
function which will use these to work out the cost of the holiday.

```
TYPE
    daysofweek  = (Saturday, Sunday, Monday,Tuesday,
                   Wednesday, Thursday, Friday);
    seasons     = (spring, summer, autumn, winter);
    peoplerange = 0..100;  {can't take more}
    dollies     = 0..maxint;  {sky's the limit}

FUNCTION holidaycost  (
                arrival    : daysofweek;
                season     : seasons;
                people     : peoplerange) : dollies;

CONST
    basicrate   = 120;  {dollies}
VAR
    sofar : dollies;
BEGIN
    sofar := basicrate;
    if arrival > Monday then sofar := sofar div 2;
    if season = summer then sofar := round(sofar * 1.5);
    holidaycost := sofar * people;
END;  {holidaycost}
```

The ordering is
defined in the
type statement.

Notice that the declaration for the days of the week was altered to start on
Saturday so that the > could be used to good effect with the arrival day.

Looping with state indicators

As was mentioned before, enumerated types have a special use inside a program, where they make manipulating state-values natural and clear. One of the values that a program often needs is the state of a particular computation or iteration. This is illustrated in the next example.

Example 8.2   Prime numbers

| Problem | Given a positive integer, decide whether it is prime or not.

| Solution | The basic method for deciding whether a number is prime is to divide it by successive smaller numbers and if any divides evenly, then the number is not prime. There are several well-known refinements to this outline, i.e.

- 1, 2 and 3 are prime;

- try dividing by 2 first;

- then start dividing from 3, and skip all even numbers as divisors;

- stop dividing when the divisor exceeds the square root of the number.

To explain the last refinement, note that if the number has a divisor, and that divisor is greater than the square root, then a divisor smaller than the square root must already have been found. So once all the smaller numbers have been tried, the process can stop.

| Examples |

Number : 37	Approx. square root : 6
Divisors : 2 3 5	Result : Prime
Number : 217	Approx. square root : 14
Divisors : 2 3 5 7	Result : Not prime
Number : 211	Approx. square root : 14
Divisors : 2 3 5 7 9 11 13	Result : Prime

| Algorithm | The algorithm can be phrased in a pseudo-code chart as shown overleaf. There are two points at which the loop can stop, and neither is at the start or end of the loop, so a while statement or repeat statement is not immediately applicable. What we do is regard the loop as having **states**, which can be expressed in the symbolic type

```
TYPE states = (stilldividing, factorfound, nofactors);
```

The state of the loop starts off as *stilldividing*. Then when one of the stopping conditions becomes true, the state changes. After the loop, the state can be tested to establish the result.

A straight-
forward
algorithm.

Prime number tester

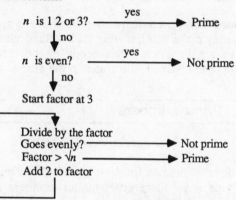

For a clever
algorithm, see
the problems.

Program   The actual prime tester is written as a function, so that it may be called from other programs. The program itself is very basic, and just calls the function for one number at a time.

```
PROGRAM Primetesting (input, output);
    VAR  number : integer;

    FUNCTION prime (n : integer) : boolean;
    TYPE
        natural   = 0..maxint;
        states    = (stilldividing, factorfound, nofactors);
    VAR
        factor    : integer;
        root      : natural;
        state     : states;
    BEGIN
      if (n <= 3) then prime := true else
      if not odd(n) then prime := false else
      BEGIN
        root := trunc(sqrt(n));
        write('Square root is approx: ', root:1,
        '    Trial factors are: ');
        factor := 3;
        state := stilldividing;
        REPEAT
          write(' ', factor:1);
          if n mod factor = 0 then state := factorfound else
          if factor > root then state := nofactors else
          factor := factor + 2;
        UNTIL state <> stilldividing;
        writeln;
        prime := not (state = factorfound);
      END;
    END; {prime}

BEGIN
    writeln('****** Prime testing program ******');
```

Looping with
state indicators.

```
    write('Type in a number (greater than 0): ');
    readln(number);
    case prime(number) of
      true  : writeln(number:1, ' is prime');
      false : writeln(number:1, ' is not prime');
    end; {case}
  END.
```

Sample test runs might be:

****** **Prime testing program** ******
Type in a number (greater than 0): 211
Square root is approx: 14   Trial factors are: 3 5 7 9 11 13 15
211 is prime

****** **Prime testing program** ******
Type in a number (greater than 0): 213
Square root is approx: 14   Trial factors are: 3
213 is not prime

****** **Prime testing program** ******
Type in a number (greater than 0): 12343
Square root is approx: 111   Trial factors are: 3 5 7 9 11 13 15
17 19 21 23 25 27 29 31 33 35 37 39 41 43 45 47 49 51
53 55 57 59 61 63 65 67 69 71 73 75 77 79 81 83 85 87
89 91 93 95 97 99 101 103 105 107 109 111 113
12343 is prime

It may seem wasteful in this last example to be dividing by multiples of 3, when we know that 3 doesn't go. The same applies to multiples of 5 and 7 and so on. However, recognising multiples in order to exclude them as divisors will take a division operation in itself, which will not save anything. There are other methods of testing for primes, and a good one is discussed in the problems.

8.2 Strings

Pascal recognises that character elements are frequently replicated to form strings for storing names, addresses, sentences and in fact any kind of text data. Strings have a special place in Pascal's array mechanism. Unfortunately, the extra privileges accorded to strings do not go far enough for many applications, and most Pascal systems have extended them. These extensions are usually sensible enough, but using them renders a program non-standard and hence difficult to move to other Pascal systems. For that reason, we mention only the most important ones at the end of this section, and advise strongly that the use of extensions is kept to a minimum, and clearly marked in a program.

Pascal's string features are rudimentary.

The form of strings

In order to ensure that strings are stored efficiently, there is a special form of array declaration for them:

String type

> *identifier* = PACKED ARRAY [*bound type*] of char;

The addition of the word *packed* informs the Pascal system that it can squeeze up the items, several to a memory word. Words usually contain 32 bits, large enough for four characters, so that a saving in space is made. The computer can also deal more efficiently with characters stored in this way, rather than one per word. To recognise this, Pascal has a few additional properties for strings.

String values and operators

String literals were introduced right at the start of the book, and consist of characters enclosed in quotes. A string constant of n characters is considered to be of the type

        PACKED ARRAY [1..n] of char;

which enables them to be used in expressions with array variables of the same type.

Strings may be compared using all six relational operators. For example, we can declare

```
CONST
  n            = 6;
  default      = 'Holmes';
TYPE
  namerange = 1..n;
  names        = PACKED ARRAY [namerange] of char;
VAR
  yourname, myname : names;
```

and then have

```
myname := 'Watson';
yourname := default;
if myname = yourname then ...
if myname < yourname then ...
```

The length of a string is part of its type.

However, strings are of fixed length, so it is not possible to say

```
myname := 'Wu';   yourname := 'Moriarty';
```

as these constants do not have exactly six characters, as required by this particular type.

Reading and writing strings

Writing out constant strings is a familiar operation. Since there is an equivalent type, and variables of it can be defined, it is also possible to write out string variables. This does not apply to plain arrays of characters, which is why it is so important to include the keyword *packed* in the declaration.

Pascal does not give any additional assistance for reading a string. Thus a string has to be read character by character. This is fine if the data is exactly the same length as the string. Take for example the declarations:

```
CONST
      namemax    = 10;
TYPE
      namerange  = 1..namemax;
      names      = packed array [namerange] of char;
VAR
      name  : names;
```

Then the data J Robinson which is exactly 10 characters long can be read with the loop

```
FOR i := 1 to namemax do read(name[i]);
```

However, if the name is shorter or longer than will fit, additional checks and reactions are needed. The usual conventions are that

- shorter strings are padded with blanks,
- longer strings are truncated.

Given this, it becomes reasonable to define a special readname procedure:

```
PROCEDURE readname (VAR name : names);
  CONST
    space = ' ';
  VAR  i : namerange;
  BEGIN
    for i := 1 to namemax do
      if eoln  then name[i] := space else read(name[i]);
    readln;
  END; {readname}
```

A useful procedure for reading strings.

Example 8.3 Multilingual interfaces

| Problem | A program is being written for general use within several countries, and it is a requirement that the output should be in whatever language is spoken in that country. However, we do not want to change the program every time. How can the words printed out be made

independent of the Pascal code?

| Solution | The solution is to make the words data and store them in files, one for each language. At the start of the program, the langauge required is set, and the words from that file are read into one or more arrays. Instead of writing out actual strings, the program is altered to write out the contents of the array instead.

| Algorithm | As an example, take the days of the week. Within the program, we can refer to these by means of an enumerated scalar, in English, i.e.

```
TYPE
   daysofweek   = (Monday, Tuesday, Wednesday, Thursday,
                    Friday, Saturday, Sunday);
```

The actual words to be printed will be stored in a file. For example, the French versions are

```
    lundi
    mardi
    mercredi
    jeudi
    vendredi
    samedi
    dimanche
```

and could be stored in a file called *French.days*.

The longest name is eight letters long, so the declarations for name, as given above, will be appropriate, as will the *readname* procedure. The array of day names is then simply an array of this type.

| Program | The declarations required are:

```
CONST
   daynamemax  = 8;
TYPE
   namerange   = 1.. daynamemax;
   names       = packed array [namerange] of char;
   daysofweek  = (Monday, Tuesday, Wednesday, Thursday,
                   Friday, Saturday, Sunday);
   daynames    = array [daysofweek] of names;

VAR
   dayfile     : text;
   filename    : names;
   dayname     : daynames;
```

Then the reading in of the French names and writing them can be done by first reading in the filename, and then the strings, as in:

```
write('Which file for the day names? ');
readln(filename);
reset (dayfile, filename);
for day := Monday to Sunday do
  readname(dayfile,dayname[day]);

write(dayname[Friday]);
```

Non-standard
reset: see
section 4.4.

This last will write out a full eight characters for each string, which may not be what is required in all circumstances. For that reason, a procedure similar to *readname* can be written, which will only write out the letters of a name, omitting any trailing blanks.

```
PROCEDURE writename (name : names);
  CONST space = ' ';
  VAR  i : namerange;
  BEGIN
    FOR  i := 1 to daynamemax do
      if name[i] <> space then write(name[i]);
  END; {writename}
```

Switching to another language would be done by changing the file name, and reading in the new words.

Extensions for strings

A popular extension of Pascal for handling strings is the addition of a predefined type which will accept strings of different lengths. For any string variable, the programmer has to specify the maximum string length, but within that, strings of varying lengths can be mixed. For example, one may declare

These are useful but make a program non-portable.

```
VAR  S : string[25];
```

and assign

```
S := 'ABCDE';
```

The string *S* now has an actual length of 5, but still retains its potential length of 25. Later on, another assignment such as

```
S := 'LMNOPQR';
```

will extend *S* .

These strings are very useful because they can be parameters to *read* and *readln* statements. The normal convention is that an end-of-line ends a string, so that *readln(S)* will accept a string of any length less than 25, and enable it to be written out exactly, and compared successfully with strings of other lengths. What happens when the data is longer than 25 depends on the particular implementation.

String extensions usually also include a suite of routines to manipulate strings by taking pieces out of them, finding substrings, joining strings together and so on. The details of these will be included with the documentation of your Pascal system.

8.3   Records

Many programming applications are centred around the processing of data, which may assume a fairly complicated form. An example would be the full information required for a passport, which would include names, date of birth, sex, marital status, various facial characteristics and so on. All these items combine to form a single unit and there will be times when they need to be treated as such. Pascal provides for such a grouping mechanism in its record construct.

Form of a record type

A record type is declared as a list of fields of other types, enclosed in keywords. The types of the fields can be anything, either all different or all the same or a mixture.

Record type

```
identifier = RECORD
          field : type;
          field : type;
              . . .
          field : type;
        END;
```

An example of a natural application of a record type would be a date: this comprises three fields, but may well be treated as a unit by itself on occasion. Such a definition, with its subsidiary definitions, would be:

```
CONST
    past   = 1750;
    future = 2500;
TYPE
    days   = 1..31;
    months = 1..12;
    years  = past..future; {The limit of the program's lifetime!}

    dates  = RECORD
                day      : days;
```

```
            month    : months;
            year     : years;
          END;
complex = RECORD
            re,
            im : real;
          END;
```

Since a field can be of any type, it could be a record itself. For example,

Records within records.

```
TYPE
  sexes      = (male, female);
  newborns   = RECORD
                 sex    : sexes;
                 birth  : dates;
               END;
```

Record values

The range of values for any one record is the product of every value of every field. In other words, any kind of composite value can be accommodated in a record type. However, there are no literals for record values.

Record operators and functions

The important operator as far as records are concerned is that for **field selection**, which is indicated by a dot. Any field of a record can be selected by giving the record variable name (not the type name) followed by a dot and the field name. If there are records within records, then several dots can be used to access the lower fields as in

Introducing the dot operator.

```
VAR baby : newborns;

baby.sex := female;
baby.birth.day := 21;
baby.birth.month := 3;
baby.birth.year := 1986;
```

There are no predefined functions that apply to record types. Records can be used as parameters, as can fields of a record.

Record values cannot be read or written in their entirety by the predefined read and write statements. It is necessary to treat each scalar field separately. As for enumerated types, it is a good idea to construct procedures for each of these operations. So, for example, one would define *readdate* and *writedate* procedures to handle variables of the type *dates*. However, entire records can be input from and output to files using the *get* and *put* procedures, as discussed in section 10.4.

Example 8.4   Complex roots of an equation

Problem   We have an equation which we suspect has complex roots. Can
Newton-Raphson be used?

Solution   The answer is yes. There is no problem in using the Newton-
Raphson method to find a complex root, but of course we shall
have to do complex arithmetic. Pascal does not have a predefined complex
type, but we can define one. We shall then have to define procedures or
functions for every operation that we wish to perform on the new type.

Algorithm   The type we need forms a record:

```
TYPE complex = record
               re,
               im : real;
               end;
```

We shall need to provide all the basic arithmetic operations for this type, i.e.
addition, subtraction, multiplication, division, absolute value, reading and
writing. Furthermore, we shall need a means of converting a real constant
into a complex form. An example of one of the procedures would be:

```
PROCEDURE cadd (var c : complex;  a,b : complex);
  BEGIN
    c.re := a.re + b.re;
    c.im := a.im + b.im;
  END;  {cadd}
```

Once we have these procedures, we find that life is still not very easy!
Suppose we have the simple quadratic $x^2 + 2x + 2$ to solve. Instead of being
able to write this as a Pascal expression, we have to break it up into its
individual operations and call the appropriate procedures. The calls will
look like this:

```
{calculate f := x * x + 2x + 2}
cmult(f, xold, xold);          {f := xold * xold}
cconst(two, 2);                {convert 2 to two}
cmult(temp, two, xold);        {temp := 2 * xold}
cadd(f ,f, temp);              {f := f + temp
cadd(f, f, two);               {f := f + two}
```

This is very tedious, but at least the job can be done.

After the function itself, we also have to calculate its derivative and the
new value of x. We have used the existing Newton procedure, suitably
updated with parameters, and have added the extra monitor parameter to
enable partial results to be printed out easily.

Program

```
PROGRAM NewtonRaphson(input,output);
{Implements the Newton-Raphson method for
complex roots of a specific equation}

TYPE
  complex = record
    re,
    im : real;
  END;
  range = 0..maxint;
VAR
  imax        : integer;
  iterations  : range;
  tolerance   : real;
  xnew, xold  : complex;

PROCEDURE cconst (var c : complex; r : real);
  BEGIN
    c.re := r;
    c.im := 0;
  END; {cconst}

PROCEDURE cadd (var c : complex;  a,b : complex);
  BEGIN
    c.re := a.re + b.re;
    c.im := a.im + b.im;
  END; {cadd}

PROCEDURE cmult (var c : complex;  a,b : complex);
  BEGIN
    c.re := a.re * b.re – a.im * b.im;
    c.im := a.re * b.im + a.im * b.re;
  END; {cmult}

PROCEDURE cdiv (var c : complex; a,b : complex);
  BEGIN
    c.re := (a.re * b.re + a.im * b.im)/(sqr(b.re) + sqr(b.im));
    c.im := (b.re * a.im – a.re * b.im)/(sqr(b.re) + sqr(b.im));
  END; {cdiv}

PROCEDURE csub (var c : complex; a,b : complex);
  BEGIN
    c.re := a.re – b.re;
    c.im := a.im – b.im;
  END; {csub}

FUNCTION cabs (b : complex) : real;
  BEGIN
    cabs := sqrt(sqr(b.re) + sqr(b.im));
  END; {cabs}

PROCEDURE cwrite (c : complex);
  BEGIN
```

```
          write('(',c.re:1:4,',',c.im:1:4,')');
      END; {cwrite}

  PROCEDURE cread (var c : complex);
      BEGIN
          read(c.re, c.im);
      END; {cread}

  PROCEDURE initialise;
      BEGIN
          writeln('********Newton-Raphson root-finding ',
              'program*******');
          writeln('for x * x + 2x + 2');
          writeln;
          write('Initial estimate for root:');
          cread(xnew); readln;
          write('Required error limit:');
          readln(tolerance);
          write('Maximum number of iterations permitted:');
          readln(imax);
          writeln;
          writeln(' i     x');
      END; {initialise}

  PROCEDURE Newton (var xold, xnew : complex; var i : range;
      imax : range; tolerance : real; monitor : boolean);
      VAR
          temp, one, two, f, fdiff : complex;
          b : boolean;
      BEGIN
       i := 0;
       REPEAT
          i := i + 1;
          if monitor then begin
              write('xnew = '); cwrite(xnew); writeln;
          end;
          xold := xnew;
          {calculate f := x * x + 2x + 2}
          cmult(f, xold, xold);
          cconst(two, 2);
          cmult(temp ,two, xold);
          cadd(f f, temp);
          cadd(f, f, two);

          {calculate fdiff := 2x + 2}
          cadd(fdiff, temp, two);

          {calculate xnew := xold − f/fdiff}
          cdiv(temp, f, fdiff);
          csub(xnew, xold, temp);

          {calculate xnew − xold}
          csub(temp, xnew, xold);
       UNTIL (cabs(temp) < tolerance) or (i = imax);
      END; {Newton}
```

```
        BEGIN
          initialise;
          Newton (xold, xnew, iterations, imax, tolerance, true);

          if iterations = imax
          then begin
            write('Failed to converge: x=');
            cwrite(xnew);
            write('x0 = ');
            cwrite(xold);
            writeln('in i =',iterations:3);
          end else begin
            write('Root is:');
            cwrite(xnew);
            writeln;
            writeln('   ',iterations:3,' iterations required');
          end;
        END.
```

Testing

*******Newton-Raphson root-finding program*******
for x * x + 2x + 2 with suspected complex roots

Initial estimate for root: 5.0 6.0
Required error limit: 1e-6
Maximum number of iterations permitted: 50

i   x
xnew = (5.0000,6.0000)
xnew = (1.9583,3.0417)
xnew = (0.3970,1.6053)
xnew = (-0.4557,0.9799)
xnew = (-0.9445,0.8799)
xnew = (-1.0080,1.0059)
xnew = (-1.0000,1.0000)
xnew = (-1.0000,1.0000)
Root is:(-1.0000,1.0000)
8 iterations required

Running the program again with an initial guess of (5.0, -6.0) will find the other complex root.

The with-statement

Writing out long selected field names can be tedious. Pascal provides a shorthand which factorises out the common parts of a field name – the with-statement. The usual form of the with-statement is:

With-statement

WITH   *record variable name* DO BEGIN
    statements;
END; {with}

The scope of the with-statement extends from the BEGIN to the END and within this scope any reference to the fields of the record mentioned can be given without their prefix. For example, the group of statements above could be rewritten as

```
baby.sex := female;
WITH baby.birth DO BEGIN
    day := 21;
    month := 3;
    year := 1986;
END; {WITH}
```

This version is not any shorter, but it is perhaps easier to read and to write, because there is less repetition.

The syntax of the with-statement includes a version for having a list of record names, an example of which would be:

```
WITH baby, baby.birth DO BEGIN
    sex := female;
    day := 21;
    month := 3;
    year := 1986;
END; {WITH}
```

It is permissible to mention a record more than once, as was done here, but it is not correct to mention two records of the same type. In this case, the Pascal system would not know to which record each field belonged.

It is also possible to have a with-statement applying to only one statement, in which case the begin-end is omitted. The good use of this option is with read and write statements, as in:

```
with baby.birth do write(day, month, year);
```

Variant records

The information that is gathered together to form a record type could have inherent variations. For example, in a record that has a field for marital status, there may be additional fields for the name and occupation of the spouse. However, if a particular record of this type had the marital status listed as single, then these latter fields would not apply. In fact, it may well be erroneous to store or access them. Pascal provides for this eventuality in a limited way with the concept of records with variants.

Form of a variant record type

A record type may specify one field as a **tag field.** Thereafter, for each value of the tag field, a different group of fields may be specified. Each of these groups is known as a **variant**. The form of a record with variants is:

Variant record type

```
identifier = RECORD
  fixed fields
  CASE tag-field : tag-type OF
    tag-values : (variant fields);
    tag-values : (variant fields);

      . . .

    tag-values : (variant fields);
  END; {RECORD}
```

The tag field may be of any of the discrete types, i.e. integer, character, boolean, enumerated, or subranges of these. Each value of this type must be listed with a corresponding list of fields. There may be none, one or more fields for each tag value. The fixed fields are always listed first in the record, and are optional. Examples of variant record declarations are:

```
TYPE
  names       = packed array [namerange] of char;
  occupations = 000 .. 999; {coded}
  status      = (married, divorced, single, widowed);

  person = RECORD
      name    : names;
      birth   : dates;
      CASE MaritalStatus : status of
        married   : (spouse : names;
                            occupation : occupations);
        divorced  : (since : dates);
        single    : ( );
        widowed   : (dependents : integer);
    END;

  kinds       = (cartesian, polar);
  coordinates = RECORD
    CASE kind : kinds of
      cartesian   : (x,y : real);
      polar       : (theta : angles;
```

```
            radius : real);
END;
```

When a variable is declared of one of these types, initialisation of the tag field becomes important. For example, if we declare

```
VAR
    P, Q  : person;
    C, D  : coordinates;
```

then valid assignments of values would be:

Tags provide
essential
control over the
variants.

```
readname(P.name);
readdate (P.birth);
P.MaritalStatus := single;
readname(Q.name);
readdate(Q.date);
Q.maritalStatus := widowed;
read(Q.dependents);

C.kind := cartesian;
read(C.x, C.y);
D.kind := polar;
read(D.theta, D.radius);
```

Once the tag field has been given a value, only those fields of the corresponding variant are defined. Thus a variant record provides a secure way of hiding unwanted information. It would not be valid to now refer to *P.dependents* or *C.radius*, since these fields are incompatible with their respective records' tag fields.

Example 8.5   Roots of a quadratic

Problem   Solve the quadratic equation $ax^2 + bx + c = 0$ for given values of a, b and c.

Solution   This may seem a come-down after the complexity of example 8.4, but what we want to do here is to cater for all sorts of roots. The first thing to remember is the formula for the roots of the equation. It is

$$x = \frac{-b \pm \sqrt{b^2 - 4ac}}{2a}$$

The problem is that the the expression inside the square root may be negative, in which case, the roots are complex and are calculated slightly differently. Another check to be made is whether the coefficient a is zero, because then the formula must not be applied.

Algorithm The algorithm is based on checking the coefficients and the discriminant $b^2 - 4ac$ and performing one of four different calculations. In so doing, a message about the classification of the roots can also be given to the user.

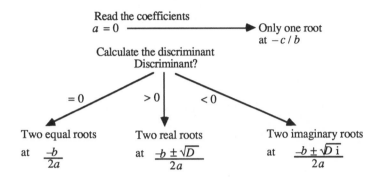

If the procedure is to be reused, it must be made self-contained. In other words, it must communicate through parameters only. The input parameters will be the coefficients, a, b and c. The output parameters will be the roots. But how are these to be expressed? The number of roots and their meaning will differ according to the discriminant calculated on the basis of the coefficients. To recap, we have the following possibilities:

- no roots

- one root

- two real roots (possibly equal)

- two imaginary roots, each with two components.

Catering for all possible cases.

We therefore employ a variant record to express all these variations in a single type.

The definition of the fields for the record follows the list above. Before defining the record, though, we should consider how to represent the imaginary roots. These are given by

(realpart, impart) and (realpart, –impart)

and we can re-use the type *complex* defined earlier.

Program

```
PROGRAM TestQuadratics (input, output);
  TYPE
    rootsorts      = (none, onereal, tworeal, twoimaginary);
    complex        = record
                        realpart,
```

```
                                          impart    : real;
                              end;
                  rootrec        = record
                    case sort : rootsorts of
                      none          : ( );
                      onereal       : (R : real);
                      tworeal       : (R1, R2 : real);
                      twoimaginary  : (i1, i2 : complex);
                  end;

              VAR
                  a,b,c : real;
                  roots : rootrec;
```

A clean, self-
contained
interface.

```
                  PROCEDURE quadratic (a, b, c : real;  var roots : rootrec);
                  VAR
                    D : real; {discriminant}
                    twoa : real;  {optimisation}

                  BEGIN
                      twoa := 2 * a;
                      with roots do begin
                        if (a = 0) and (b = 0) then
                          sort := none
                        else
                        if a = 0 then begin
                          sort := onereal;
                          R := -c / b;
                        end else begin
                          D := b * b - 4 * a * c;
                          if D = 0 then begin
                            sort := tworeal;
                            R1 := -b / twoa;
                            R2 := R2;
                          end else
                          if D > 0 then begin
                            sort := tworeal;
                            R1 := (-b + sqrt(D)) / twoa;
                            R2 := (-b - sqrt(D)) / twoa;
                          end else begin
                            sort := imaginary;
                            i1.realpart := -b / twoa;
                            i2.realpart := i1.realpart;
                            i1.impart := sqrt(-D) / twoa;
                            i2.impart := - i1.impart;
                          end;
                        end;
                      end;
                  END; {Quadratic}

              BEGIN
              writeln('***** Solving quadratics ******');
              write('Type the coefficients ');
              readln(a,b,c);
              quadratic(a,b,c,roots);
```

```
     with roots do
     case sort of
        none           : writeln('Not a quadratic');
        onereal        : writeln('One real root ', R:6:2);
        tworeal        : writeln('Two real roots ', R1:6:2, '   ', R2:6:2);
        twoimaginary   : writeln('Two imaginary roots (',
                           i1.realpart:6:2,',',i1.impart:6:2,')   ',
                           '(',i2.realpart:6:2,',',i2.impart:6:2,')');
     end;
     END.
```

8.4   Sets

Pascal is one of a few languages that provides for grouping and manipulating items without respect to order. The type mechanism is the **set**, which has most of the properties and operations of the mathematical concept of a set.

By far and away the most common use of sets is the test for set membership. This has already been introduced in Chapter 4, along with the *in* operator. To recap, examples of such uses of **set literals** are

Familiar uses of set membership.

```
if month in [sep, apr, jun, nov] then days := 30;
borderlines := mark in [49, 59, 69, 74];
isadigit := ch in ['0'..'9'];
```

If the sets are to be used more often, or manipulated in any way, then a **set type** should be defined, along with **set variables** of that type. The declaration can be split into four stages.

Form of a set type

1.   **Define the base type.** A set has to be defined on a base type, which may be a small subrange of integer, char, boolean or enumerated or any subrange of these. Examples of base types are: Four steps in defining a set.

```
TYPE
   months      = (jan, feb, mar, apr, may, jun, jul, aug, sep, oct,
                  nov, dec);
   markrange   = 0..100;
   smallrange  = 'a'..'z';
   capitalrange = 'A'..'Z';
```

2.   **Define the set type.** The form of a set type definition is

Set type

```
identifier = SET OF base type;
```

Examples of set types are:

```
TYPE
    monthsets   = set of months;
    marksets    = set of markrange;
    smallsets   = set of smallrange;
    capsets     = set of capitalrange;
    charsets    = set of char;
```

Notice the use of the suffixes '-range' and '-set' to distinguish between bases and the sets themselves.

3.   **Declare the set variables.** Set types, like any other types, do not exist as items that can be manipulated. We first have to declare variables of that type. Examples are:

```
VAR
    allmonths, months30  : monthsets;
    class, border        : marksets;
    smalls : smallsets;
    letters, digits        : charsets;
```

4.   **Initialise the sets.** Like any other variable, a set variable does not have an initial value. That is, it does not start off as the empty set, any more than an integer variable starts off as zero. It is necessary, therefore, to initialise the set to some value, by listing the elements, or ranges of them, in square brackets, for example:

It is easy to
forget this part!

```
allmonths  := [jan..dec];
months30   := [sep, apr, jun, nov];
class      := [50, 60, 70, 75];
digits     := ['0'..'9'];
letters    := [ ]; {to start with}
smalls     := ['a' ..'z'];
```

Note the special case of [ ] which denotes the empty set, and is a set literal compatible with any set type.

Set values

Check your
system for its
set limit.

Theoretically, the range of a set is restricted only by the range of its base type. However, because of the way sets are implemented, there is usually a limit placed on the maximum ordinal value in a base type. Typical limits are 256 or 4096. For a limit of 256, the following would be valid base types

```
TYPE
    secondcentury = 100..199;
    charsets      = set of char;
```

but the following would not be valid:

```
TYPE
   numbers    = integer;
   fifthcentury = 400..499;
```

Even though *fifthcentury* has only 100 possible values, it exceeds the limit on the maximum ordinal value.

As we have already noted, literal sets are enclosed in square brackets, and may contain individual elements and ranges of elements, where the elements can be constants or expressions of the base type. Unfortunately, literal sets cannot be given names under the CONST section.

Set functions and operators

There are no predefined functions defined for whole sets. Sets can be passed as parameters to user-defined functions.

Neither input nor output to text-files is possible for whole sets – a restriction that we have already seen for whole records and whole arrays. Procedures for accomplishing this are described below.

There are several operators applicable to sets. The relational ones are:

in	set membership
= <>	set equality and inequality
<= >=	set inclusion

For manipulation of sets, the three operators are:

+	set union
*	set intersection
–	set difference

We shall now see how these are used in typical cases.

Manipulating sets

1. **Creating sets from sets**. A large set may have disjoint subsets, which can be formed by set difference, rather than by listing the elements in each case. For example, we can declare and initialise: *Four common uses of sets.*

```
VAR months31 : monthsets;

months31 := allmonths – months30 – [feb];
```

(This is exactly what the old rhyme says: '... all the rest have thirty-one, excepting February alone ...'.) Notice that the set operations work on sets, not elements, and it would have been incorrect to say – *feb* instead of – [*feb*].

2. **Creating sets from data.** The elements of a set cannot always be fixed as constants in a program. For example, not all schools and universities have the same class borders for marks as given earlier. To create a set dynamically, we initialise it to the empty set and use set union:

    ```
    class := [ ];   border := [ ];
    for i in 1 to 4 do begin
      read (mark);
      class := class + [mark];
      border := border + [mark − 1];
    end;
    ```

3. **Printing a set.** A set is not a simple type, and it cannot be printed in its entirety using a simple Pascal write statement. To print all the elements present in a set, we have to loop over the whole base type and use tests on set membership. For example

    ```
    for mark := 0 to 100 do if mark in classes then
      write (mark);
    ```

    There is no simpler way. In fact, to perform any operation on all elements of a set, we need such a combination of a for-statement and an if-statement.

4. **Cardinality of a set.** Sometimes it is necessary to know how many elements there are in a set (its cardinality). To count the elements, once again we have to loop through all possibilities and use tests on set membership. In general, such a function could be defined as:

Called *card* on
some systems.

```
FUNCTION cardinality (s : someset) : integer;
  VAR
   i  : somebase;
   count : integer; {0..maxsetsize}
  BEGIN
   count := 0;
   for i := lower to upper do if i in s then
     count := count + 1;
   cardinality := count;
  END; {cardinality}
```

The parts in italics will need to be specified for the particular set type and different versions of the function will have to be included for each set type for which it is required. In some Pascal systems, a single predefined function, called *card*, is provided which will work for any set type.

Example 8.6   Training schedules

| Problem | Employees at Zanyland Inc. attend training courses and a record of each course attended is kept on a file. We wish to

discover which employees have attended which course, and which courses overall have been used.

| Solution | One could construct arrays with the names of each employee who has done a course. Alternatively, if the employees are

identified by number, and the courses by letters, then sets can be used.

| Algorithm | Assume that the data looks like this

```
100 AHF
123 JHU
99 U
77 JHAF
213 BAF
190 AB
180 AJHUF
170 JHUF
110 BHAF
115 AHF
```

We need to keep a set of employee numbers for each course, and a set of all courses taken. This is done with the data structures:

```
CONST
 numbermax  = 250;
TYPE
  courses       = char;
  coursesets    = set of courses;
  numbers       = 000..numbermax;
  numbersets    = set of numbers;
VAR
  classlist      : array[courses] of numbersets;
  taken          : coursesets;
```

The algorithm then consists of reading in a number followed by courses until an end of line, and for each course, we add the number to the set in the array indexed by its character. The important statement is:

```
classlist[c] := classlist[c] + [number];
```

To get the full set of courses taken, we construct the union of all courses read in, as in

```
taken := taken + [c];
```

The rest of the program is concerned with printing out the sets neatly, four numbers to a line.

| Program |

The program is suprisingly simple. A striking feature of it is that the procedures do not use parameters. This is because there are only two main data structures, they are used from all parts of the program, and it would be superfluous to keep passing them in and out of the procedures. We do, of course, declare all other variables locally where they are needed.

```pascal
PROGRAM Trainingschedule (input, output);
  CONST
    numbermax      = 250;
    space          = ' ';
  TYPE
    courses        = char;
    coursesets     = set of courses;
    numbers  = 000..numbermax;
    numbersets     = set of numbers;

  VAR
    data       : text;
    classlist  : array[courses] of numbersets;
    taken      : coursesets;

  PROCEDURE InitialiseSets;
  VAR c : courses;
  BEGIN
    for c := 'A' to 'Z' do
      classlist[c] := [ ];
    taken := [ ];
  END; {InitialiseSets}

  PROCEDURE ReadEmployee;
  VAR c : courses;
      number : numbers;
  BEGIN
    read(data,number);
    write(number);
    read(data,c); write(c:5); {the space}
    while not eoln(data) do begin
      read (data,c); write(c);
      classlist[c] := classlist[c] + [number];
      taken := taken + [c];
    end;
    readln(data); writeln;
  END; {ReadEmployee}

  PROCEDURE PrintClassLists;
  var c : courses;

    PROCEDURE PrintSet(class : numbersets);
    CONST numbersperline = 4;
    VAR n : numbers;
        i : 1..numbersperline;
    BEGIN
      i := 1;
```

```
        for n := 0 to numbermax do
          if n in class then begin
            write(n:8);
            if i = numbersperline
            then begin
              writeln;
              i := 1;
            end else i := i + 1;
          end;
      END; {PrintSet}

  BEGIN
    writeln;
    writeln('Class Lists');
    for c := 'A' to 'Z' do
      if classlist[c] <> [ ] then begin
        writeln('Course ',c);
        PrintSet(classlist[c]);
        writeln;
      end;
    writeln;
    write('Courses used were :');
    for c := 'A' to 'Z' do
      if c in taken then write(c,space);
    writeln;
  END; {PrintClassLists}

  BEGIN
    writeln('**** Employee Training Statistics ****');
    reset (data, 'train.dat');
    InitialiseSets;
    writeln('Number  Courses');
    WHILE not eof(data) do
      ReadEmployee;
    PrintClassLists;
  END.
```

| Testing | A sample run would give:

**** Employee Training Statistics ****

Number   Courses
```
  100     AHF
  123     JHU
   99     U
   77     JHAF
  213     BAF
  190     AB
  180     AJHUF
  170     JHUF
  110     BHAF
  115     AHF
```

Class Lists
Course A
```
   77    100    110    115
```

```
        180    190    213
Course B
        110    190    213
Course F
         77    100    110    115
        170    180    213
Course H
         77    100    110    115
        123    170    180
Course J
         77    123    170    180
Course U
         99    123    170    180
```

Courses taken were : A B F H J U

8.5   Abstract data types

Records provide a very powerful means of grouping data together, as we have seen from the many examples in the previous section. Several of these examples involved modelling familiar concepts that have well accepted formats, such as dates, polar coordinates or complex numbers. Using records allows us to extend the repertoire of predefined Pascal types to make a richer language for our particular needs.

Consider, however, that the predefined types have, in addition to their specified range of values, sets of properties, operations, functions and input-output facilities. The record structuring facility does not automatically provide these for user-defined types   However, it would be desirable if we could create them, so that we could, for example, read a date or add two complex numbers.

Such extensions are known as **abstract data types**. The theory is that a data type consists not only of a set of values, but also of the operations that are applicable to it. Then any variables defined of that type can **only** use the operations provided. In other words, one would provide operations to subtract and compare days, but certainly not to multiply or divide them!

Unfortunately, standard Pascal does not provide any means for grouping together a data type definition with its procedures and functions. However, modelling with **adts** (abstract data types) is a good technique to bear in mind when designing a program, as shown in the following example. We have used comments to highlight the adt, but if your particular version of Pascal provides adt facilities (usually called units or modules) then you might like to experiment with it.

We have already seen an example of an adt in action: the complex roots of example 8.5 brought out the benefits and difficulties very clearly. We follow this with another example, completing an earlier problem.

Example 8.7   Calculating floor dimensions again

Continuing with the program to calculate the area of a house given the
dimensions of its rooms (discussed in example 5.7), we can now pay attention
to the data structuring.   Feet and inches together form a linear imperial
measurement, and should go in a record, and be treated as an adt.   The
operations that we could define would be:

- read a linear length
- write out a linear length
- multiply two lengths, giving an area
- compare two lengths for equality and inequality.

Not all of these are needed in our program. Furthermore, once it comes to
comparing, it may be easier just to deal with the metric measurements. For
this reason, we shall store both sets in a composite record for the room. The
data types are:

```
TYPE
{Abstract data type for Imperial Length and area}
    feet    = 0..feetmax; {something reasonable}
    inches        = 0..11;
    ImperialLinear   = record
                        ft  : feet;
                        ins    : inches;
                      end;
    ImperialArea   = real; { sq ft}
{End of adt declarations}

    MetricLength  = real;  {metres}
    MetricArea    = real;  {sq metres}

    RoomDimensions = record
      length, breadth     : ImperialLinear;
      area : ImperialArea;
      mlength, mbreadth  : MetricLength;
      marea              : MetricArea;
    end;

VAR
    room : RoomDimensions;
```

We shall assume that the metric measurements are recalculated as needed.
The program can now be far more readable, with the *length* and *breadth* field
names being used for the dimensions, rather than *ft1* and *ins1* etc. For
example, the multiply procedure can be called by:

```
WITH room do
    multiply (length, breadth, area);
```

compared with

```
                    multiply (ft1, ins1, ft2, ins2, area);
```

as previously. Within the procedure itself, we still need to refer to the first
and second dimensions in turn.

```
                PROCEDURE multiply (dim1, dim2 : ImperialLinear;
                           VAR a : ImperialArea);
                BEGIN
                  a := (dim1.ft + dim1.ins/12) * (dim2.ft + dim2.ins/12);
                END;
```

The complete program is given here.

```
                PROGRAM Floorspace (input, output);
                  {Reads dimensions of rooms in feet and prints the area
                  in sq ft and sq metres, together with total area}

                VAR data, results : text;

                PROCEDURE CopyHeadings;

                  PROCEDURE copyline;
                  VAR ch : char;
                  BEGIN
                    while not eoln(data) do begin
                      read(data,ch);  write(results,ch);
                    end;
                    readln(data);  writeln(results);
                  END; {Copyline}

                  BEGIN {copyheadings}
                    WHILE not eoln(data) {being a blank line}do begin
                    copyline;
                  END;
                    readln(data);  writeln(results);
                  END; {Copyheadings}

                  PROCEDURE CalculateRoomsandTotal;
                  CONST gap = 25;
                        feetmax = 100;
                  TYPE
                {Abstract data type for Imperial Length and area}
                    feet     = 0..feetmax;  {something reasonable}
                    inches       = 0..11;
                    ImperialLinear   = record
                               ft : feet;
                               ins    : inches;
                             end;
                    ImperialArea  = real; { sq ft}
                {End of adt declarations}
                    MetricLength  = real;  {metres}
                    MetricArea    = real;  {sq metres}

                    RoomDimensions = record
```

```
      length, breadth    : ImperialLinear;
      area               : ImperialArea;
      mlength, mbreadth  : MetricLength;
      marea              : MetricArea;
    end;

VAR
    room               : RoomDimensions;
    totalsqft, totalsqm : real;
    aBlankLine         : boolean;
    position           : 0 .. 80;

{Operations for the adt }
  PROCEDURE readlinear (VAR L : ImperialLinear);
  VAR
      a : integer;
      unit : char;

    PROCEDURE readinteger(var n : integer;
            var follow : char);
    VAR ch : char;
    BEGIN
      n := 0;
      repeat
        read(data,ch);  write(results,ch);
        position := position + 1;
      until ch in ['0'..'9'];
      while ch in ['0'..'9'] do begin
        n := n * 10 + ord(ch) – ord('0');
        read(data,ch);  write(results,ch);
        position := position + 1;
      end;
      follow := ch;
    END; {readinteger}

  BEGIN
    readinteger(a,unit);
    if unit = "" then begin
      L.ft := a;
      if data^ in ['0'..'9']
      then begin
        readinteger(a,unit);
        L.ins := a;
      end else L.ins := 0;
    end else
      L.ins := a;
  END; {readlinear}

  PROCEDURE multiply (dim1, dim2 : ImperialLinear;
                  VAR a : ImperialArea);
  BEGIN
    a := (dim1.ft + dim1.ins/12) * (dim2.ft + dim2.ins/12);
  END;
  {end of adt ops needed so far }
```

```
                    PROCEDURE checkforblankline;
                     BEGIN
                       readln(data);  writeln(results);
                       if eoln(data) then begin
                         aBlankLine := true;
                         readln(data); writeln(results);
                       end;
                     END;

                    PROCEDURE echoto(target : char);
                     VAR ch : char;
                     BEGIN
                       repeat
                         read(data,ch);  write(results,ch);
                         position := position + 1;
                       until ch = target;
                     END; {echoto}

                     PROCEDURE convert (L : ImperialLinear; var m : real);
                      BEGIN
                        m := (L.ft + L.ins/12) * 0.3048;
                      END;

                    BEGIN
                      aBlankLine := false;
                      totalsqft := 0;    totalsqm := 0;
                      WHILE not aBlankLine do
                      WITH room do begin
                        position := 0;
                        Echoto(' ');
                        readlinear (length);
                        EchoTo ('x');
                        readlinear (breadth);
                        multiply (length, breadth, area);
                        write (results, ' ': gap-position, area:6:2, 'sq ft        ');
                        convert (length, mlength);
                        convert (breadth, mbreadth);
                        marea := mlength * mbreadth;
                        writeln (results, mlength:5:2, 'm x',
                                    mbreadth:5:2, 'm ', marea:6:2,'sq m');
                        totalsqft := totalsqft + area;
                        totalsqm := totalsqm + marea;
                        Checkforblankline;
                      END;
                      writeln(results, 'Total area :',' ':gap-13, totalsqft:6:2,'sq ft',' ':23,
                               totalsqm:6:2,'sq m');
                    END; {CalculateRoomsandTotal}

                  BEGIN
                     writeln('***** Calculating floor areas *****');
                     writeln('For the data file connecting to floor.data');
                     write('For the results connecting to floor.out');
                     Copyheadings;
                     CalculateRoomsandTotal;
                  END.
```

Summary

☐   Enumerated types are constructed from lists of identifiers. In any scope, these identifiers may occur once only.

☐   Input and output are **not** automatically provided for enumerated types.

☐   Arrays declared as packed arrays of char are known as strings and have additional properties, such as being able to be read, written and compared for equality.

☐   Particular Pascal systems may have a more powerful, but non-standard, string type which allows variable length strings and many more operations on them.

☐   Pascal's strings are of fixed length (as set by the range of the subscript) so that always the full number of characters is read or written.

☐   Records comprise fields of different types. Fields are selected using a dot operator.

☐   The with-statement enables fields of a record to be referred to without the record name.

☐   Variant records consist of a section with fixed fields (maybe none) and then a case-statement listing various options for a variant section. Only one option is valid for a given variable, and it is determined by the value of the tag field.

☐   Field names in a record, as well as across options in a variant record, must be distinct.

☐   Sets can be declared on a base type which is integer, boolean, character or enumerated, but not real or string.

☐   Some Pascal systems have a limit (say, 4096) to the largest value in a set.

☐   A set is not initialised on declaration, and assigning it the value of the empty set or some constant set is necessary before working on it.

☐   Sets cannot be read or written with the predefined read and write statements. Custom-made procedures must be defined for each set type.

☐   The cardinality of the set is the number of elements it contains at any one time.

☐   Pascal provides set operators for membership (*in*), inclusion (< or <=), union (+), intersection (*) and difference (–).

☐   Abstract data types link a type definition (usually a record) with the operations that apply to it.

Self-check quiz

1.   Is the following a valid enumerated type? vowels = ('a','e','i','o','u');
2.   If the variable *day* is of an enumerated type *days*, can one say

       read(days)? write(days)?

3.   If a string is declared 20 characters long, and contains the word 'Jones' followed by spaces, how many characters of the string would be printed by the write statement?
4.   If we declare an array of strings, can we still get at the individual characters of each string?
5.   Can records be nested inside each other?
6.   Can fields in different options in a variant have the same names?
7.   Can a set of strings be declared?
8.   Find all the errors in the following excerpt.

```
TYPE
  coins = (1, 2, 5, 10, 20, 50);
  coinset = SET OF coins;
VAR
  n : coins;
BEGIN
  read (n);
  if n in coinset then ....
```

9.   An illness can be identified by possible symptoms, which are catered for by the enumerated type

```
TYPE
  symptoms = (temperature, headache, stomach ache, cough,
              runny nose, sore eyes, spots);
```

      Declare a type called *illness* which is a set of symptoms and write a procedure to print out all the symptoms of a given illness.
10.   Given that *flu* and *cold* are both illnesses, write an expression that represents those symptoms that are common to both.

Problems

8.1   A historian is studying the period of the Roman Empire, which extends either side of 1 AD. He wishes to computerise some of his data and to be able to compare and make simple calculations about the dates. Typical dates and calculations might be:

      54 BC − 64 BC = 10 years

      33 AD − 4 BC = 37 years

      Decide on a method of inputting, storing and outputting such dates, and write procedures to read a date, write a date and subtract two dates. Write a short program to test them.

8.2   Define a record type which will hold a string of up to 80 characters, as well as its length and the position of the first non-blank character. Define any other types you need. Now write procedures or functions to read and write such strings (assuming that on input, a string is terminated by an end-of-line). The procedures should set up and use the fields for the length and first non-blank position correctly. Consider what other operations might be useful on such a data structure, and implement them as additional procedures or functions. Write a short program to test them.

8.3   Since 1970, the Zanyland population statistics have been stored on a file, with each line containing the year followed by the total people counted for that year. Write a program that will read this file and find the two consecutive years in which there was the greatest percentage increase in population. Use a record to store the year-population pair. Write the program without using any arrays.

8.4   Design a record to hold a typical inventory of wares in a hardware shop. Write a program which will allow inventory data to be read off a text file, and which will print out the complete record of any item whose stock has fallen below its reorder level.

8.5   Choose an activity with which you are familiar and design a record data structure to store information about the people, equipment or events associated with the activity. What operations would be needed for this information?

8.6   The method for finding prime numbers discussed earlier in the chapter seemed very inefficient, in that division by 9, 15, 21, etc. was still attempted after division by 3 had failed. One of the ancient Greek philosophers, Eratosthenes, discovered a better method. The idea is to put all the numbers in a 'sieve'. The first number is taken out, then all multiples of it removed. Then the next number is taken out, and all its multiples removed. By this process, all of the 'taken out' numbers will be prime. Write a Pascal program to implement the Sieve of Eratosthenes, using sets.

8.7   A supermarket is running a competition in which a customer wins a prize for collecting cards with four lucky numbers. The cards are numbered from 1 to 60 and are handed out at the tills. Each Friday the four lucky numbers are announced and any customer holding cards with those numbers may claim a prize.
       Write a Pascal program which will check a given list of four numbers (from a customer) against a list of four read off a file and indicate whether a prize has been won or not. Use sets and set operations.

8.8   Starting with the program in example 8.6 on employee training schedules, adapt it to print out the names, rather than the numbers, of employees. Also use sets to work out how many employees are doing the same combination of any two courses.

8.9   Implement an abstract data type for coordinates represented as polar or cartesian. Test it out with an example such as that in problem 3.2 (the farm fence).

8.10   Implement an abstract data type for the 24-hour clock, and test it out in the program in example 3.8.

Sorting and advanced topics

We now return to algorithms and consider the more advanced features of Pascal that permit procedures to be generalised. Conformant array parameters enable procedures to operate on arrays of different sizes; procedural parameters allow procedures to have certain operations specified by the caller; and recursion is a technique which enables operations to be defined in terms of themselves – very powerful indeed! The focus for discussing these features is sorting, and a simple but effective sorting method is described.

9.1   Sorting

Sorting is a very common operation in computing, and many systems provide high level commands which enable data to be sorted in any specified way. These commands rely on one of a number of sorting algorithms and every programmer should know at least one such sorting algorithm off by heart. Here we introduce a simple one – selection sort – which performs in time proportional to the square of the number of items being sorted. Other algorithms (e.g. quicksort) perform faster, but are perhaps more difficult to understand and remember.

Selection sort

Sorting items means moving them around in a methodical way until they are all in order. A method used by some card players is to sort cards by holding them in the right hand, finding the lowest one and taking it out into the left hand, then finding the next lowest and taking it out, until all the cards have been selected, and the left hand holds the cards in order. The following sequence illustrates how this method works.

Left hand	Right hand
	7 3 9 0 2 5
0	7 3 9 – 2 5
0 2	7 3 9 – – 5
0 2 3	7 – 9 – – 5
0 2 3 5	7 – 9 – – –
0 2 3 5 7	– – 9 – – –
0 2 3 5 7 9	– – – – – –

We could implement this by having two arrays and picking the numbers out of one, adding them to the other. However, there is a way of keeping both lists in the same array, the one growing as the other shrinks. Each time an element is picked out, the gap it leaves is moved to one end, thus creating a contiguous gap, which is used to hold the new list. The move is done by a simple swap with the leftmost element of the right hand. So, the example would proceed as follows:

Left hand	Right hand
	7 3 9 0 2 5
0	3 9 7 2 5
0 2	9 7 3 5
0 2 3	7 9 5
0 2 3 5	9 7
0 2 3 5 7	9
0 2 3 5 7 9	

Each time a reduced list is considered, until only one element is left. The algorithm can be phrased more precisely as:

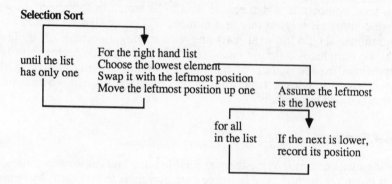

Because sorting is clearly going to be useful in many contexts, it makes sense to put it in a procedure from the beginning. The types that it will need are:

```
TYPE
    items   = integer; {for testing}
    range   = 1..max;
    tables  = array [range] of items;
```

The parameters would be the array to be sorted, and the number of items that are active in it. (The array may be 100 long, and only have 56 items stored in it, say.)

```
PROCEDURE sort (VAR a : tables; n : range);
    VAR
        temp        : items;
        i,
        smallest,
        leftmost   : range;

    BEGIN
        FOR leftmost := 1 to n – 1 do begin
            smallest := leftmost;
            for i := leftmost + 1 to n do
                if a[i] < a[smallest] then smallest := i;
            temp := a[smallest];
            a[smallest] := a[leftmost];
            a[leftmost] := temp;
        END;
    END; {sort}
```

Note the interface provided by the parameter list.

Example 9.1   Ocean temperatures sorted

Problem | An ocean-going research ship records the sea temperature at each hour of the day. The scientists on board like to see a sorted list of the temperatures in order to get a feel for the spread.

Solution | Read in the temperatures, sort them and print them out each day. The sorting procedure above can be used as is.

Program | The program starts by defining the types needed by the sort – items, range and tables. The output is in three columns for ease of reading.

```
PROGRAM SortingTemperatures (input, output);
    CONST
        max     = 24;
    TYPE
        items   = range; {degrees celsius}
        range   = 1..max;
        tables  = array [range] of items;
    VAR
```

```
                          temps   : tables;

              PROCEDURE readdata (VAR a : tables);
                VAR i : range;
                BEGIN
                  writeln('Type in the 24 temperatures');
                  for i := 1 to 24 do read(a[i]);
                  readln;
                END; {readdata}

              PROCEDURE sort (VAR a : tables;  n : range);
              {As defined above}
              END; {sort}

                BEGIN
                  writeln('****** Ocean temperatures in order ******');

                  readdata(temps);

                  sort (temps, noitems);

                  writeln('The temperatures in order are: ');
                  for i := 1 to 8 do
                    write(table[i]:6:2,'    ',table[i+8]:6:2,'     ',
                          table[i+16]:6:2,'      ');
                  writeln;
                END.
```

Testing

****** Ocean temperatures in order ******
Type in the 24 temperatures
11.1 11.08 11.03   11.56   11.98   12.01   12.0   12.13
12.13   12.5 12.4   12.09   12.5   12.8   13.01   13.1
14.5   14.6   14.51   13.5   13.32   13.04   12.9 12.8
The temperatures in order are
14.60   12.90   12.09
14.51   12.80   12.01
14.50   12.80   12.01
13.50   12.50   11.98
13.32   12.50   11.56
13.10   12.40   11.10
13.04   12.13   11.08
13.01   12.13   11.03

Sorting is a frequent requirement in computing, and it is useful to have a
sorting algorithm handy. As will be seen in following sections, the algorithm
can be applied to arrays of any size, and containing any elements, and can be
used to sort in ascending order just by changing the comparison from < to >.

Example 9.2   Sorting names and marks

| Problem | Suppose that the names and marks of a class of students have to be printed in alphabetical order. |

| Solution | Use a computer. Read all the name-mark pairs into an array, sort them according to the name using selection sort, and then print out the contents of the array.

| Algorithm | The first step is to define the data and the data structure. The data will look like this:

```
67   Jones K L
51   MacDeedle P
```

with the mark first and then the name. This enables the end of line to be used as a string terminator. We define a record with two fields – one for the name and one for the mark. In the sorting process, the name is used in the comparison part, but when the swapping is done, the whole record is copied. Thus the mark will move around with the name while sorting is proceeding.

| Program | The program is really just a rework of the sort given in the previous example, but we give it in full here to emphasise the versatility of the method. Because the types of the array being sorted are different, the sort procedure has had to be changed accordingly.

```
PROGRAM Sortingmarks (input, output, data);
  CONST
    classmax    = 200;
    namemax     = 24;
  TYPE
    namerange = 1..namemax;
    names      = packed array [namerange] of char;
    marks      = 0..100;
    students   = record
                        name : names;
                        mark  : marks;
                      end;
    classrange    = 1..classmax; {assumes at least one student}
    classes       = array [classrange] of students;

  VAR
    class        : classes;
    noofstudents,
    i                : classrange;
    data            : text;

  PROCEDURE readname (VAR name : names);
    VAR i : namerange;
    BEGIN
      for i := 1 to namemax do
```

This is the same as the previous sort, but for different types.

```
     if eoln(data) then name[i] := ' ' else read(data,name[i]);
     readln(data);
END;  { readname }

PROCEDURE sortname(var a : classes;  n : classrange);
VAR
  i,
  smallest,
  leftmost   : classrange;
  temp       : students;  {used in swapping}
BEGIN
  FOR leftmost := 1 to n − 1 do begin
    smallest := leftmost;
    for i := leftmost + 1 to n do
      if a[i].name < a[smallest].name
      then smallest := i;
    temp := a[smallest];
    a[smallest] := a[leftmost];
    a[leftmost] := temp;
  END;
END; {sortname}

BEGIN
  writeln('****** Sorting names and marks ******');
  write('For the data file '); connect(data);
  noofstudents := 0;
  while not eof(data) do begin
    noofstudents := noofstudents + 1;
    with class[noofstudents] do begin
      read(data, mark);
      readname(name);
    end;
    readln(data);
  end;

  sortname(class, noofstudents);

  writeln('The class in alphabetical order is: ');
  for i := 1 to noofstudents do
    with class[i] do
      writeln(name:namemax,'   ', mark:3);
END.
```

Access tables

A sorting optimisation.

Sorting involves a lot of swapping, and if the items being swapped are large records, this can be quite time consuming. There is a technique which can be used with any sorting algorithm to reduce the amount of physical moving of values.

For the array to be sorted, we define a companion array, the **access table**, over the same index type, with elements also of the index type thus

```
TYPE
    accesstables = array [range] of range;
VAR
    accesstable : accesstables;
```

The values of this array are initialised to the index values and all references to the array are then made via the access table.   When elements have to be swapped, only the access table elements are swapped, which could be very much quicker. Then when the elements are required in sorted order, they are extracted via the access table once again.

For example, if we have values in an array with the corresponding access table as follows:

Original array : D B F E A C G
Access table   : 1 2 3 4 5 6 7

and sort them, then the original array remains untouched and the access table becomes:

Original array : D B F E A C G
Access table   : 5 2 6 1 4 3 7

To print the original array in sorted order, we would print according to the order in the access table, that is first element 5 then element 2 then 6, and so on. The Pascal to do this is:

```
FOR i := 1 to max do write (table [accesstable [i]]);
```

and would produce, for the above data,

    A B C D E F G

This technique is not only useful for avoiding the copying of large items, but also as a means for making a complicated data structure easier to handle.

Example 9.3 Sorting with access tables

| Problem | The Zanyland Weather Department are pleased with the program developed as a result of example 6.5, and would like to add a further feature: a list of the months in decreasing order of average rainfall.

| Solution | The averages must be stored somewhere as they are calculated. A suitable declaration is:

```
VAR averagetable : monthlyrains;
```

If this table is sorted, then the average rainfall figures will be in order, but we shall have lost track of their associated months. To keep this information, we maintain the *averagetable* in its original monthly order, and employ the access table technique. Thus we imagine a league table which lists the months in the order required: the corresponding rainfall can then be found in the *averagetable*.

```
TYPE
    leagues = 1..12;
    leaguetables = array [leagues] of months;
VAR
    leaguetable : leaguetables;
```

For example, after sorting, the values in the tables might look like this:

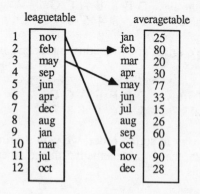

To perform the sort, we can use the selection algorithm with suitable alterations being made to the comparison and swapping actions.

Program   The program of example 6.5 can be amended to take into account the averages table, and perform the sort. An extract of it is:

```
VAR
    m : months;
    i : leagues;

BEGIN
    ('****** Rainfall statistics ******');
    readinthedata;
    writeln('Month      Average      Std Deviation');
    FOR m := jan to dec do begin
        averagetable[m] := monthlyaverage(raintable[m]);
        writemonth (m);
        writeln (' ', a:6:2,' ', monthlystddev(raintable[m],
            averagetable[m]):6:4);
    END;
    sortaverages;
```

```
      writeln ('The months from wettest to driest are:');
      for i := 1 to 12 do begin
        writemonth (league[i]));
        writeln ('   ', averagetable[league[i]]:6:2);
      end;
    END.
```

9.2   Conformant array parameters

One of the biggest nuisances in Pascal is the fact that array variables have to be of exactly the same length if they are to be compatible. This means that a general-purpose procedure such as a sort or a matrix inversion can only work for arrays of one size. For any other size, a separate procedure must be provided.

In the Pascal standard there is an optional feature which gets around this problem. Parameters that are arrays can be declared in the parameter list with a maximum range for the subscripts. Then any array variable which has subscripts within this maximum range, and has the same type of elements, will be able to be passed as an actual parameter.

Providing variable length arrays to procedures.

Form of conformant array parameters

A parameter list can also include formal parameters of the form:

Conformant array parameter declaration

identifier : array [*lowid..highid* : *subscript type*] of *element type*

Then any array of the same element type with subscripts of the same type which lie within the range *lowid* to *highid* can be passed as an actual parameter to this formal. Multi-dimensional arrays can be specified in the same way.

The important point about this kind of declaration is that the identifiers of the range are treated as variables that can be used but not altered; for the subscripts must consist of identifiers. When the procedure is called, the range of subscripts of the actual array is picked up, and actual values for *lowid* and *highid* filled in. Since a procedure with a conformant array parameter will in all probability need to index through the array, it is good practice to start off by declaring an index variable that will apply, i.e.

    VAR i : *subscript type*;

Example 9.4 Searching string tables

Problem | In the program that wrote out foreign spellings for days of the week (section 8.2), there is also a requirement that it read them. Moreover, it is desirable that the program should work for any set of foreign names specified as data.

Solution | The words for days are to be stored in a file, and read into an array of strings. A potential day can then be read and passed to a **search** procedure, which will return the index to the array for that string, or some error code if the string is not a valid name.

If we reflect on this, we realise that searching is an operation that could be applicable in many circumstances. Reading a month name, or a department name, or even a person's name, and checking that it appears on a list could be done in the same way. The only difficulty is that different enumerated types could not be used for the subscripts. If we sacrifice the use of enumerated types at this level, and use integer subranges instead, we can come up with a very nice generalised procedure for reading and identifying strings.

Examples | Given a table containing days of the week in French, i.e.

lundi	vendredi
mardi	samedi
mercredi	dimanche
jeudi	

which is read into an array with subscripts 1..7, then passing the word

vendredi

as a parameter to the proposed search procedure should return a 5. With the data

spring
summer
autumn
winter

read into an array indexed 1..4, a call to the same search procedure with a parameter

summer

will return a 2.

Algorithm | The searching algorithm is an example of a double-exit loop: either the word is found in the table, or the end of the table is reached before the word is found. State indicators are the best way of expressing the solution, as shown overleaf.

The one issue to settle, then, is how the procedure should report that a word did not match any in the table. The best way is to have a boolean as a parameter, and to rely on the caller checking it before assuming that the index returned is meaningful.

Table Search

In the program that follows, three string tables are set up and searched. Moreover, reading in a table is also an operation that can be generalised, so another procedure with conformant array parameters is added.

Program

```
PROGRAM Searchingtables (input, output);
   CONST
      namemax = 24;
      deptmax = 20;
   TYPE
      positive      = 1..maxint;
      namerange     = 1..namemax;
      names         = packed array [namerange] of char;
      dayrange      = 1..7;
      seasonrange   = 1..4;
      deptrange     = 1.. deptmax;
      days          = array [dayrange] of names;
      seasons       = array [seasonrange] of names;
      depts         = array [deptrange] of names;

   VAR
      daytable      : days;
      seasontable   : seasons;
      depttable     : depts;
      word          : names;
      there, stop   : boolean;
      n             : positive;

   PROCEDURE readname (VAR name : names);
      VAR i : namerange;
      BEGIN
         for i := 1 to namemax do
            if eoln then name[i] := ' ' else read(name[i]);
```

```
        readln;
      END; {readname}

PROCEDURE getintable (
                VAR T : array [low..high : positive] of names);
  VAR i : positive;
  BEGIN
    for i := low to high do readname (T[i]);
    writeln('Table with ', high − low + 1:1, ' elements read.');
  END; {getintable}

PROCEDURE search (T : array [low..high:positive] of names;
      x : names;
      VAR index : positive;
      VAR result : boolean);

  TYPE
    states = (searching, found, notthere);
  VAR
    i : positive;
    state : states;
  BEGIN
    state := searching;
    i := low;
    REPEAT
      if x = T[i] then state := found else
      if i = high then state := notthere else
      i := succ(i);
    UNTIL state <> searching;
    CASE state of
      found :  begin
                  index := i;
                  result := true;
                end;
      notthere :  result := false;
    END;
  END; {search}

BEGIN
  writeln('****** Demonstrating conformant arrays ******');
  writeln('Type in the day names (7): ');
  getintable(daytable);
  writeln('Type in the season names (4): ');
  getintable(seasontable);
  writeln('Type in the department names (20): ');
  getintable(depttable);

  stop := false;
  repeat
    writeln('Type in a day, a season, a department or QUIT');
    readname(word);
    if word = 'QUIT                    ' {literal must be 24 long}
    then stop := true
    else begin
      search (daytable, word, n, there);
```

```
                    if there
                    then writeln('This is day No. ', n:1)
                    else begin
                       search (seasontable, word, n, there);
                       if there
                       then writeln('This is season No. ', n:1)
                       else begin
                          search (depttable, word, n , there);
                          if there
                          then writeln ('This is department No. ', n:1)
                          else writeln ('This word is not in any of the tables.');
                       end;
                    end;
                  end;
               until stop;
            END.
```

The above procedure implements a **linear search**. If the data to be searched is ordered, then there are far more efficient searching methods, but these are beyond the scope of this book.

9.3   Procedural parameters

Parameters enable different **values** to be passed to and from procedures, and to be given formal names within the procedures. This same facility can be applied to **actions** by declaring a procedure or function as a parameter. The form of the declaration is exactly the same as that for the heading of the procedure or function itself, i.e.

Procedural parameter declaration

PROCEDURE *name (formal parameter declarations)*;

FUNCTION *name (formal parameter declarations) : type*;

This is not a facility that is often used in programming, partly because many Pascal systems do not support it. The example most often quoted is in numerical analysis where methods for finding roots of functions, integrating them, differentiating them and so on can be written to be independent of any particular function; the function is then passed to the solving procedure as a parameter. This notion of independence is the key to the need for procedures as parameters. In the context of the examples we have seen so far, the sort procedure could benefit from such a feature.

Multi-way sorting

The selection sorting procedure developed in section 8.1 is defined to sort in

descending order. This aspect of the sort is confined to the single expression
in the middle where the comparison is done, i.e.

> if a[i] < a[smallest] then ...

If we make this comparison a call to a boolean function, i.e.

> if inorder (a[i], a[smallest]) then ...

then we can declare this function as a parameter to the sort procedure, as in

```
PROCEDURE sort (var a : somearray;  n : range;
                function inorder (x,y, : items) : boolean);
```

Calling the sort procedure needs actual parameters for the three formals
listed, and the following would satisfy:

```
TYPE
  items    = names;
  range  = 1..50;
  somearray        = array [range] of items;

VAR
  table  : somearray;
  size  : range;

FUNCTION descending (x, y : names) : boolean;
  BEGIN
    descending := x > y;
  END;  { descending}
```

The resulting call would then be

> sort (table, size, descending);

The power of this facility becomes apparent when we define

```
FUNCTION ascending (a,b : items) : boolean;
  BEGIN
    ascending := a < b;
  END; {ascending}
```

and can call on the same procedure to order the names in the other direction
with

> sort (table, size, ascending);

Procedures as parameters do not occur in all languages, as they are
considered difficult to implement at runtime. However, it is a good idea to
gain practice with them, as the concept of parameterised action is central to
proper programming in advanced languages.

Alternatives to procedural parameters

If your particular Pascal system does not support procedural parameters, it is still possible to get the effect described above by using an enumerated scalar and a case statement. This is how it would be done. You first have to decide on all the possible orderings that one would wish to use on the sort. Let us suppose that these are simply the two mentioned above. *If your Pascal system does not have them.*

```
TYPE orderings = (up, down);
```

Then the definition of the procedure includes a parameter of this type, as in

```
PROCEDURE sort (var a : somearray;  n : range;
                direction : orderings);
```

and inside the procedure, the comparison is replaced by a case-statement which selects the appropriate function, as in

```
case direction of
  up : relation := ascending (a[i], a[smallest]);
  down : relation := descending (a[i], a[smallest]);
end;
if relation then ...
```

The disadvantage of this 'fix' is that the sort procedure itself has to be aware of all the names of the different functions that do the comparisons, whereas with procedural parameters, the functions are collectively known only by their formal name.

Example 9.5   The independent Newton-Raphson

In an earlier example in Chapter 5, we postulated that it would be nice to make the numerical methods procedures that we were developing completely self-contained, so that they communicated only by parameters. We achieved our aim, except for the functions being solved. With procedural parameters, we can now complete the interface.

As an example, consider the Newton-Raphson procedure header with parameters:

```
PROCEDURE Newton (var xold, xnew : real;  var i : range;
                  imax : range; tolerance : real;
                  monitor : boolean);
```

The procedure makes use of the function *f* and its derivative, say *fdiff*. We can add these in as follows:

```
PROCEDURE Newton (var xold, xnew : real;  var i : range;
                  imax : range; tolerance : real;
                  monitor : boolean;
                  function f (x : real) : real;
                  function fdiff (x : real) : real);
```

A further improvement can be made by substituting a boolean function for the test for convergence. This is left as an exercise for the reader.

9.4   Recursion

Simple last-line recursion

Solutions to problems that involve iteration can often be expressed in the following general terms:

> **The operation**
> Do something
> If the data is not 'finished',
>   then do the same operation on amended data.

An example of this kind of thinking would be counting people for party invitations. If a party list is written out as

> John
> Mary & Peter
> David & Anne & Catherine & Thomas
> George
> William & Harry
> Aunt Edith
> Granny & Grandpa

and we wish to count both the people who are coming and the number of invitations needed, then we can express the algorithm as

> **Count a person**
> Read a name
> Add one
> If an ampersand follows, count a person

Essentially, we are re-using the operation by calling it from itself. This is known as **recursion**. In Pascal, the above operation could be part of another procedure as follows:

```
PROCEDURE partyplan;
VAR
   people, invitations : 0 .. 1000;

PROCEDURE countaperson;
```

```
BEGIN
  readname;
  people := people + 1;
  if ampersandfollows then
    countaperson;
END; {countaperson}
```

```
BEGIN
  people := 0;
  invitations := 0;
  while not eof do begin
    countaperson;
    invitations := invitations + 1;
  end;
  writeln('For the ', people:1,' people, you will need ',
          invitations:1, ' invitations.');
END.
```

where *ampersandfollows* and *readname* are suitably defined.

If the recursive call comes at the very end of the operation, then the recursion can be replaced directly by a loop. For example, we could have just as easily written:

```
PROCEDURE countaperson;
BEGIN
  repeat
    readname;
    people := people + 1;
  until not ampersandfollowing;
END; {countaperson}
```

Recursion usually only becomes preferable to looping when parameters are involved. Recursive algorithms share with loops the two essential properties that

- there must be a stopping condition,
- some variables must change their values each time.

Recursion with parameters

When a recursive call is made on a procedure with parameters, it follows the same execution pattern as an ordinary call. The parameters and local variables of the caller are remembered (or 'stacked') and the new procedure is entered with the new parameters. At the end of the call, the program returns to where it was, and the caller's parameters and variables become visible again. With a recursive procedure, the parameters and variables have the same name and meaning each time, though they may have different values, and thus they can give the effect of an array that is constructed as time goes by, and then disappears. By deftly altering the order of the 'do something' and 'do the operation again' in the general algorithm above, we can obtain the effect of looking at the array in reverse. This is aptly illustrated by the next example.

Example 9.6   Based number writing

| Problem | Write a procedure to print out positive integers of any size to a given base. |

| Solution | This problem was tackled in section 3.5 for three-digit integers, and we remarked at the time that we had to know about the three digits, so that we could take the hundreds first, the tens next and finally the units. But if we express the solution like this:

Print the left part of the number; write the rightmost digit

and consider that printing the left part is exactly the same operation again, then it is not necessary to know in advance how long the number is. When we eventually get down to a single digit then printing the left part does nothing, the rightmost digit is written, and we return to the previous piece of the number.

| Example | Suppose we print 102 to base 8. This proceeds in steps as follows:

Print the left part of 102, i.e. 102 div 8 = 12;   Write 102 mod 8 = 6

Print left part of 12, i.e. 12 div 8 = 1;   Write 12 mod 8 = 4

Print left part of 1, there is none; Write 1 mod 8 = 1

and the digits printed out are 146, in that order.

| Algorithm | The stopping condition here coincides with the left part running out. We can confirm that the variables will change because the procedure is called with the value of parameter *number* being the *number div base*. In algorithmic terms, the solution becomes:

> **Print number to a base:**
>   If number < base, then write it out
>   Otherwise
>   Print number div base to base
>   Write out number mod base

The procedure, together with a test program, follows on easily.

| Program |

```
PROGRAM Basetester (input, output);
VAR number, base : 0 .. maxint;

PROCEDURE print (n, b : integer);
```

```
BEGIN
  if n < b then write(n:1)
  else begin
    print (n div b, b);
    write(n mod b:1);
  end;
END; {print}

BEGIN
  writeln('****** Testing printing to a base ******');
  write ('Number and base (positive only): ');
  readln(number, base);
  write(number:1,' to ', base:1,' is ');
  print(number, base);
  writeln;
END.
```

Backtracking with recursion

Recursion effectively enables us to build up a history of values and then go back and use them again. It is very effective if there is a choice of paths to follow at a given time. One can travel recursively down one, find it no good, come back up to the crossroads with everything restored to what it was before, and proceed down some other path. This technique is used widely in game playing programs, for chess, noughts and crosses, or any situation where there are choices to be made. A full discussion of this fascinating area is beyond the scope of this book, but is sure to be taken up again in future courses in advanced programming, recursive techniques or data structures.

Recursive data types

A data type which is still to be discussed (in Chapter 10) is the **pointer**. The structures that can be built with pointers are inherently recursive. Hence many of the algorithms to create and manipulate such structures are excellent examples of recursion at work.

9.5   Finer points about procedures

Levels of nesting

A program with procedures is said to consist of several **levels**. The outermost level is level 1, which is that of the program itself. Thus all declarations made under the program header are at level 1. Level 1 is also known as the **global** level, and the variables and procedures declared there are called **globals**.

Within these outer procedures at level 1, further declarations can be made. These would then be at level 2. Procedures inside them would be at level 3, and so on, for as many levels of nesting as are required. Declarations within a procedure are called **local** declarations, and the identifiers that they introduce are known as local to that procedure. Parameters acquire the same

Procedure is used to mean both procedure and function.

Globals and locals defined.

level as the locals, not as the procedure. Thus if we had the little skeleton program

```
PROGRAM skeleton (input, output);

    VAR i, j : integer;

    PROCEDURE order (VAR n, m : integer);

        VAR temp : integer;
        ...
        END; {order}

    BEGIN
    ...
    END.
```

then *i, j* and *order* are at level 1, but *n, m* and *temp* are considered to be declared inside *order* and therefore are all at level 2.

Scope and visibility

With all these places where declarations can be made, it is necessary to sort out which identifiers are visible where, and what happens if the same name is used more than once. The **scope** of an identifier is the extent of the procedures over which the identifier is visible and can be used. We therefore have:

Pascal's Rule of Scope

An identifier is visible in the block (i.e. program, procedure or function) in which it is first declared *and* in all enclosed blocks in which it is not redeclared.

The term 'enclosed blocks' refers to the nesting. If we view nested procedures as a set of nested boxes, then what the rule is saying is that the inner boxes can see outwards, but not vice versa. One way of remembering this is to imagine all the boxes being built with one-way glass: someone in a box can see out, but no-one outside can see in.

The forward directive

The order in which declarations are made also affects visibility. Pascal requires that any use of an identifier must be preceded by its declaration. Thus if two procedures are declared at the same level, their order of declaration will dictate who can call whom. The procedure currently being declared cannot actually see the following ones. This problem can be overcome by declaring the procedure as *forward*, then giving its details later on. For example, if procedure *A* calls *B* and vice versa, then we could declare them as follows:

Use of the
forward clause.

```
PROCEDURE B;  forward;

PROCEDURE A;
 BEGIN

   ...
   B;
 END;

PROCEDURE B;
 BEGIN

   ...
   A;
 END;
```

Occlusion

As stated in the Rule of Scope, an identifier is not visible if it is redeclared in an inner block. The effect of this is that if two variables in the same scope have the same name, only the innermost one is visible. The proper name for this phenomenon is **occlusion**. The identifier which is hidden because of the inner declaration is said to be **occluded**.

The external directive

In many Pascal systems there is a facility for compiling procedures independently and putting them in a library. This would be a particularly useful feature for us, now that we have all these self-contained procedures defined!

The details of how this is done vary from system to system, and consultation of the appropriate manual is required. Usually, the procedure is submitted to the compiler, preceded by any types and constants that it needs (but not variables, obviously) and the compiler recognises it as a separately compiled procedure and puts it in the specified library. To use the procedure, then, we declare it in a program as usual, but followed by a directive such as *external*. For example, we might have

```
PROCEDURE Newton (var xold, xnew : real;  var i : range;
      imax : range; tolerance : real; monitor : boolean); external;
```

It is also possible in this way to link into procedures which were written in other languages. Usually the language name is given so that the compiler can set up the correct parameter linkage.

If your system has this facility, it would be a good idea to compile the methods in this book into a library for future use.

Summary

☐   The data in an array can be sorted by various methods, one of which is selection sort.

☐   The sort procedure can be generalised so that the size of the array can vary and the order of sorting is given by the caller.

☐   The Pascal Standard allows formal array parameters to be given bounds that can vary depending on the size of the actual parameter at the time the procedure is called. These are called conformant array parameters.

☐   The lower and upper bounds of such an array parameter are treated as variables whose values cannot be altered by the procedure.

☐   Procedures can themselves be passed as parameters, allowing considerable versatility of action at runtime.

☐   Pascal procedures and functions can be defined in terms of themselves using recursion.

☐   Recursive procedures, like loops, must be careful to specify a stopping condition.

Self-check quiz

1.   Why does the main loop of the sorting algorithm specify $n - 1$ as the upper bound?
2.   When sorting data, why is the record the most useful type for the items?
3.   Give the heading and parameters of a procedure which will sort arrays of different lengths, where the items in the array are of type *element*.
4.   Write a function which will search a simple integer array for a zero value and return its index. The array should have variable bounds.
5.   Describe two ways of defining a procedure which can sort an array either in ascending order or in descending order.
6.   Work through the Basetester program of example 9.6 for the following data: 123 to base 5.
7.   Explain how the recursion in the print procedure of Basetester actually prints the digits of the answer in the correct order, and not backwards.
8.   What output would be produced by the following program when given the input AB123CDE69F?

```
PROGRAM Printing (input, output);

PROCEDURE sift;
  VAR ch : char;
  BEGIN
    read(ch);
```

```
        if ch in ['0' .. '9'] then begin
           sift;
           writeln(ch);
        end;
     END; {sift}

  BEGIN
     while not eof do begin
        sift;
        writeln('*');
     end;
  END.
```

Problems

9.1   Add to the *Searchingtables* program of example 9.3 a sorting procedure which is
       defined for conformant arrays of names. Use it to sort each table of words after it is
       read in. Given that the tables are then in alphabetical order, can you think of a way
       in which the search procedure could be optimised to detect more quickly that a word
       is not in the table?

9.2   In the *Sortingmarks* program of example 9.2, we postulated that it would be useful to
       be able to sort on the name field or on the marks field of the table of students.
       Using a function as a parameter, as described in section 9.3, extend the program to
       print out two lists – one in alphabetical order of name, and one in descending order
       of marks.

9.3   A palindrome is a word or sentence that reads the same forwards as backwards,
       disregarding punctuation. Famous palindromic sentences are:

> Madam, I'm Adam!
> Able was I, ere I saw Elba.

       Checking for a palindrome involves successively comparing pairs of characters, one
       from each end of the input. This can be expressed nicely as a recursive check, i.e.

> It is a palindrome if the leftmost and rightmost chars are the same
> and the inner portion of the sentence is a palindrome.

       Write a recursive function which tests whether a given string is a palindrome or not.
       The string is assumed to be stripped of all punctuation and spaces, and to have all
       characters in lower case. Test the function in a short program. Then extend the test
       program by adding a procedure which reads in a proper sentence and prepares it for
       input to the palidrome function by stripping punctuation and spaces.

10

Dynamic data structures

Pascal has a relatively small number of features, compared to other widely used languages such as Ada, C or FORTRAN 77. Nevertheless, mastery of every aspect is not needed in a first course, and the features usually omitted are pointers and unformatted files. Both of these are concerned with storing and manipulating an unspecified amount of data. The wide range of algorithms that are applicable to such data makes pointers a good starting point for a second course in programming – usually called *Data Structures* or *Advanced Programming*. In this chapter, therefore, we simply introduce pointers and show the basic algorithms for list processing. The section on files discusses some of the deficiencies of Pascal, and mentions the common extensions that are available. The chapter closes with a case study based on pointer manipulation.

10.1 Pointers

In Pascal, every variable declared in the VAR section is given a name – its **identifier**. Identical items can be grouped in an array, so that one name can stand for a whole list of items. Each item is known by a **designator** comprising the array name and a subscript to that array, and can be accessed directly by its designator. The drawback of arrays is that the number of items must be known in advance, and, once set, it cannot be expanded. This can lead to situations such as shown in the following diagram.

The shaded
areas are
wasted.

list

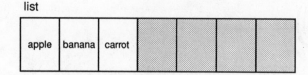

where much of the array is empty.

Pascal provides for lists of varying size to be created. Each item in a list is linked to the next by means of a pointer, and a pointer by itself can point to the first item. The list shown above would then be represented as

No waste – but
an overhead for
the pointers.

list

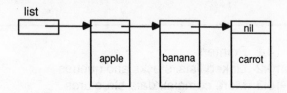

If another item needs to be added to the list, another **node** and pointer are created and linked up. When no longer required, nodes can be removed from lists. Moreover, this adding and removing does not have to be done at the start or end of the list – it can be done anywhere within the list, simply by reorganising the pointers.

The cost of
using pointers.

The price that one pays for such flexibility is twofold. Firstly there is the **overhead** of one pointer per node, plus one for the start of the list. A pointer usually takes up at least as much space as an integer. If the data in the nodes requires more space than the pointer – and it usually does – then the overhead is not significant. However, one would not use pointers to hold lists of characters, say: it would be more economical to waste characters at the end of a packed array than to provide a pointer per character.

The second part of the cost of pointers is a **lack of accessibility**. Each element of an array is directly accessible by means of its subscript; not so for nodes in a pointer list. They can only be accessed by starting at the name of the list and following a chain of pointers until the required node is reached. Thus, once again, one would not use pointers if diverse items in the list need to be accessed all the time, as is the case in a sort. But if the list is to be processed sequentially most of the time, then a linked list is not a drawback.

The form of pointer declarations

The syntax for declaring a pointer type is simply:

Pointer type

$identifier = \uparrow type;$

The pointer symbol ↑ can also be expressed as a circumflex ^, or an @ on some systems with restricted character sets.

10.2 Linked lists, stacks and queues

There are four steps to setting up and accessing a linked list using pointers. We give them all in general form here and then explain them using an example. Throughout the forms, the term *nodes* in italics stands for whatever record type is to constitute the list. Consequently, the term *tonodes* is used for the type that points to *nodes*. Other identifiers in italics have a similar importance, i.e. they convey the general sense of the item, but could be any identifier required by the particular circumstances.

1.   **Define the node and pointer types**

Four steps in defining a linked list.

```
TYPE
  tonodes = ↑ nodes;
  nodes   = RECORD
              link : tonodes;
              other data fields
            END;
```

The nodes are records with an extra field for the link to the next node.

2.   **Declare the header**

```
VAR
  list : tonodes;
```

This will define a variable which can be used to point to a dynamically created node. As yet it has no value, i.e.

list

Pascal has a special pointer value called *nil* which can be assigned to pointer variables to indicate specifically that they point nowhere. This value can be tested for, and is conventionally used as the link value for the last node in a list. Pointers are considered to be bound to their node type, but *nil* is a pointer literal and is compatible with all pointer types.

3.   **Create space for a new node**

```
new (list);
```

Space large enough for a node of the correct type is taken from an area in the Pascal system known as the **heap**. The address of this area is put into the pointer variable mentioned. This produces

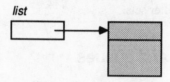

4.   **Access fields in the node.** If the node is a record, access to a field is via
     the dot notation, plus the up-arrow, to indicate that a pointer must be
     followed first.

     list ↑.field

Example 10.1   Party people

In the example in section 9.4, various people were to be invited to a party,
and they were listed as families, for example

>   Tom & Pat
>   Nigel & Judy & William & Michael

Each family, therefore, is a list of people, and the list is of variable size. We
could set up such a list with the declarations:

```
TYPE
    topeople =  ↑people;
    people   = record
            next   : topeople;
            name : names;
          end;
VAR
    head, guest : topeople;
```

As each name is read in, a space for a new name can be created (together with
its pointer), and linked up to the others. The loop to do this would be:

```
head := nil;
repeat
  new(guest);
  readname (guest↑.name);
  guest↑.link := head;
  head := guest;
until nomoreampersand;
```

Working through this sequence for Nigel, Judy, William and Michael, we see
that the list is created looking like this:

327

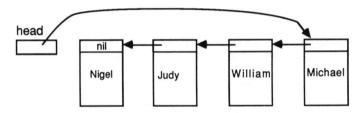

The names have been inserted in the list in reverse order. A means of linking them in a more obvious order is discussed after the quick resumé of the properties of pointers.

Pointer values and operators

Pointer values are generated identifiers. The nodes that a pointer may point to are kept in the area of memory called the **heap**. Therefore a valid pointer value is any address in the heap. It is not possible to have pointers pointing to a variable or area of memory, other than one created through the procedure *new*. There is no notation for pointer literals except for the special value *nil*. The heap defined.

Pointer values can be assigned and compared for equality. They can also be followed down to their nodes, or **dereferenced**, by using the up-arrow. Thus if *head* is a pointer, *head↑* represents the node it points to. Such indirect names are legitimate wherever variables of that type are legitimate. Thus given the two pointers and nodes

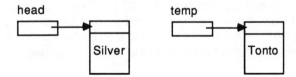

the assignment

      head↑ := temp↑;

will copy the entire contents of the node pointed to by *temp* into the node pointed to by *head*. Pictorially, we have:

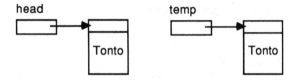

This is quite different to saying

```
head := temp;
```

which would only copy the pointer, giving

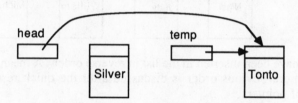

In this case, note that the node originally pointed to by *head* would be inaccessible after the assignment, unless the pointer to it had previously been copied somewhere.

Use of *new* and *dispose*.

There are two special procedures for pointers, i.e. *new* and *dispose*. *New* acquires an area from the heap, as already described, and *dispose* can be used to return unwanted nodes to the heap. The system may then be able to reuse that space.

Pointer values cannot be read or written. Input and output of fields of nodes they point to are subject to the input and output provisions of their own types.

Stacks and queues

The list that was built up in the example 10.1 is known as a **stack**, since new nodes are added at the top or front of the list. Sometimes it is essential that the nodes be added at the end, maintaining the chronological order of arrival. This structure is a great British institution, known as a **queue**.

Creating an ordered list or queue

In order to create a list of nodes in the order in which they are provided, it is necessary to know at all times where the end of the list is. Nodes can then be linked using this pointer. The appropriate loop for creating a list of names, as described above, in order is

```
VAR
    head, last, guest : topeople;

    head := nil;
    repeat
        new (guest);
        readname (guest↑.name);
        guest↑.link := nil;
        if head = nil
            then head := guest
            else last↑.link := guest;
```

```
            last := guest;
         until nomoreampersand;
```

This sequence will create the following list:

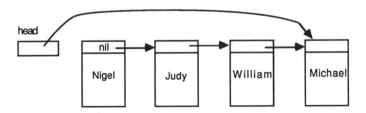

Scanning a list

Once a list is created, it can be scanned by following the pointers. Notice that we can only scan the list in the direction in which the pointers were created. Thus for the loop just created above, we could print out the names with the following loop:

```
VAR
  head, current : topeople;

current := head;
while current <> nil do begin
  writename(current↑.name);
  current := current↑ .next;
end;
```

There are many variations on the basic stack and queue, depending on whether deletions can occur at the front or back or both. In the most general case, nodes can be added anywhere in the list, which would be useful, for example, if they had to be maintained in alphabetical order.

10.3 More complex data structures

Stacks and queues are **linear lists**: all such lists have the property that they have only one pointer to another node. There is no reason why a node should not branch off into several sublists, and these do not even have to be of the same type. The following example is a simple illustration of this facility. Even more complex and formalised structures can be developed, as would be covered in a course on data structures. One of the formal structures is given the name **tree** and can be very useful.

Example 10.2 Holiday camp data

| Problem | The Zanyland Holiday Camp Recreation Section likes to keep track of the interests of people who are attending the camp. For each family, it records

- the surname
- the sex, sports and hobbies of each adult
- the sex and age of each child.

Children are assumed to be interested in everything, but knowing their age helps to group them with their peers. Since families can vary a lot in size, a dynamic means of storing this data is needed.

| Solution | Use pointers. We can set up a structure for a family as shown overleaf. Then the structure can be processed for all adults, or all children, or all those interested in tennis, say, just by following the appropriate pointers.

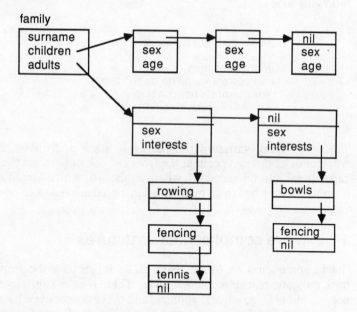

| Algorithm | The data type definitions are the most important part of this example. Once a diagram, such as here, has been drawn, it is relatively simple to write down the corresponding Pascal types. Then to test that the structure is as required, and to have basic processes for accessing, we devise procedures to read in a family and print out its details again.

There are actually three kinds of list here – the adults, children and the interests. In each case, the principle of creating nodes and linking them up is the same, but it is not possible to use a single procedure to read in all three, as the types are different. What still remains to be decided is the form of the input data. We shall assume that it is entered interactively, with prompts for each field. An empty string will signal the end of the group of items. The complete program follows.

Program

```
PROGRAM Holidaydata (input, output);
  CONST
    namemax    = 24;
    empty      = '                        ';
  TYPE
    namerange  = 1..namemax;
    names      = packed array [namerange] of char;
    sexes      = (male, female);
    ages       = 0 .. 16;
    hobbies    = names;

    tochildren = ↑ childnode;
    childnode  = record
                        next    : tochildren;
                        sex     : sexes;
                        age     : ages;
                 end;
    tohobbies  = ↑ hobbynode;
    hobbynode  = record
                          next    : tohobbies;
                          hobby : hobbies;
                 end;
    toadults   = ↑ adultnode;
    adultnode  = record
                          next      : toadults;
                          sex       : sexes;
                          interests : tohobbies;
                 end;
    families   = record
                          surname : names;
                          children : tochildren;
                          adults    : toadults;
                 end;
  VAR
    family : families;

  PROCEDURE readname (VAR name : names);
    BEGIN
      {as defined in section 8.2}
    END; {readname}

  PROCEDURE readhobbies (VAR head : tohobbies);
    VAR
      temp, last : tohobbies;
      hobbyname : hobbies;
    BEGIN
```

```
        head := nil;
        last := nil;
        repeat
          write('Interest (return for none)? ');
          readname (hobbyname);
          if name <> empty then begin
            new(temp);
            temp↑.hobby := hobbyname;
            temp↑.next := nil;
            if head = nil
            then head := temp;
            else last↑.next := temp;
            last := temp;
          end;
        until hobbyname = empty;
      END; {readhobbies}

    PROCEDURE readadults (VAR head : toadults);
      VAR
        temp, last : toadults;
        ch : char;
        finished : boolean;
      BEGIN
        head := nil;
        last := nil;
        finished := false;
        repeat
          repeat
            write('Sex? (M, F, or Q for no more): ');
            read(ch);
          until ch in ['M','m','F','f','Q','q'];
          writeln;
          if ch in ['Q','q'] then finished := true else
          begin
            new(temp);
            if ch in ['M','m']
              then temp↑.sex := male
              else temp↑.sex := female;
            temp↑.next := nil;
            readhobbies(temp↑.interests);
            if head = nil
              then head := temp
              else last := temp;
            last := temp;
          end;
        until finished;
      END; {readadults}

    PROCEDURE readchildren (VAR head : tochildren);
      VAR
        temp, last : tochildren;
        ch : char;
        finished : boolean;
      BEGIN
        head := nil;
```

```
        last := nil;
        finished := false;
        repeat
          repeat
            write('Sex? (M, F, or Q for no more): ');
            read(ch);
          until ch in ['M','m','F','f','Q','q'];
          writeln;
          if ch in ['Q','q'] then finished := true else
          begin
            new(temp);
            if ch in ['M','m']
              then temp↑.sex := male
              else temp↑.sex := female;
            temp↑.next := nil;
            readhobbies(temp↑.interests);
            if head = nil
              then head := temp
              else last := temp;
            last := temp;
          end;
        until finished;
      END;  {readchildren}

PROCEDURE printhobbies (head : tohobbies);
  VAR scan : tohobbies;
  BEGIN
    scan := head;
    while scan <> nil do begin
      write(scan↑.hobby, ' ');
      scan := scan↑.next;
  END; {printhobbies}

PROCEDURE printadults (head : toadults);
  VAR scan : toadults;
  BEGIN
    scan := head;
    while scan <> nil do begin
      case scan↑.sex of
        male : write('male');
        female : write('female');
      end;
      write(' with interests ');
      printhobbies (scan↑.interests);
      writeln;
      scan := scan↑.next;
    end;
  END;  {printadults}

PROCEDURE printchildren (head : tochildren);
  VAR scan : tochildren;
  BEGIN
    scan := head;
    while scan <> nil do begin
      case scan↑.sex of
```

```
                    male : write('boy');
                    female : write('girl');
                end;
                write(' age ');
                writeln(scan↑.age);
                scan := scan↑.next;
            end;
        END;  {printchildren}

    BEGIN
        writeln('***** Reading holiday data *****');
        writeln('Testing for one family only');
        write('Surname: ');
        readname(family.surname);
        writeln('Adults');
        readadults(family.adults);
        writeln('Children');
        readchildren(family.children);
        writeln;
        writeln('The ', family.surname, ' family''s data is: ');
        writeln('Adults:');
        printadults(family.adults);
        writeln('Children:');
        printchildren(family.children);
    END.
```

Testing

***** Reading holiday data *****
Testing for one family
Surname: Jones
Adults
Sex (M, F or Q for no more): m
Interest (return for no more)? bowling
Interest (return for no more)? swimming
Interest (return for no more)? tennis
Interest (return for no more)?
Sex (M, F or Q for no more): f
Interest (return for no more)? swimming
Interest (return for no more)?
Sex (M, F or Q for no more): q
Children
Sex (M, F or Q for no more): m   **Age** 6
Sex (M, F or Q for no more): f   **Age** 3
Sex (M, F or Q for no more): q

The Jones family's data is:
Adults:
male with interests bowling swimming tennis
female with interests swimming
Children:
boy aged 6
girl aged 3

10.4 Files in general

The text files that we have used up to now consist of items of type character and include special end-of-line markers. Pascal actually permits new file types to be declared. These files can consist of items of any type, and in particular of records. This means that programs that process many items of data and then have to store the processed form, can do so efficiently. Files can be accessed sequentially, from the first item to the last: there is no provision for random access to files, although some (non-standard) implementations do provide such a feature.

Form of a file declaration

A file type is declared as follows:

File type declaration

> *identifier* = FILE OF *type identifier*;

Variables of this type can then be defined. For example, in section 8.3, a record for type *Roomdimensions* was defined. A corresponding file would be declared as in:

    TYPE Roomfiles = FILE of Roomdimensions;

    VAR Roomfile : Roomfiles;

File values and operators

A file can contain theoretically an infinite number of items. In practice, there will be some limitation imposed by the available hardware.

Files must be opened, connected and closed (if necessary) as already described in section 4.4. The procedures and function that can be used are:

reset (F)	opens the file for reading
rewrite(F)	opens the file for writing
eof(F)	returns true if the file is positioned past its end

The same extension to reset is used to make an association between the file name and a file on the disk. Note that both general files and text files do not actually have to exist on some external device: Pascal does allow the concept of a **local file**. Thus it is possible to declare and use a file within a program, without connecting it to any device. At the end of the program, then, no 343 record of the file would remain.

With each file is associated a file pointer. The file pointer can be used to consult the buffer variable, which is known by the name of the file followed by an up-arrow, for example, *Roomfile↑*. At any time, the file pointer indicates the current position in the file, and the buffer variable contains the value of the item at that position, if one exists.

Reading and writing the file is done by using the buffer variable in conjunction with the following two procedures:

get(F)   moves the pointer to the next item in the file
             and copies the value there into the buffer
put(F)   appends the item in the buffer to the end of the file

When a file is opened for reading, the first item is copied into the buffer, provided that the file is not empty. If *X* is a variable of the same type as the file's items, then the sequence for reading is:

X := F↑;
get(F);

This copies the contents of the buffer into *X* and then moves the file pointer on. The sequence for writing is:

F↑ := X;
put(x);

This assigns the value in *X* to the buffer variable and then transfers this to the end of the file. When a file is opened for writing, the value of the function *eof* is always true, and it is an error to inspect the contents of the buffer variable.

In many earlier versions of Pascal, get and put were the only procedures for accessing items in files. The most recent standard permits the read and write statements to be used as well, which means that the buffer variable can be ignored. Turbo Pascal provides only this method. Thus to read a value from a file we have

read(F, X);

and to write a value we use simply:

write(F, X);

As with text files, several items can be listed as parameters, so that the following are also valid:

read(F, X, Y);
write(F, P, Q, R);

10.5 Case study 6: Electronic diary

| Problem | Students studying computer science at Zanyland University
have to undertake a group project in their second year. The
number of groups and the number of students in each project group varies
from year to year. One of the difficult tasks at the beginning of the course is
establishing when members of a particular group can meet to discuss their
project, since they may be taking different courses and have different
timetables. They would like to get computer assistance in arranging
meetings.

| Solution | We can write a program which will read in:

- a list of course numbers and their lecture days and times
- lists of the courses taken by students in each project group

and then print out for each group the times when they could possibly meet.
We ought to consider carefully the data structures that are most appropriate
for this problem. Will linked lists be best, or sets or arrays?

| Algorithm | There is a good deal of design work that needs to be done for
this program. Let us start with the overall structure of the
program. We need to read in the course timetable and then, for each project
group, the individual students' timetables. The main program could
therefore look like this:

```
PROGRAM MeetingTimes (input, output);

BEGIN
    writeln('*** The meeting time organiser *****');
    Initialise;
    SetUpFiles;
    ReadTimetable;
    while not eof do begin
      StartProject;
      while not ABlankLine do
        ReadaStudent(some parameter?);
        ComputeandPrintFreetimes;
    end;
END.
```

The next design decision concerns the data structures. The main computation
is one of finding intersections of times, which points us to sets. However,
Pascal sets can only handle small numbers and characters, not complex
records like a day-time pair, so we would need to convert each block on the
timetable into a numeric code. This is easy enough if the timetable is
regarded as having 5 days and 8, say, periods per day. A student's timetable
can therefore be represented as a set of numbers between 1 and 40. To work
out the free times, we can do the following:

```
      freetimes := [1..maxperiods];
      student := project.first;
      while student <> project.last do begin
        freetimes := freetimes − student↑.timetable;
        student := student↑.next;
      end;
```

In other words, we start off with all the periods in the *freetimes* set and work through the list of students in the project, subtracting out the timetables. What is left is the free time for all.

We have therefore assumed that the students in a project will be represented by a linked list. This is sensible, because we do not know how many students there will be per group. The *project* type will have a pointer to the first and last student in the group, and the handling of the list is just as explained in section 10.2.

What about the timetable itself? The data for a student will include course numbers, presumably, and this has to be looked up in the list of courses read in initially. If we want to look up a number, then an array is ideal, but in this case, that may be very wasteful. Course numbers may be in the thousands, and the students doing the projects may only take a small selection of these. Therefore, once again, we shall use a linked list for the courses. Each course will keep its number and the set of periods that it uses. Notice that the number of elements in the set is quite variable, so that one course may have three periods and another six, without any trouble.

| Program | A first stab at the timetable data structures, main program, and the procedure to read in the information is: |

```
PROGRAM MeetingTimes (input, output);
  CONST
    space = ' ';
    periodsperday = 8;
    periodmax = 40;  {5 x periodsperday}
  TYPE
    coursenos = 000..999;
    periods = 1..periodmax;
    periodset = set of periods;
    tocourses = ↑courses;
    courses = record
      number : coursenos;
      pattern : periodset;
      next : tocourses;
    end;
    courselists = record
      first, last : tocourses;
    end;

  VAR
    courselist : courselists;

  FUNCTION ABlankLine : boolean;
  BEGIN
```

```
    ABlankline := eoln;
  END;

PROCEDURE ReadTimetable;
VAR course : tocourses;

  PROCEDURE readpattern(var course : tocourses);
  VAR
    ch : char;
    n : integer;
    period : periods;

    FUNCTION converttoperiod
            (day : char; period : integer) : periods;
    VAR p : integer;
    BEGIN
      case day of
      'M', 'm' : p := 0;
      'T', 't' : p := periodsperday;
      'W', 'w' : p := periodsperday*2;
      'H', 'h' : p := periodsperday*3;
      'F', 'f' : p := periodsperday*4;
      end;
      converttoperiod := p + period;
    END; {converttoperiod}

  BEGIN
    with course↑ do begin
    pattern := [ ];
    next := nil;
    read(number);
    while not eoln do begin
      repeat read(ch) until ch <> space;
      read(n);
      period := converttoperiod(ch,n);
      pattern := pattern + [period];
    end;
    readln;
    end;
  END; {readpattern}

BEGIN
  writeln('Type in a course number, followed by ');
  writeln('the periods given as days and slots');
  writeln('where days are MTWHF and slots are 1..8');
  writeln('e.g.');
  writeln('301  M1  T1   H3');
  courselist.first := nil;
  courselist.last := nil;
  while not ABlankLine do begin
    new(course);
    readpattern(course);
    if courselist.first = nil
    then courselist.first := course
    else courselist.last↑.next := course;
    courselist.last := course;
```

```
            end;
       END; {Readtimetable}
```

You can take the rest of it from here!

Summary

❑   Pointers to dynamically created variables (usually records) enable lists and structures to be built up.

❑   The pointer symbol ↑ (or ^ or @) is used to declare a pointer type, to dereference from the pointer to the variable it is pointing to.

❑   Pointer variables are declared as usual in the VAR declarations; the dynamic variables they point to are created at runtime on the heap using the *new* procedure.

❑   Linear lists such as stacks and queues, as well as more complex structures, can be built up by making use of pointers.

❑   Files of any type can be declared in Pascal.

❑   They can be accessed via the usual read and write procedures, or via a buffer variable and the get and put procedures.

Self-check quiz

1.   What are the two disadvantages of using pointers for structures?
2.   What does the *new* procedure do?
3.   What is the difference between a stack and a queue?
4.   What would happen if a program tried to read a file that had no data in it?

Problems

10.1   The two types of data in case study 6 have different life spans: the course timetable will be set for a year, and probably change little between years, while the students' timetable could change every term. Reading in the course days and times every time we need to set up meetings could be tedious. It would be better to have one program to do this, and another to read the students' data. To connect these two, we need a file.

Write a program which will read in the class timetable interactively and store the information in a general file. Then modify the program in case study 6 to read this file in, prior to requesting the students' timetables.

10.2   The seating on large airplanes consists of ten seats in a row of the form

Seat letter: A B C   D E F G   H I J
               W S S S A S S S A S S W

where **W** indicates a window, **S** a seat and **A** an aisle. Different airplanes have different arrangements of seats, but the seat letters always reflect their position, even if some letters have to be missed out. For example, a small plane with only four seats across might have the following arrangement:

Seat letter: A C   H J
                  W S S A S S W

Rows of seats are also divided into between one and three cabins for first, business and economy class. For example, in a 100 row plane, there could be rows 1 – 12 for first class, rows 14 – 40 for business class and rows 41 – 101 for economy. (Notice that it is customary in aviation not to use the number 13 for a row, as it is deemed unlucky.) Devise a way of storing the seating information for various types of planes so that it can be readily used by a seat reservation program. Then write the reservation program, which accepts seats requests for a certain type of plane and a number of seats of a given class. The program should allocate seats using two simple rules: a group of people should be seated in the same row, preferably with no aisle intervening; and window and aisle seats should be allocated before centre seats.

10.3   Design a way of showing the seating plans of an airplane on the screen. Use the graphical facilities you have to best advantage, including colour for the classes, and so on.

Appendix A

Tables

Reserved words

and	end	nil	set
array	file	not	then
begin	for	of	to
case	function	or	type
const	goto	packed	until
div	if	procedure	var
do	in	program	while
downto	label	record	with
else	mod	repeat	

Predefined identifiers

Constants

true	false	maxint

Types

boolean	char	integer	real	text

File variables

input	output

Functions

abs	arctan	chr	cos
eof	eoln	exp	ln
odd	ord	pred	round
sin	sqr	sqrt	succ
trunc			

Procedures

dispose	get	new	pack
page	put	read	readln
reset	rewrite	unpack	write
writeln			

Directives

forward

See also the tables of operators in the summary to Chapter 3 and of types in section 8.1.

Appendix B

Collected forms

These forms serve as templates for creating valid Pascal constructs. Keywords and symbols in plain type must appear. Words in italics must be replaced by suitable items. Symbols such as ( ) in italics indicate that the construct is optional. Words in plural indicate that a list of such items may appear, separated either by commas or semicolons, depending on context. The section or sections where the construct is described is given in each case. For a more precise definition of the syntax, consult the bubble diagrams that follow.

Programs and procedures

Program   2.1

```
PROGRAM name (files);
  declarations
  BEGIN
    statements
  END.
```

Simple procedure declaration   2.4

```
PROCEDURE name;
  declarations
  BEGIN
    statements
  END; {name }
```

Simple procedure call 2.4

```
name ;
```

Procedure declaration 5.2

```
PROCEDURE name (formal parameter declarations);
  declarations
  BEGIN
    statements
  END; {name}
```

Procedure call 5.2

```
name (actual parameters);
```

VAR parameter declaration 5.2

```
VAR  formal parameter identifiers : type identifier ;
```

Conformant array parameter declaration 9.2

```
identifier : array [lowid..highid : subscript type] of element type;
```

Procedural parameter declaration 9.3

```
PROCEDURE name (formal parameter declarations) ;
FUNCTION name (formal parameter declarations) : type ;
```

Function declaration 5.3

```
FUNCTION name (formal parameter declarations) : type  ;
  declarations
  BEGIN
    statements
  END;  {name}
```

Statements

Output statements   2.2, 4.4

```
write (list of items ) ;
writeln (list of items) ;
writeln;
```

For-statement   2.5

```
FOR loop variable := lower to upper DO BEGIN
    statements
END;
```

Assignment statement   3.2

```
variable := expression ;
```

Input statements   3.3, 4.4

```
read (list of variables);
readln (list of variables);
readln;
```

If-statement   3.4

```
IF condition THEN statement
    ELSE statement;
```

While statement   4.2

```
Initialise the conditions
WHILE conditions DO BEGIN
    Statements to perform the loop
        and change the conditions
END;
```

Repeat statement 4.2

Initialise the conditions
REPEAT
   Statements to perform the loop
      and change the conditions
   UNTIL *conditions;*

Compound statement 3.4

BEGIN
   statements
END ;

Case-statement 4.3

CASE *key-expression* of
   key-values : *statement*,
   key-values : *statement*,
   . . .
   key-values : *statement*,
END; {CASE}

Opening a text file 4.4

reset (F);   {to open for reading}
rewrite (F);   {to open for writing}

With-statement 8.3

WITH *record variable name* DO BEGIN
   statements;
END; {with}

Declarations and types

Constant declaration   2.3

```
CONST
   identifier = value;
   identifier = value;
      . . .
   identifier = value;
```

Variable declaration   3.2

```
VAR
   identifiers : type;
   identifiers : type;
      . . .
   identifiers : type;
```

Type declaration   6.1

```
TYPE
   identifier = type;
   identifier = type;
      . . .
   identifier = type;
```

Subrange type   3.2, 6.1

```
   identifier = lower bound  .. upper bound ;
```

Array type   6.2, 6.3

```
   identifier = ARRAY [bound type] of element type;
```

Enumerated type   8.1

```
   identifier = (list of identifiers);
```

String type   8.2

```
identifier = PACKED ARRAY [bound type] of char;
```

Record type   8.3

```
identifier  =  RECORD
        field : type;
        field : type;
          . . .
        field : type;
      END;
```

Variant record type   8.3

```
identifier = RECORD
   fixed fields
   CASE tag-field :  tag-type  OF
    tag-values  : (variant  fields);
    tag-values  : (variant  fields);
      . . .
    tag-values  : (variant  fields);
   END; {RECORD}
```

Set type   8.4

```
identifier = SET OF base type;
```

Pointer type   10.1

```
identifier = ↑ type;
```

File type   10.4

```
identifier = FILE OF type ,
```

Appendix C

Syntax diagrams

These diagrams provide a precise description of the syntax of Pascal. The rounded boxes indicate keywords or operators, and the rectangular boxes refer to other diagrams. To use the diagrams to find the syntax of a construct, look for a keyword, and then follow the arrows, filling in the rectangular boxes with the appropriate construct.

Letter

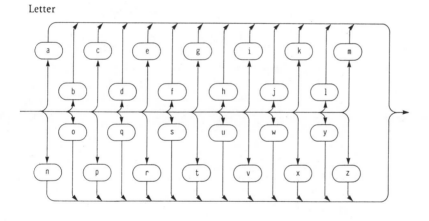

Digit

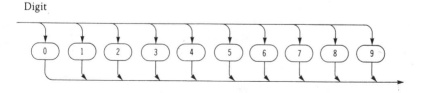

The publishers wish to thank Springer-Verlag for permission to reproduce this appendix from *Pascal User Manual and Report* 3rd edition by K. Jensen and N. Wirth.
© 1985 Springer-Verlag New York Inc.

Identifier and Directive

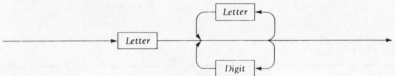

Unsigned Integer

UnsignedNumber

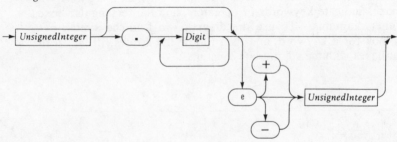

CharacterString

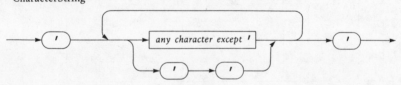

ConstantIdentifier, VariableIdentifier, FieldIdentifier, BoundIdentifier,
TypeIdentifier, ProcedureIdentifier and FunctionIdentifier

Identifier

Unsigned Constant

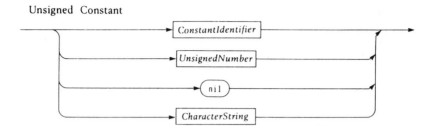

Constant

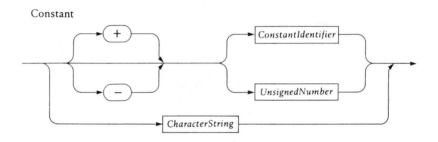

Variable

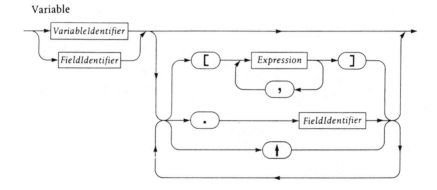

Factor

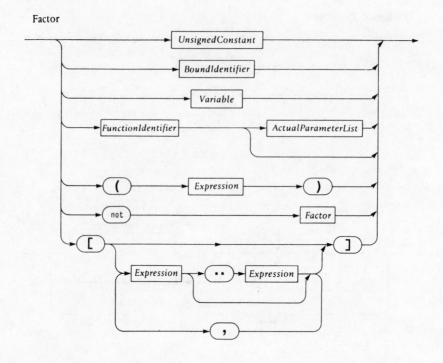

Term

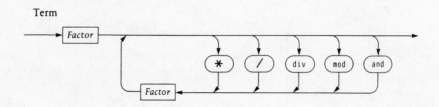

SimpleExpression

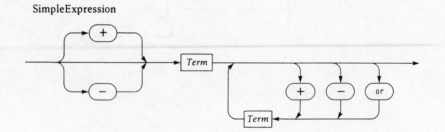

Expression

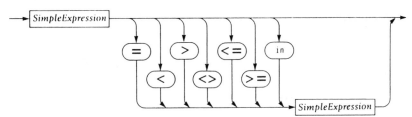

ActualParameterList

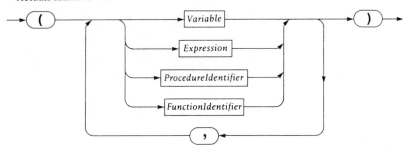

WriteParameterList

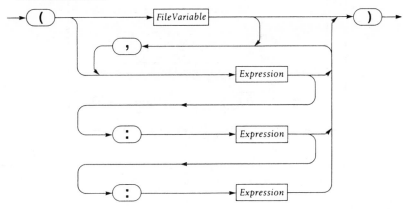

IndexTypeSpecification

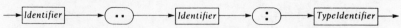

ConformantArraySchema

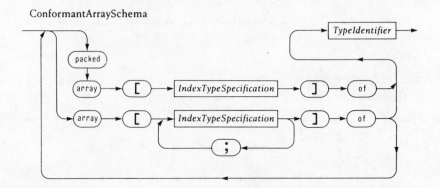

FormalParameterList

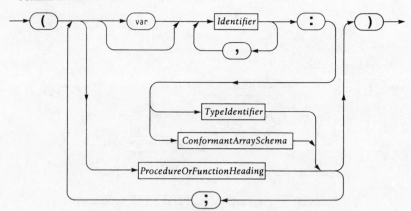

ProcedureOrFunctionHeading

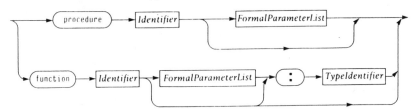

OrdinalType

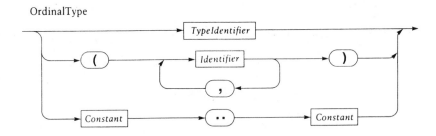

Type

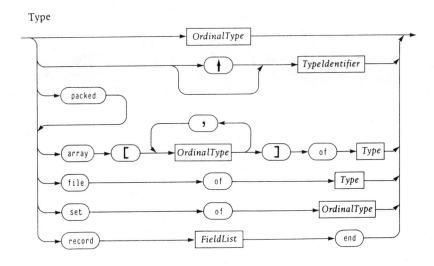

FieldList

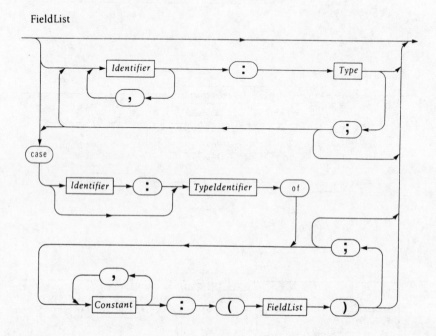

Statement

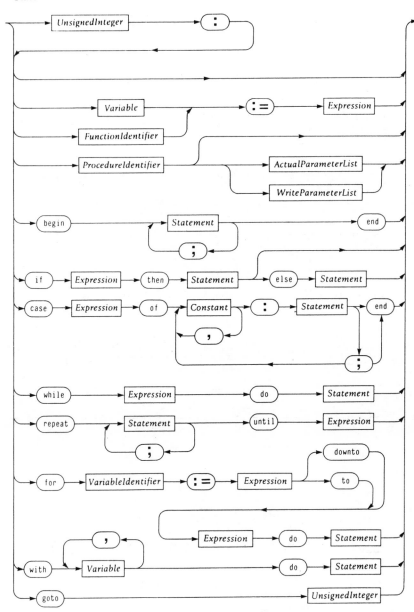

Block

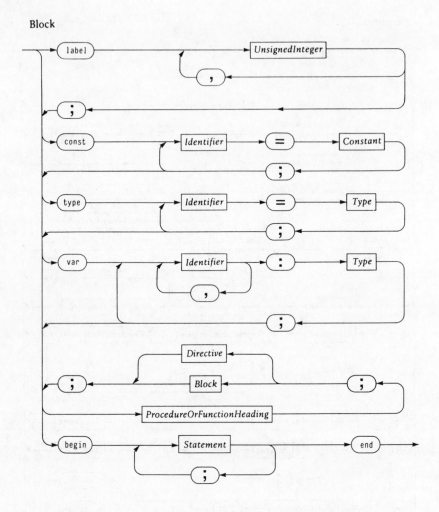

Program

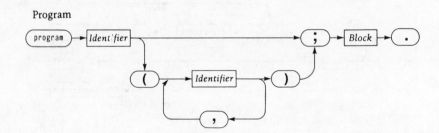

Appendix D

Using Turbo Pascal

Turbo Pascal™ is a small, fast Pascal system suitable for interactive use on microcomputers. It has many extensions to Pascal for handling graphics and files and for interfacing to various operating systems such as MS-DOS. Once a program uses these extensions, it becomes non-standard and hence cannot easily be run on another Pascal system. Even if one avoids non-standard features, there are still aspects of Turbo which encroach on the way in which a program is written. These can be divided into **limitations** and **file interfaces.**

Limitations

Several of the limitations present in version 4.0 of Turbo Pascal have been removed in version 5.0. The differences are pointed out here.

Procedural parameters
In Turbo procedures and functions may not be passed as parameters. This means that the algorithms discussed in section 9.3 cannot be implemented directly. In version 5.0, there is provision for procedure variables which gives some of the functionality of procedural parameters.

Conformant arrays
Turbo does not yet implement conformant arrays. Therefore the algorithms discussed in section 9.2 cannot be used.

Buffer variable, get and put
Turbo does not implement the buffer variable, nor does it have *get* and *put* procedures for accessing files. This is not serious, because the standard read and write procedures can perform the functions of *get* and *put* on general files, as described in section 10.4. The lack of the buffer variable means that programs cannot look ahead at the next item in a file.

Local files

Turbo Pascal does not support local files: all files must be connected to a device.

Range checking

Turbo Pascal does not check subrange bounds or array subscript bounds unless the compiler directive {$R+} is specified at the start of a program. This is a very useful feature, and no program should be without it! In versions 4.0 and onwards, it is possible to set range checking on in the compiler's environment, so that it applies to all programs.

File interfaces

Pascal was originally designed to work in a batch environment, that is without interactive input and output. As a result, the read and write procedures are not defined in the most suitable way for modern programming. Nevertheless, to ensure that programs are reasonably portable, it is best to use implementations which conform to the standard. Fortunately, Turbo Pascal Version 5.0 is now nearly standard. The read and write procedures operate on the input files in the same way as on any other text files, allowing items on a line to be read by several successive reads.

In Turbo Pascal 4.0, when the read procedure is applied to the predefined file *input,* the data is only available once a line of text has been completed by typing the <RETURN> key. In essence, this limitation makes version 4.0 difficult to use when writing character processing programs which are to conform to standard Pascal.

The other problem concerns connecting files to physical devices, and is fully discussed in section 4.4.

Answers to quizzes

Quiz 1

1. The hardware, software and devices that are available.
2. Several programs sharing a single (large) computer.
3. A microcomputer usually has all the necessary software and devices to make it a general purpose tool; a microprocessor is usually designed and programmed for a single embedded application; a personal computer is another name for a microcomputer, but with the emphasis being on software which is used in the home (e.g. spreadsheets, word processors, games); there are different sorts of chips – memory chips, processor chips etc. and several go into a single microprocessor.
4. Mips (millions of instructions per second) or Megaflops (millions of floating point operations per second) are most usual.
5. RAM is random access memory for reading and writing, whereas ROM is for read-only access.
6. A compiler translates a program in a high level language like Pascal into the machine code of the computer.
7. Unambiguous, precise, finite, self-checking and clear notation.
8. The codes which directly drive the hardware instructions of the computer.
9. A compilation error indicates an error in the formulation of a construct in a language, whereas an execution error indicates an error in the logic of the program.
10. User manual, product guide, technical manual, implementor's guide.

Quiz 2

1. After a write statement, output will proceed directly after the last item written; after a writeln statement, output will proceed at the start of a new line.
2. VAR not VARIABLE
   BEGIN needed for PROCEDURE tops
   FOR loop :=, not =
   1 to 10 not 1 .. 10
   writeln('!') – remember the quotes around a character.
   END. – fullstop at the end of a program.
3. Yes, if they are declared in different procedures.
4. (sqr(x) – 1) / (sqrt(x) – 2)
5. The declaration always comes first.
6. Although the statements under the for-statement are indented, there is no *begin-end* bracketing them. Therefore the loop applies only to the first statement, and we get

5 times 5 times 5 times 5 times 5 times 5 times 5 times 5 times 5 times 5 times 5 times 5 times ******* is *******

where the ******* indicates that the value is indeterminate because the loop variable *multiple* does not have a defined value at the end of the loop. The two ways of correcting the loop are:

- put the statements in a procedure and let the loop call the procedure;
- bracket the statements with *begin-end*.

7.   6

8.   There is an interval of 8 between the 7 numbers and an offset of −13. Therefore we can run a loop from 0 to 6, multiplying the loop variable by 8 and subtracting 13.

```
VAR i : 0 .. 6;
FOR i := 0 to 6 do
  write( i * 8 – 13, ' ' );
```

9.   One computer produced ~ ~ ~ 3.250~ ~ ~ ~ ~ ~ ~ 3 3 ~ 3e+00 but you should check with your own.

10.

```
CONST pi = 3.141592;

writeln(pi, sqr(pi), sqr(sqr(pi)), sqr(sqr(sqr(pi))));
writeln(pi, sqrt(pi), sqrt(sqrt(pi)), sqrt(sqrt(sqrt(pi))));
```

Quiz 3

1. | K = 1,000 | cannot use a comma in a number. |
      | Prize = D50 | D50 is not a valid constant – must just use 50. |
      | 2ndPrize = D25 | Identifier must start with a letter. D25 not valid. |
      | i,j,k | k is being redefined. |
      | start, end | end is a keyword. |

2.   • State in advance how many items there will be.
      • Precede the data with a count.
      • Put a special terminator after the items.
      • Make use of an end-of-file property.

3.   **67 98 91**

4.   *Pre* can only have one of the values, so once one is found, there is no sense in checking further: the statements should be connected with *else*, i.e.

```
if pre = 'm' then write('milli') else
if pre = 'c' then write('centi') else
if pre = 'K' then write('kilo');
```

5.   The then-part consists only of the statement *temp := x*, since there is no *begin-end* bracketing the indented statements. So *temp* will sometimes get set to *x* and the other two statements will always be executed, the last with unpredictable results in some cases.

6.   *write(−maxint)* will get close.

7.   Assuming that the field width for integers is 10 characters, we have ~~~~~~1948194800

8.   *mod* is not defined for negative divisors.
      exp cannot raise a negative number to a real power.
      ln is not defined for negative values.
      arctan – no restriction.

9.   In a computer with 11 digits of precision, the 9 digit constant can be stored comfortably. Writing it out with a field width of 10:6 will give ~~3.141593. However, in a 4 digit computer, the full constant will not even be stored. Only 3.141 will fit. Therefore, writing it out with 10:6 will yield ~~3.141000.

10.   shift := trunc(time) div + 1;

Quiz 4

1. By writing out the character with the appropriate value, for example ASCII 7, as in write(chr(7)).
2. No, for-loops only operate on discrete types such as characters. Strings do not qualify.
3. ord(chr(ch)) − ord('0')
4.
```
          read(ch);
          while not (ch in ['0'..'9']) do begin
            write(ch); read(ch);
          end;
```

5. Usually CNTRL-Z or ESC does it. Check your own computer.
6. There is usually an assign procedure or an extension to reset. Check your own computer.
7. Yes, provided it is a file that is being used for output!
8. 'gr' is not a valid key-value. 'a' appears twice. The end-statement is followed by a comment as in end {case}.
9. The conditional loops are:

```
total := 0;    total := 0;
sec := 0;                        sec := 1;
while sec < 60 do begin          repeat
  sec := sec + 1;                  write(sec:2); readln(temp);
  write(sec:4:1); read(temp);      total := total + temp;
  total := total + temp;           sec := sec + 1;
end;                             until sec > 60;
```

10. To adapt the for-loop, we must run it over all the readings, expressed as integers i.e. from 1 to 600, and divide by ten when printing.

```
          total := 0;
          for sec := 1 to 600 do begin
            write(sec / 10:4:1); read(temp);
            total := total + temp;
          end;
```

Notice that equality on real numbers is avoided.

Quiz 5

1. False, false, true, false
2. Yes.
3. No.
4. No.
5. PROCEDURE P (x,y : integer; VAR z : real; w : real);
6. Yes.
7. No.
8. No.
9. The output from *Picture* would be

```
1   0
2   2 2 2
3   6 3 3 3 3 3
4   12 4 4 4 4 4 4 4 4 4 4 4
```

10. The parameters to *modify* are listed separately because the one is a value parameter and the other is VAR.

Quiz 6

1. Yes, in the same scope.
2. No, reals cannot be used in subranges.
3. The program should halt with an execution error message.
4. Yes.
5. Yes.
6. Compilation error.
7. Execution error.
8. Yes, a row (not a column).
9. No, unfortunately.
10.

```
FUNCTION mean (a : vector;  n : range) : real;
  VAR
    i : range;
    total : real;
  BEGIN
    FOR i := 1 to n do
      total := total + a[n];
    mean := total / n;
  END; {mean}
```

The function will only deal with arrays of length n, where n is less than the upper bound of the fixed array type, *vector*, as given in the *range* type.

Quiz 8

1. No. Values of an enumerated type must be identifiers.
2. No, unfortunately.
3. 20
4. Yes.
5. Yes.
6. No.
7. No.
8. (a) Enumerated types cannot consist of integers – only newly declared identifiers. (b) Enumerated types cannot be read with the read procedure. (c) *Coinset* is a type, so we cannot use it with the *in* operator. We must define, declare and initialise a set for the coins, such as

```
TYPE
  change = set of coins;
VAR
  pocket : change;
pocket := [ ];

if n in pocket then ...
```

9.
```
TYPE
  illness = set of symptoms;

{Assumes the existence of a writesymptom procedure}
PROCEDURE writeillness ( bug : illness);
  VAR s : symptoms;
  BEGIN
    for s := temperature to spots do
      if s in bug then writesymptom (s);
  END;
```

10.   flu * cold

Quiz 9

1. The main loop takes i to $n-1$ so that the inner loop always has at least one value to compare a_i to.
2. The record can contain a key value as well as other information.
3. PROCEDURE sortany (VAR a : array[low .. high : integer] of element);
4.

```
FUNCTION search (a : array[m..n] of integer) : integer;
  VAR i : integer;
  BEGIN
    i := m;
    while (i <= n) and (a[i] <> 0) do
      i := i+1;
    search := i;
  END; {search}
```

5. See section 9.3.
8. The program reads a character, and if that is a digit it holds it and calls the *sift* procedure recursively. As soon as a non-digit is found, the recursive calls *unwind* and the digits are printed in reverse order. If the data is typed on a screen and interspersed with the output, we would have:

```
A*
B*
123C321*
D*
E*
69F96*
```

Quiz 10

1. Overhead of storage for pointers providing the links, and lack of direct accessibility by name to the nodes of the list.
2. It creates space on the heap for a variable of the type referenced by the pointer parameter, and sets the parameter to point to this space.
3. Items are added on the top only, so that they end up in reverse order if unstacked (last-in-first-out). On queues, items are added at the end and removed from the front so that they maintain their order (first-in-first-out).
4. It would halt with an execution error.

Answers to selected problems

Chapter 1

This set of problems is intended to lead you into a greater awareness of the size and capabilities of computer hardware and software you will be using. There are no common answers to the questions, but some help on 1.5 is offered.

The number of bytes in this text book is approximately (418 pages by 50 lines by 70% full on average by 85 characters per line) = 1243K. This will fit comfortably on two 800K diskettes.

Chapter 2

2.7   The way of tackling this problem is to take a verse from the output and underline those parts that change each time, i.e.

> <u>3</u> men went to mow, went to mow a meadow,
> <u>3</u> men, <u>2</u> men, <u>1</u> man and his dog, went to mow a meadow.

We set up one loop for the verses, based on how many men there are, and one loop to repeat all the men in reverse order. A first attempt at a program for five men is:

```
PROGRAM MowaMeadow (output);
  VAR
    man, companions : 1 .. 5;
  BEGIN
    writeln('****** One man went to mow ******');
    FOR man := 1 to 5 do begin
      writeln(man,' men went to mow, went to mow a meadow,');
      FOR companions := man downto 2 do
        writeln(companions, ' men, ');
      writeln('1 man and his dog, went to mow a meadow. ');
  END.
```

A point to note is that the inner loop is skipped when the loop variable *man* is one. If you run the program, you will notice that it has one defect: the first line is written as '1 men ...' rather than '1 man ...'. How would the program have to be altered to display correct grammar?

Chapter 3

3.4   The pattern for the else-if sequence for class marks was given in section 3.4. The point to remember when amending it for printing each symbol in a large format is that **compound statements** are needed to group more than one procedure call after each *then* or *else*.

```
if mark >= 75
then eye
else
  if mark >= 70
  then begin
    eye; eye; dash; one;
  end
  else
    if mark >= 60
    then begin
      eye; eye; dash; two;
    end
    else
      if mark >= 50
      then begin
        eye; eye; eye;
      end
      else
        eff;
```

The handling of the two second classes could have been grouped as follows:

```
else
  if mark >= 60
  then begin
    eye; eye; dash;
    if mark >= 70 then one else two;
  end
```

3.6   The solution to this problem involves a mixture of the algorithms for summing numbers and for finding the largest one, and the mixture is all wrapped up in loops for the weeks and days. It is vital to have a clear picture of the algorithm before proceeding to the program. The positioning of the checks and loops is shown in the pseudo-code chart as follows:

Initialise wettest day total and number
Initialise driest week number

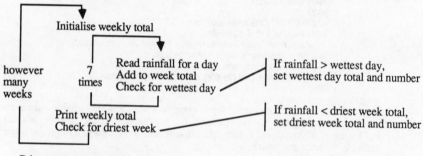

Print wettest day number
Print driest week number

Notice that the checking for the wettest day and driest week involves keeping track of two variables – the actual rainfall and the day or week number. In order to find the maximum rainfall for the wettest day, the total can be initialised to zero; for the driest week, the initialising is not so clear and it is necessary to choose something impossibly large.

Recording the wettest day also has its problems because in the loop, the day number will run from 1 to 7, but ultimately, the wettest day must be recorded in the range 1 to 28. To perform this mapping, the week number must be taken into account.

3.8   The solution to the Golf Course problem is based on finding the lowest number; the handling of the handicap and par are very much side issues. Obviously, the algorithm for finding the highest number (section 3.4) can be adapted to find the lowest. A point to note is how the question suggests that the prompts, data and results should all appear on a single line. This will require deft use of write, read, and writeln. What follows is a suitable main program, omitting the procedures that it calls. Notice how the use of procedures makes the main program really easy to read.

```
PROGRAM GolfScorer (input, output);
  CONST
    par            = 30;
    NoofHoles      = 9;
    maxplayers     = 6;
    maxscore       = 100;
  VAR
    player,
    winner            : 1 .. maxplayers;
    handicap,
    total,
    result,
    winningresult     : 0 .. 100; {say}

  BEGIN
    writeln('***** Golf Scoring Program ******');
    writeln;
    PrintHeading;
    player := 1;
    ReadHandicap;
    ReadandTotalShots;
    PrintOutcome;
    winner := player;
    winningresult := result;
    FOR player := 2 to Noofplayers do begin
      ReadHandicap;
      ReadandTotalShots;
      PrintOutcome;
      CheckforWinner;
    END;
    AnnounceWinner;
  END.
```

3.11   Printing simple trigonometric graphs in Pascal is quite straightforward. We make use of the field width facility to print an asterisk so many spaces across the page. The precise number of spaces is calculated by taking the sine, multiplying by 30 and subtracting one (for the asterisk).

The x-axis is going to run in whole degrees, so we can use an integer variable for it. A good interval between stars would be 5 degrees. The initial program is:

```
PROGRAM TrigGraph1 (output);
CONST pi = 3.141592;
VAR d : integer;
```

```
                    BEGIN
                      writeln("****** Sin Graph ******");
                      writeln;
                      d := 0;
                      while d <= 90 do begin
                        writeln("*":round(sin(d*pi/180)*30));
                        d := d + 5;
                      end;
                    END.
```

This will produce the characteristic curve, with 19 (that is, 90 / 5 + 1) points plotted. The second part of the question involves shifting the *x*-axis to the centre of the page by adding on a factor. However, running the graph from −180 to 180 means that it will sometimes be to the left of the *x*-axis (as seen on the page) and sometimes to the right. The writeln statements must take this into account. The revised program, complete with constants for all the values needed by the program is:

```
            PROGRAM TrigGraph2 (output);
              CONST
                pi       = 3.14159;
                start    = −180;  {degrees}
                finish   = 180;   {degrees}
                centre   = 38;
                scale    = 30;
                interval = 10;    {degrees}
              VAR
                d, y : integer;
              BEGIN
                writeln("****** Full sin graph ******");
                writeln;
                d := start;
                WHILE d <= finish do begin
                  y := round(sin(d * pi / 180) * 30);
                  if y = 0
                  then writeln("*" :centre)
                  else
                    if y <= 0
                    then writeln("*":centre − abs(y), 'I': abs(y))
                    else writeln('I':centre, '*':y);
                  d := d + interval;
                END;
              END.
```

Run the program to see the actual output.

This program can be extended considerably to include such goodies as reading in the limits and interval, printing the scales on the axis, having more than one function plotted, and so on. However, once these facilities are considered, the program should be completely rewritten using procedures. There is further discussion of graph printing in section 4.5.

3.13   There are two problems here – the conversion and the tabulation. For the conversion, we shall need some assignment statements, and conversion from reals to integers. The tabulating is more difficult. Probably three columns per line on the card will be easy to read, and we assume that the engineers will supply the starting value for card, e.g. 10kg. However, we should also try to devise a program that is not tied to a 20 × 3 card, but that can be adapted to print a table of any reasonable size.

Tackling the conversion first, we know that one kilogram is 2.2046lbs, and a lb has 16oz. Therefore for *k* kilograms, we can calculate the lbs as *k* * 2.2. This could be a real number. For example, 4.3kg gives 9.46lbs. We need to isolate the fraction and multiply it by 16. This can be done using the trunc function to get the integer part of the lbs and subtracting this from the original, that is $9.46 - 9 = 0.46$. Multiplying by 16 gives 6.16, which in whole numbers, rounded, is 6oz. The complete sequence of steps, in Pascal, would be:

```
VAR  kg, whole, frac : real;
     lbs, oz : integer;

whole := kg * 2.2;
lbs := trunc (whole);
frac := whole – lbs;
oz := round (frac * 16);
```

The tabulation part draws on the experience of example 2.8, to get several values across the line. Putting three columns across, with 20 lines down, we have 60 values. At 0.1kg intervals, this enables us to print 6kg per page. Unlike example 2.7, though, we would like to print the values downwards in columns, as in

kg	lb	oz	kg	lb	oz	kg	lb	oz
0.0	0	0	1.0	4	7	4.0	8	13
0.1	0	4	2.1	4	10	4.1	9	1
0.2	0	7	2.2	4	14	4.2	9	4

Two nested loops will satisfy this as shown in the algorithm (assuming we number the rows, and columns from 0):

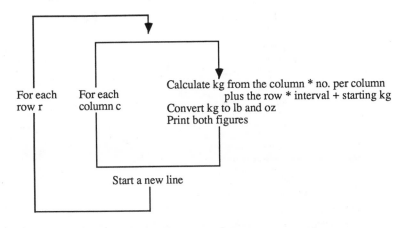

Do a few examples yourself to check that the formula is correct. The complications are that we are dealing in tenths of a kg and that there is a variable starting point. The program should now follow easily.

3.17   Compare your results to the analytic solution $v_T = \sqrt{\dfrac{mg}{k}}$ or 0.4427.

3.19   The answers should be (a) 0.33333 (b) –0.11111

Chapter 4

4.1   It is surprisingly easy to perform this conversion. Each character is read in and checked and then written out either as is or converted to lower case. The checks depend both on the character itself and on the previous character. Looking at the previous character enables initials and the first letter of double surnames to remain in capitals.

```
PROGRAM Convert (input, output, oldfile, newfile);
    {Copies a file of names in capitals to a new file with
    names in both cases}
    VAR oldfile, newfile : text;

    PROCEDURE CopyandConvert;
      CONST
        space = ' ';
      VAR
        ch, previous : char;
      BEGIN
        previous := space; {to force a capital to start with}
        WHILE not eoln(oldfile) do begin
          read(oldfile,ch);
          if previous in [' ', '.', '-', '"']
          then write(newfile,ch)
          else
            if ch in ['A'..'Z']
            then write(newfile, chr(ord(ch) – ord('A') + ord('a')))
            else write(newfile,ch);
        END; {while}
        readln(oldfile);
        writeln(newfile);
      END; {CopyandConvert}

    BEGIN
      writeln('****** Converting from capitals ******');
      writeln;
      write('For the old file connect to old.file');
      write('For the new file connect to new.file');
      reset(oldfile, 'old.file');
      rewrite(newfile, 'new.file');
      WHILE not eof(oldfile) do
        CopyandConvert;
      close(newfile); {if necessary}
    END.
```

4.2   The extension to the existing program will involve closing the file, resetting it again, and then processing it in a similar way, making use of the *readaword* and *skipagap* procedures as before. Each time a word is read, its length (*letters*) is compared with the average in order to decide whether to increment the counter or not.

4.3   The solution to this problem will bear some similarity to that for controlling the apparatus discussed in the second example in section 4.4. As each of the numbers is read, it must be checked against the previous one, and when they are no longer equal, something must be done. The action required is the writing out of the instruction *(n*m)*, where *m* is the number and *n* is the count of the occurrences of that number.

4.4   This, and the next problem, are typical character processing programs. Characters are read from a file, one by one, examined, processed and written out again. The programs are made more interesting by the introduction of the notion of a paragraph; at each new paragraph, after a blank line, the counters and conditions can begin anew.

The body of the comments program is governed by a single boolean variable, *inacomment*, which records whether we are processing a comment or not. Depending on the value of this condition, the occurrence of a { or } at specific points will either be correct or an error. This is all shown in the program.

```
PROGRAM  Comments (input, output, data, results);
  VAR
    data, results        : text;
    ch                   : char;
    inacomment,
    endofparagraph       : boolean;
    commentcount,
    noncommentcount  : 0 .. maxint;

  PROCEDURE CheckforOpenComment;
    BEGIN
      if ch = '{' then
        if inacomment {already}
        then writeln(results, '*** { found in a comment'
        else inacomment := true;
    END; {CheckforOpenComment}

  PROCEDURE CheckforCloseComment;
    BEGIN
      if ch = '}' then
        if not inacomment
        then writeln(results, '*** } no opening comment')
        else inacomment := false;
    END; {CheckforCloseComment}

  PROCEDURE CountandWrite;
    BEGIN
      if inacomment
      then commentcount := commentcount + 1
      else begin
        noncommentcount := noncommentcount + 1;
        write(results, ch);
        if eoln(data) then writeln(results);
      end;
    END; {CountandWrite}

  PROCEDURE CheckforParagraph;
    {Detects a blank line}
    BEGIN
      if eoln(data) then readln(data);
      if eoln(data) then begin
        readln(data);
        endofparagraph := true;
        if inacomment then writeln(results, '*** No ending bracket');
        writeln(results);
      end;
    END; {CheckforParagraph}

BEGIN
  writeln('****** Comment checker ******');
  writeln;
  write('For data file, connect to comments.dat');
  write('For results file connect to comments.out');
  reset(data,'comments.dat');
  rewrite(results,'comments.out');
  WHILE not eof(data) do begin
    endofparagraph := true;
    commentcount := 0;
```

```
                    noncommentcount := 0;
                    inacomment := false;
                    while not endofparagraph do begin
                      read(data,ch);
                      CheckforOpenComment;
                      CountandWrite;
                      CheckforCloseComment;
                      CheckforParagraph;
                    end;
                    writeln('Comment is ', trunc(commentcount * 100 /
                            (commentcount + noncommentcount)):1,
                            '% of the text');
                END;
              END.
```

4.13 Two things happen every three months: the children become adults, and new children are born. As formulated here, everything happens in pairs, so we can base our calculations on pairs, too. The program is centred around a simple while loop, which stops when we run out of room. The results you should get are:

***** Rabbit populations *****

We assume that a pair of rabbits of 3 months or over produces 2 more rabbits every 3 months.

In 27 months there will be more than 500 rabbits.

4.14 First consider the rules that can be broken. They are:

- too many questions answered overall (>5);

- too many questions answered from A (>3);

- too many questions answered from B (>3).

To monitor whether the rules are being obeyed we use three counters. As soon as a section counter exceeds its quota, a boolean is set. After all the marks have been read, the booleans are tested in order to write out any message regarding a rule being broken. The algorithm is:

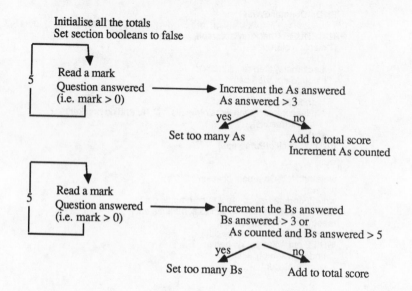

4.15 To check your answers, substitute them back into the equation. There are three
roots: one negative, one at zero and one positive.

Chapter 5

5.2 There are three nested loops here. The outermost one runs down the page for each
group of tables. It goes from 1 to 4, there being 4 groups of 3. The next loop goes
down the lines of each group, from 1 to 12. The final loop goes across the page for
the three tables in a group. In addition, each group must have three headings
printed. It therefore makes sense to parcel up the printing of a group into a
procedure, with two parameters indicating the first and last tables. A suitable
program would be:

```
PROGRAM OldenDays (input, output);
VAR
  down : 1..4;

  PROCEDURE PrintThreeAcross (first, last : integer);
  VAR
    across, line : 1..12;
  BEGIN
   for across := first to last do
     write(across:2, ' times table   ');
   writeln;
   for line := 1 to 12 do begin
    for across := first to last do
      write(line:2, ' x ',across:2, ' = ', line*across:3,' ':5);
    writeln;
   end;
   END; {PrintThreeAcross}

BEGIN
  writeln('******* Times Tables up to 12 *****');
  for down := 1 to 4 do begin
   PrintThreeAcross ((down-1)*3+1,down*3);
   writeln; writeln;
  end;
  END.
```

5.11 Check your answers by substituting into the equation. Compare the speed of
conversion for this method with that of the Newton-Raphson method (problem
4.15).

5.12 We give here the full Pascal version of the program.

```
PROGRAM Splitter (input, output, all, pos, neg);
VAR
  all, pos, neg : text;

PROCEDURE printfile (VAR f : text);
  VAR n : integer;
  BEGIN
    reset(f);
    WHILE not eof(f) do begin
      read(f, n);
      write(n, '   ');
    END;
    writeln;
  END; {Printfile}

BEGIN
  writeln('****** Splitting a file ******');
```

```
                    writeln;
                    writeln('For the data file connect to all.file');
                    writeln('For the positives file connect to pos.file');
                    writeln('For the negatives file connect to neg.file');
                    reset(all, 'all.file');
                    rewrite(neg, 'neg.file');
                    rewrite(pos, 'pos.file');
                    WHILE not eof(all) do begin
                       read(all, n);
                       if n >= 0
                       then write(pos, n, '   ')
                       else write(neg, n, '   ');
                    END;
                    close(pos);  close(neg);
                    printfile(pos);
                    printfile(neg);
                 END.
```

Since the printing is done for both files, it is profitable to put it in a procedure. Notice, however, that the file parameter has to be declared as VAR.

If the separate files are not needed later on, they could have been left as local files, unconnected to any device and existing only during the run of the program.

5.13   We give here the development of the algorithm for this, fairly large, program. This problem will have to be tackled from the top level downwards. We start by identifying the main sections and loops of the solution as follows:

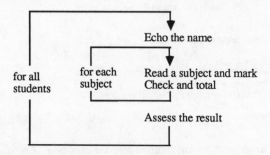

Echoing the name is virtually the same process as copying a line – which was done in example 4.6. The additional complication is that we must restrict the name to 20 characters, so that all the data can fit on one line of the results. So the copying must stop after 20 characters, if it hasn't stopped already. This means adding another stopping condition to the loop, and remembering to keep track of the number of characters copied so far. The algorithm becomes:

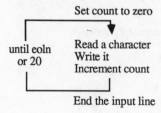

Moving on to reading the individual subjects and marks we realise that a simple

    read (subject, mark);

will only work once: the next time the read-statement will assign to the subject the space after the number, not the letter which is further on. Therefore, the spaces in between each pair have to be skipped. The skipping process will end when the next subject code is encountered, or in the last case, at the end of a line. Taking these possibilities into account, the following algorithm emerges.

An important point is that the skipping loop is only meant to be used if a symbol is imminent, since it does not look for the end of the line. The reading will therefore only end correctly if the last mark is right at the end of the line. This assumption must be made clear to the person putting in the data. (How would the algorithm have to be changed to take account of random spaces at the end of the line?)

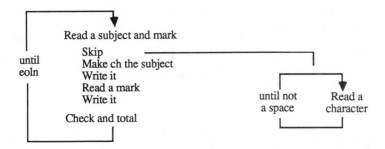

The checking and totalling procedure has several operations to perform. One of these is to find the lowest mark as the pairs are read in. This process was covered in Chapter 2 for finding the *highest* number, and can be re-used with the obvious change of < for >. The top level of this section is:

Check and total

                Add to total
                Reset lowest if necessary
                Increment subjects taken
                Consider as a pass
                Consider as a higher pass
                Consider as a language or science

The three checks follow one after each other, with the conditions in increasing order. That is, we first check for a pass, then a higher pass, then a language or science higher pass. The appropriate construct is therefore successive else-ifs.

Finally, assessing the result involves removing the lowest mark (if applicable), dividing by 6 and then calculating the symbol. Mapping a mark to a symbol was developed in the previous section, and the case-statement from that section can be brought straight across, with the special symbols for breaking the rules being handled first.

With this problem, it is going to be important to choose test data carefully to test each of the conditions. One way of doing this is to keep most of the subject marks the same, and vary only one or two so as to produce all the effects required. A sample set might be:

```
Adams Q T
E 60   a 50   M 65   c 70   h 78   P 55
Bright A B
E 60   a 50   M 65   c 70   h 78   P 35
Cairns J K
E 37   a 50   M 65   c 70   h 78   P 35
Dobson B N
E 37   a 50   m 65   c 70   H 78   P 35
```

with the corresponding results:

Name	Subject marks						Excluded	%	Symbol
Adams Q T	E 60	a 50	M 65	c 70	h 78	P 55	–	63.00	C
Bright A B	E 60	a 50	M 65	c 70	h 78	P 35	–	59.67	H
Cairns J K	E 37	a 50	M 65	c 70	h 78	P 35	–	55.83	X
Dobson B N	E 37	a 50	m 65	c 70	H 78	P 35	–	55.83	L

5.14   The *anybox* procedure below contains several loops, the middle one of which is nested. Notice that the loops start at 2 and end one short, to take account of the initial and final symbol or row being different. *Anybox* is declared with two parameters, supplying the size required.

```
PROCEDURE anybox (across, down : integer);
  VAR
    a : 1..80;
    d : 1..20;
  BEGIN
    for a := 1 to across do write('_'); writeln;
    for d := 2 to down – 1 do begin
      write('|');
      for a := 2 to across – 1 do write(' ');
      writeln('|');
    end;
    for a := 1 to across do write('_');  writeln;
  END; {anybox}
```

The scaling requirement is fairly tricky. It was not specified whether the scaling has to be uniform on both sides: we assume that it does. However, the scaling need not be the same for each box. So for dimensions 8m by 3m, a scaling of 6 would be appropriate, giving a box 48 by 18. However, dimensions of 8m by 8m would have to be scaled by only 2, for a box 16 by 16. The factor has to be worked out each time, and of course it should be indicated on the printout.
    The program that could call *anybox*, including the scaling and checking is:

```
PROGRAM lotsofboxes (input, output);
  CONST
    maxsize      = 10;
    screenwidth  = 80;
    screendepth  = 24;
    maxfactor    = 8; {screenwidth / maxwidth}
  VAR
    width,
    depth    : 1..maxsize; {in metres}
    factor : 0 ..maxfactor;
    n        : 1 .. 4;

  { declare anybox here}

  BEGIN
    writeln('****** Four variable sized boxes ******');
    for n := 1 to 4 do begin
      write('Give width and depth in metres (1 ..10): ');
```

```
            readln(width, depth);
            factor := trunc(screendepth / depth);
            if factor > 0 then
                if width * factor > screenwidth then begin
                    {try the other way round}
                    factor := trunc(screenwidth/width);
                    if factor > 0 then
                        if depth * factor > screendepth then factor := 0;
                end;
            if factor = 0
            then writeln('Box too large for an 80x20 screen')
            else begin
                writeln('Scaled by ',factor);
                anybox (width * factor, depth * factor);
            end;
        end;
    END.
```

Chapter 6

6.1   The simplest way to set up a histogram is to regard it as a frequency count, as
discussed in section 6.1. The two differences are that we want to map the incoming
numbers onto a small range of intervals or **bars**, and that we want to print the
frequencies out as lines of asterisks.   The mapping is relatively simply
accomplished by dividing a mark by the maximum bar, however there is a problem
at the upper end. The way the problem was specified, any mark larger that 100
goes in the last bar, and this could include marks that go into the next bar as well,
such as 115. Careful programming is needed to ensure that this is treated correctly.

   Printing out presents no problems. Note that the case of no items in a bar is
catered for by the for-statement, which is 'vacuous' if the lower bound exceeds the
upper bound right at the outset. A first attempt at the program is:

```
PROGRAM HistogramTest (input, output);
CONST
  itemmax = 500;

TYPE
  marks = 0..120;
  itemrange = 0 .. itemmax;
  itemarrays = array[itemrange] of marks;

VAR
  i : itemrange;
  markarray : itemarrays;

PROCEDURE PrintHistogram (M : itemarrays;  n : itemrange);
CONST
  barmax = 10;
TYPE
  barrange = 0 .. barmax;
  frequencies = array [barrange] of itemrange;
VAR
  bar : barrange;
  potentialbar : 0..maxint;
  f : frequencies;
  total, i : itemrange;
BEGIN
  for bar := 0 to barmax do f[bar] := 0;
  total := 0;
  for i := 1 to n do begin
    potentialbar := M[i] div barmax;
    if potentialbar > barmax
```

```
                    then bar := barmax
                     else bar := potentialbar;
                    f[bar] := f[bar] + 1;
                    end;
                    for bar := 0 to barmax do begin
                    if bar = barmax
                    then write (bar*10 : 3,' +      ')
                    else write (bar*10 : 3, ' - ', bar * 10 + 9:2,'   ');
                    for i := 1 to f[bar] do write('*');
                    writeln;
                    end;
               END; {PrintHistogram}

          BEGIN
               writeln('**** Histogram Test ****');
               writeln;
               i := 0;
               while not eof do begin
                  readln(markarray[i]);
                  i := i + 1;
               end;
               printhistogram (markarray, i);
          END.
```

A limitation of the program as it stands is that it assumes that each bar fits on one line. Since the number of input items can go up to 500, there may well be more for a given bar. The printing part should therefore be made more sophisticated to print bars of several lines.

The second part of the question – allowing the bar ranges to be passed as a 2-D array – is interesting. The change will affect only the first part of the procedure i.e. the frequency counting. At this point it is obvious that *PrintHistogram* should be split into several procedures and maybe a few functions too!

6.8   Taking ln of $f = Ae^{kx}$ gives $\ln f = \ln A + kx$. So for the *LeastSquares* procedure use as data not (x_i, f_i) but $(x_i, \ln f_i)$ The output from the procedures, a and b, gives A and k as $A = e^a$, $k = b$. Solution: $A = 3.071$ $k = 0.5056$.

6.9   (a)   (1, 2, 0, 1)
       (b)   No solution – matrix singular
       (c)   (2, 2, 2, 1) – for SOR method rows 3 and 4 must be swapped.

Chapter 8

8.1   For the input, it would be nice if the dates could remain in the traditional format. However, if the read statement is used for the number, the BC or AD part will have to be separated from the year by a space. Alternatively, the number could be read character by character and converted to an integer by a procedure.

For storing the dates, there are two possibilities. Either the year can be an integer, and a separate field of, say,

          TYPE eras = (BC, AD);

could indicate what era it refers to, or we could investigate storing BC dates as negative numbers. Either way, there will be an impact on the operations. Using negative numbers might make the arithmetic easier, but the other option might be easier for writing. Try them both!

8.2   The point to emphasise here is that the types for the array subscript and for the length are different. The array will go from 1 to 75, but the length field needs to include zero, to indicate an empty string. One could assume that if a string is empty, then the position is immaterial, so position can be of the same type as the array subscript, and be preset to 1. The relevant types are therefore:

```
TYPE
   range      = 1..stringmax;
   index      = 0..stringmax;
   strings    = packed array [range] of char;
   textlines  = record
                  data : strings;
                  length : index;
                  position : range;
                end;
```

8.3   The technique of keeping a running maximum is now quite familiar. The interest in this example comes from the use of a record to keep the data pairs. This contributes considerably towards keeping the program tidy, and to ensuring that the pairs always move together.

   The program below also goes to some lengths to produce decent output in a file, echoing the data as it comes in and printing out the increase each year. Notice that the test data is carefully chosen so that the answer can be easily checked.

```
PROGRAM Population (input, output);
  TYPE
  years            = 1970 .. 2000;
  populationcounts = 0 .. maxint;
  readings    = record
                  year     : years;
                  people   : populationcounts;
                end;
  VAR
  data, results    : text;
  thisyear, lastyear,
  year1, year2     : readings;
  increase,
  greatestsofar    : real;

  PROCEDURE process (var R : readings);
    BEGIN
      with R do begin
        readln(data, year, people);
        write(results, year:4,people:12);
      end;
    END; {process}

BEGIN
    writeln('***** Population Statistics *****');
    writeln;
    write('For the data file connect to stats.data');
    reset (data, 'stats.data');
    rewrite (results, 'stats.out');
    write('For the results file connect to stats.out');
    writeln(results, 'Zanyland Population Statistics');
    writeln(results);
    writeln(results,'Year  Population    %Increase');
    greatestsofar := 0;
    process (lastyear);
    writeln(results);
    WHILE not eof (data) do with thisyear do begin
        process (thisyear);
        increase := (people - lastyear.people)/lastyear.people * 100;
        writeln(results, increase:10:2,'%');
        if increase > greatestsofar then begin
          greatestsofar := increase;
          year1 := lastyear;
```

```
              year2 := thisyear;
            end;
            lastyear := thisyear;
        END;
        writeln(results);
        writeln(results, 'The greatest percentage increase was ',
                greatestsofar:6:2,'% between ',year1.year:4,
                ' and ',year2.year:4);
        writeln('See the file for the results');
    END.
```

The data and results are:

```
    1970    1400000
    1971    1410000
    1972    1420000
    1973    1440000
    1974    1450000
    1975    1460000
    1976    1470000
```

Zanyland Population Statistics

Year	Population	%Increase
1970	1400000	
1971	1410000	0.71%
1972	1420000	0.71%
1973	1440000	1.41%
1974	1450000	0.69%
1975	1460000	0.69%
1976	1470000	0.68%

The greatest percentage Increase was   1.41% between 1972 and 1973

8.6   The algorithm will use set difference to take values out of the sieve, and set union to construct the set of primes. Although we know the size of the base set, conditional rather than counting loops will be needed. In the outer one, the stopping condition will be the sieve being empty, which may occur before the last number needs to be considered.

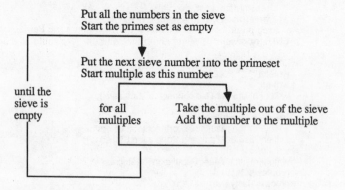

Put all the numbers in the sieve
Start the primes set as empty

Put the next sieve number into the primeset
Start multiple as this number

until the sieve is empty

for all multiples

Take the multiple out of the sieve
Add the number to the multiple

Of course, the primes do not have to be put into a set themselves – they could just be written out, but this way there is more illustration of set manipulation!

```
        PROGRAM Eratosthenes (input, output);
        CONST
            maxset = 255;
        TYPE
```

```
baserange      = 0..maxset;
sets    = set of baserange;
VAR
  sieve, primes   : sets;
  n, next,
  multiple, count  : baserange;

BEGIN
  writeln('****** Primes using a sieve ******');
  write('Primes up to (<= ', maxset:1, ')? ');
  repeat
    readln(n);
  until  (n >= 2) and (n <= maxset);
  sieve := [2..n];
  primes := [ ];
  next := 2;
  count := 0;
  REPEAT
    if next in sieve then begin
      primes := primes + [next];
      count := count + 1;
      multiple := next;
      while multiple <= n do begin
        sieve := sieve – [multiple];
        multiple := multiple + next;
      end;
    end;
    next := next + 1;
  UNTIL sieve = [ ];
  writeln('The ', count:1, ' primes up to ',n:1, ' are:');
  for next := 2 to n do
    if next in primes then write(next:1,' ');
  writeln;
END.
```

Running the program gives the expected output:

****** Primes using a sieve ******
Primes up to (<= 255)? 50
The 15 primes up to 50 are:
2 3 5 7 11 13 17 19 23 29 31 37 41 43 47

8.8   The major sticking point for this extension is that we cannot use Pascal sets to store names. There are two ways of going about the solution. We could abandon sets as inadequate, and use linked lists or arrays of strings instead. Adding each employee onto the class list is then no longer the simple

```
classlist[c] := classlist[s] + [employee]
```

but will necessitate extending the list or array. Printing is not really more difficult. However, if we are to work out how many employees are doing the same combination of any two courses, then we want to hold on to the sets, because they will enable us to use intersection to ascertain the answers.

The second approach is to keep the employee numbers and use them in the class lists, but to maintain an additional list of names for each number. All the calculations are done on the numbers, and only the printing process need change to print out names instead. If the names list is kept as an array, indexed by number, then in fact the only change will be in *printset* where *write(n:8)* becomes

```
write(namelist[n]:8);
```

Chapter 9

9.1   A sorting procedure for a conformant array of names would be declared as:

```
PROCEDURE sortnames (VAR T : array[low..high : positive] of names);
```

and the standard procedure would need to refer to *low* and *high* instead of 1 and *n*. The procedure would then be called by

```
sortnames (daytable);
sortnames (seasontable);
sortnames (depttable);
```

If the tables being searched are known to be in alphabetical order, then as soon as the search has gone past the possible place for *x*, it can stop. The change comes in the loop as follows:

```
REPEAT
  if x = T[i] then state := found else
  if (x > T[i]) or (i = high) then state := notthere else
  i := succ(i);
UNTIL state <> searching;
```

9.2   Following the method outlined in Section 9.3, we need to declare a function for each type of ordering that we want, and link these in to a procedural parameter in the sort. The actual functions will be:

```
FUNCTION namesordered (s1, s2 : students) : boolean;
  BEGIN
    namesordered := s1. name < s2.name;
  END;

FUNCTION marksordered (s1, s2 : students) : boolean;
  BEGIN
    marksordered := s1.mark > s2.mark;
  END;
```

The sort procedure is delared as

```
PROCEDURE sortclass (VAR C : classes; n : classrange;
              FUNCTION inorder (a,b : students) : boolean));
```

and the comparison statement in the inner loop becomes

```
if inorder(C[i], C[smallest]) then ...
```

The calls to the sort would be:

```
sortclass (class,n,namesordered);
sortclass (class,n,marksordered);
```

If we wanted to keep the different lists, then we could declare some new variables and sort into them instead, for example:

```
VAR
  namelist: classes;

namelist := class;
sort (namelist, n, namesordered);
```

9.3   The recursive function is

```
FUNCTION IsPalindrome (s : phrase; left, right : range) : boolean;
```

```
BEGIN
  if left >= right  {the stopping condition}
  then IsPalindrome := true
  else
    if s[left] = s[right]
      then IsPalindrome := IsPalindrome(s,left+1,right−1)
      else IsPalindrome := false;
END; {IsPalindrome}
```

It would be called by an expression such as *IsPalindrome(data, 1, n)*.

Chapter 10

10.1   The program has to take a linked list and store it on a file. Unfortunately, pointer values cannot be meaningfully reinstated from a file. Therefore, we have to write out the records one by one, without the pointers, and when we read them back, we add the pointers again. The file definition would be something like this:

```
storedcourses = record
    number : coursenos;
    pattern : periodset;
  end;
coursefiles = file of storedcourses;
```

Index